Mentally Handicapped People: Living a

To Carol
and Simon, Helen, Adrian and Rachel

Mentally Handicapped People: Living and Learning

David Clarke RNMS, SRN DN(A), RCNT, CertEd(Lond), RNT

Senior Tutor
Southampton University Hospitals Combined School of Nursing

With a foreword by

HARRY McCREE OBE, RNMS, SRN

District Nursing Officer, Winchester and Central
Hampshire Health District

BAILLIÈRE TINDALL · LONDON

Published by BAILLIÈRE TINDALL
a division of Cassell Ltd
35 Red Lion Square, London WC1R 4SG

an affiliate of
Macmillan Publishing Co. Inc.
New York

First published 1982

ISBN 0 7020 0894 X

Typeset in IBM Press Roman by Academic Typing,
Gerrards Cross, Buckinghamshire
Printed in Great Britain by
Mansell (Bookbinders) Ltd, Witham, Essex

British Library Cataloguing in Publication Data

Clarke, David
  Mentally handicapped people,
  1. Mentally handicapped — Care and treatment
  I . Title
  362.3   HV3004

ISBN 0-7020-0894-X

Contents

Foreword

At a time when the debate concerning the range and nature of services that should be available for mentally handicapped people has crystallized to the extent that official DHSS policy is described in *Care in Action* as the model of care set out in the report of the Committee of Enquiry into Mental Handicap Nursing and Care, it is particularly appropriate that this book should be published. David Clarke's experience in mental handicap as a practising nurse, nurse teacher and tutor to house parents make him extremely well qualified to explore those issues most relevant to the process of implementing these new policies; and he does this by seeking to understand the shortcomings of the present services and by identifying and illuminating those areas of skill and knowledge most necessary to take the service into the future.

The next decade will surely require a very considerable investment in staff training and retraining if the new policies are to be given effect and fulfil the great hopes of mentally handicapped people and their families. This will require that future practitioners have available manuals that describe in clear unambiguous terms the nature of the problem to be overcome; this book handsomely achieves that aim.

A great difficulty for some staff during this period of transition will be the fact of being required to provide care in a setting that does not easily facilitate the process of implementing the new patterns of care — to introduce in some environments the principles of normalization will tax ingenuity to the utmost. But the task will be more easily accomplished if the attitudes of care staff to the relevance of the concept are positive. And fundamental to the achievement of the appropriate attitude will be an understanding of the past and how the various concepts of mental handicap have influenced the provision of care.

While some disagreement remains as to the most appropriate method of preparing staff for this task of providing skilled and sensitive care, there is widespread enthusiasm among parents and professionals for a model of care based upon the rights of mentally handicapped people and for the promotion of a life-style in which the assessment of individual need is paramount. Fundamental to the process of ensuring these rights is the need for an acceptance by professionals, and others, of the right of mentally handicapped people to remain in their own communities and to be assisted to acquire skills. To remain dependent when, with the application of technology currently available, independence could be achieved, must count as a denial of those rights. This book is therefore most timely in that it sets out very clearly the issue of rights within the historical development of services and describes the various initiatives currently being developed in Great Britain and the United States of America to meet more adequately the needs of mentally handicapped people including both residential options and family support.

This book will undoubtedly prove a substantial addition to the literature available on the care of mentally handicapped people. It focusses with clarity on those major issues most relevant to achieving high-quality care, including the often forgotten process of evaluation, and draws extensively from the results of research activity in this field. In doing so David Clarke does not avoid those areas of contention still not entirely resolved, particularly the role of this hospital service. Nevertheless he sets out the facts with great fairness and does not shirk a personal view.

The hope for any new model of care must be that it recognize the essential partnership between parents and professionals. *Mentally Handicapped People: Living and Learning* clearly recognizes this and in so doing could prove of major assistance to practitioners to enjoy and share a new dignity with their clients.

July 1981   HARRY McCREE OBE, RNMS, SRN

Preface

During the last twenty years there have been major and sometimes dramatic changes in the ways in which mentally handicapped children and adults are cared for. These changes are in part a reflection of changing attitudes and a growing awareness of the problems faced by the mentally handicapped and those who care for them.

A fundamental reason for these changes is the recognition that mental handicap is not only a medical problem, but also a social and educational one. This has led to the involvement of a number of professionals in the caring process through research, practical intervention and support.

In the past nursing care of the mentally handicapped has been based on the traditional general nursing model with an emphasis on patient's symptoms, diagnosis and physical treatment. The current model of nursing care known as 'the nursing process' places its emphasis on assessment of people's needs in terms of the help they need with the activities of daily living. The traditional model of care has been seen to be particularly inappropriate for the mentally handicapped and for this reason references to clinical nursing procedures, human biology and medical conditions have been omitted as they can be obtained from other sources.

As a result of teaching parents, nurses, social workers and other care staff involved in the care of the mentally handicapped, I became increasingly aware that a large part of the material I used in teaching was scattered throughout the literature, and was therefore difficult to obtain. This book is an attempt to bring together a number of aspects of caring for the mentally handicapped through discussion of examples of research and good practice.

The book is divided into six parts, each discussing related themes of care. Part I is intended as an introduction and includes a broad overview of the philosophy of caring for the mentally handicapped, an introduction to the clinical concept of mental handicap and a discussion of legal and educational concepts.

Part II is included as reference material for those who need it for a deeper understanding and examination purposes. It discusses in depth the causes and effects of mental handicap with chapters on inheritance, chromosomal and genetic abnormalities, environmental causes, cerebral palsy and epilepsy.

A growing awareness of the problems faced by parents led to Part III, which discusses the family and mental handicap and practical measures in supporting the family.

It is recognized that for a variety of reasons many mentally handicapped people will be unable to live with their families but nonetheless have the right to a 'normal life' in the community. This move towards community life is reflected in Part IV, which discusses the sociological implications of integration and segregation, describes a number of examples of patterns of community care iin both this country and others and discusses methods of evaluating the quality of care.

The debate about integration or segregation is not concerned only with administrative provision but also with skill development and levels of individual independence. This theme is fully discussed in Part V through an analysis of the effect of the environment on behaviour and a discussion of the principles and practice of teaching new skills using behavioural techniques.

Part VI discusses a number of issues raised by the text and includes policy, practice and change.

This book is intended for anyone with an interest in mental handicap but specifically for nurses who are studying for a qualification in caring for the mentally handicapped. I am sure that other professionals involved in helping the mentally handicapped, such as teachers, social workers, psychologists, speech therapists, physiotherapists, occupational therapists, and doctors, will find it useful. It is designed to provide an opportunity for the reader to explore current thinking, research and care programmes for the mentally handicapped.

It is difficult to know where to begin in acknowledging all the help I have received in writing this book. So many people have helped in different ways: those who have given me opportunities and opened doors; the many mentally handicapped people who by their dignity and humour have taught me so much; and the many colleagues from a number of disciplines who have had the interest and patience to discuss aspects of the book and in some cases have been kind enough to read and comment on the manuscript.

It will be seen from the text that I have used the literature extensively and I acknowledge with thanks these sources, particularly Dr

A. Kushlick and the Wessex Health Care Evaluation Research Team.

The original idea for the book came from Mrs Christobel Grau and her initial support and interest was invaluable. I have been supported and encouraged throughout by Mr A. Smith, Director of Nurse Education, Southampton, who gave willingly of his time and expertise in discussing the manuscript. I am greatly indebted to Harry McCree for writing the foreword.

I acknowledge with grateful thanks the help received from Mrs Ann Griffiths and Mrs Joyce Heley in typing parts of the manuscript.

Although it is a *cliché*, it is true that this book would not have been written without the enormous help and support of my wife Carol, who not only typed the majority of the manuscript but discussed the draft copies and prepared the manuscript for publication.

November 1981   DAVID CLARKE

PART I
Concepts of Mental Handicap

Introduction

Part I is composed of four interrelated chapters which attempt to answer a number of questions related to mental handicap. They are intended to introduce the reader to some important concepts of the care and management of mentally handicapped children and adults and provide a basis for further reading.

Chapter 1 presents an overview of some aspects of mental handicap. These include the definition of mental handicap and the concept of measuring intelligence; the incidence and prevalence of mental handicap; and some characteristic physical, physiological and social differences. The text goes on to describe the provision of the various services for the mentally handicapped in terms of residential care; day care and schools; adult training; research; and specialist treatment facilities. The point is made that the mentally handicapped are more 'like' other people than they are different from them and that no one form of administrative provision or professional discipline is sufficient to help them to live as normal a life as possible.

Chapter 2 provides an explanation of the clinical factors which may cause mental handicap and is intended as a general introduction to the more detailed content of Part II. The chapter discusses normal cell division and differentiates between mitosis and meiosis. There follows a brief discussion of some chromosomal and genetic abnormalities and an outline of the difference between these and environmental causes. The difficulty of diagnosis and the lack of available treatment are highlighted and the point is made that continued research is vital.

Chapter 3 concerns the concept of the law and mental handicap. It is more comprehensive and is intended as a source of reference for both students and professional workers. It traces the development in the UK of legislation relating to the mentally handicapped and describes mental disorder as it is defined in the Mental Health Act 1959. The text discusses important sections of the Mental Health Act 1959 which relate to the hospital admission and discharge of mentally handicapped children and adults. The laws relating to issues such as signing a contract, making a will, marriage, voting, holding a driving licence and terminating a pregnancy are discussed as they affect mentally handicapped people.

Chapter 4 provides a brief explanation of how education for the mentally handicapped has evolved and introduces some important educational concepts. A more detailed discussion of intelligence and intelligence testing gives an explanation of the method of calculating an individual's IQ, provides examples of intelligence tests and discusses some of the advantages and disadvantages of intelligence testing. The importance of the environment is introduced through a discussion of the possible effects of socialization. This theme is extended by a discussion of negative care practices which can limit opportunities to learn. Finally the important issues of integration and continuing education are discussed and the point is made that no mentally handicapped child or adult, whatever his or her age, should be denied the opportunity to learn the skills that make for a full and satisfying life.

Mentalhandicap 1

Mental handicap has been a source of speculation, fear and scientific enquiry for hundreds of years. It has been regarded in turn as an administrative, medical, eugenic, educational and social problem. These changes reflect the way that society has managed and cared for mentally handicapped people. From earliest recorded history they were regarded with fear and the suspicion that they were in some way possessed by demons. This led to treatment which varied from putting the person to death or leaving him to die, to keeping him to provide amusement at Court[5] and in the market place, or according him religious or divine status.

Gradually, as society's knowledge of mental handicap widened and society itself changed, other more humane patterns of care evolved. The Victorian era saw the proliferation of large 'colonies' and institutions which in some areas form the basis of present-day residential facilities.[9] The past two decades have seen a rapid increase in the level of knowledge and understanding of mental handicap. This new knowledge has stimulated development in a number of ways, including research into causation, prevention and treatment; definition and measurement of intellectual functioning; techniques of assessment and teaching new skills; and evolution of new patterns of care related to the mentally handicapped person's needs, both in residential care and in the community. As knowledge has increased there has been a growing understanding and concern for the mentally handicapped which is reflected in a greater degree of public awareness. This awareness has been stimulated by organizations such as the National Society for Mentally Handicapped Children and the National Association for Mental Health (Mind) which publish books and pamphlets, run conferences and workshops, act as advisory bodies and constantly promote the interests of the mentally handicapped in the media. The influence of the media has been crucial in stimulating public awareness, by exposing the inadequate provisions in hospital care and also by broadcasting imaginative television programmes such as the 'Let's Go' series which demonstrated a number of social skills that the moderately handicapped adolescent could learn. Despite this progress the general public are still unsure and even apprehensive about mental handicap. This is due partly to the terminology used. Mental handicap is a relatively new term, now in general use and preferred to mental deficiency or mental subnormality, which are legal terms.[1] To call someone 'deficient' or 'subnormal' implies a static condition incapable of improvement, whereas if someone is termed 'handicapped' it carries the implication that the person can be helped to overcome his disadvantages. It may be argued that mental handicap is too wide a term to be helpful, but experience has shown that terminology is important in determining people's attitudes and expectations and in avoiding misconceptions.

One common misconception is that the mentally handicapped are mentally ill and therefore need to be in hospital to receive treatment. Whilst it is true that they may suffer from mental illness in just the same way as any 'normal' person might, they are not mentally ill. Another common misconception is that mental handicap is in some way contagious and is a disease or illness that can be treated or cured. Mental handicap is not a disease and is not contagious.[8]

These examples of misconceptions prompt the question 'What is mental handicap?' and the next section discusses the various definitions that are used to describe the condition of mental handicap.

DEFINITIONS OF MENTAL HANDICAP

Traditionally, mental handicap has been defined in terms of a score achieved on an intelligence test, called the intelligence quotient (IQ).[8] The average 'normal' score or IQ is taken as 100 although there is a range of 30 points below and above 100 which is regarded as being normal. This can be seen in the scale in Fig. 1. However, mental handicap is more than a low score on an intelligence test and encompasses such factors as social ability in relation to environmental demands. This is recognized by the World Health Organization in their classifications:

1. *Mild mental handicap* (IQ 52-67) may be only a matter of delayed development. Children can be educated and adults can work in ordinary employment following training. They may lead independent lives and never be classified as being mentally handicapped.[8]

2. *Moderate mental handicap* (IQ 36-51). Affected persons are obviously handicapped but may learn self-help skills and work in sheltered employment.[8]

3. *Severe mental handicap* (IQ 20-35). There may be delayed development or failure to develop physical and communication skills. Often affected people are also physically handicapped but they can still show limited independence.[8]

4. *Profound mental handicap* (IQ 0-19). Affected people require 24-hour care for survival. Physical and sensory development may be grossly impaired, with physical handicap.[8]

Another way of considering mental handicap is to assess the individual's

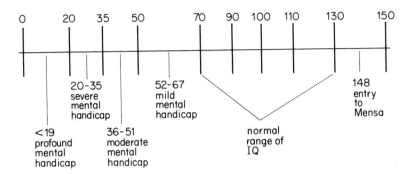

Fig. 1. A scale showing the different classifications of mental handicap recommended by the World Health Organization.

abilities and limitations in specific areas. These areas might be verbal or communication skills; performance or practical skills involving manipulation, balance and work performance; and finally social skills which involve interaction and living skills. Characteristicially the mentally handicapped tend to do better with performance skills than with verbal skills. Even when verbal and performance skills are well developed, the mentally handicapped person may not have acquired the necessary social skills to live an independent life.

The dimensions of maturation and learning are added to the concept of mental handicap when we consider the definition proposed by the American Association of Mental Deficiency (AAMD).

Fig. 2. A model showing different skill areas. The circle represents 100% of abilities.

'Mental retardation' refers to subaverage general intellectual functioning which originates during the developing period and is associated with impairment in one or more of the following: (1) maturation, (2) learning, (3) social adjustment.[1]

'Maturation' refers to the rate of sequential development of self-help skills in infancy and early childhood. 'Learning' refers to the facility with which knowledge is acquired as a function of experience. 'Social adjustment' is particularly important in adulthood where it is assessed in terms of the degree to which the person is independent and able to meet social responsibilities and standards set by the community.[1]

Intellectual ability is only one aspect of mental handicap and does not always give an accurate guide to the individual's all-round ability. The IQ certainly does not tell us how a person will behave socially or his ability in the future.

So far we have discussed varying definitions of mental handicap. Although these definitions can be seen to use rigid criteria such as the intelligence quotient, classification of this kind is helpful in estimating the incidence and prevalence of mental handicap, which are discussed in the next section.

INCIDENCE AND PREVALENCE OF MENTAL HANDICAP

Incidence refers to the proportion of babies who are born suffering from mental handicap; for example, the incidence of Down's syndrome is 1 : 600-700 live births.[5] It is more usual to use the term prevalence when discussing the number of mentally handicapped children or adults. *Prevalence* refers to the number of mentally handicapped people in proportion to the general population. It is estimated[1] that the overall prevalence of mental handicap related to the world

Table 1. Prevalence of severe mental handicap

Case register	Age group	Prevalence/1000 population	
Wessex 1964	15–19	3.54	urban
	15–19	3.84	rural
Camberwell 1972	5–9	4.39	urban
	10–14	4.17	urban
Salford 1973	5–9	5.73	urban
	10–14	5.81	urban
Sheffield 1975	5–9	2.95 }	urban/rural
	10–14	4.65 }	

By permission of the Controller of Her Majestys' Stationery Office.[4]

Table 2. Incapacity associated with mental handicap (rate per 100 000 total population)

Place of residence	Degree of mental handicap	Non-ambulant		Behaviour difficulties requiring constant supervision		Severely incontinent		Needing assistance to feed, wash or dress		No physical handicap or severe behaviour difficulties		Incapacity not assessed		Total	
		0-14 years	15+ years	0-14 years	15+ years	0-14 years	15+ years	0-14 years	15+ years	0-14 years	15+ years	0-14 years	15+ years	0-14 years	15+ years
Home	Severe	10.49	3.18	4.83	3.17	5.00	1.69	15.90	9.29	12.79	53.90	0.73	0.94	49.24	71.65
Hospital or other residential care	Severe	6.10	7.23	4.86	15.58	3.65	6.97	3.63	16.58	1.69	49.36	0.10	0.94	19.96	96.19
	Mild	0.34	1.51	0.88	5.29	0.15	0.64	0.23	1.96	3.85	42.40	0.21	0.15	5.55	53.17
Total		16.81	11.92	10.27	24.01	8.75	9.30	19.68	27.82	17.04	146.46	1.04	3.03	72.90	221.00

By permission of the Controller of Her Majesty's Stationery Office.[2]

Table 3. Some stages in the development of normal children[7]

Movement	Manual dexterity	Language
No head control. General body movements	Grasp reflex	Sucking reflex. Crying
Some head control	Hands normally closed	
Head mostly up when supported sitting. Lifts head off couch when lying on tummy	Hands mostly open. Can shake rattle for few seconds	Makes noises back when spoken to
Creeps on hands and knees. Can twist round to pick object up when sitting	Gives toy to person. Casts objects on to floor	Two or three words with meaning
Runs. Kicks ball without over-balancing	Builds tower of six to seven cubes. Unscrews lids. Puts on shoes, socks	Many words joined together, e.g. 'Daddy go'
Skips on one foot. Goes downstairs one foot per step	Copes with all buttons. Can copy a cross with pencil	
Skips on both feet	Can tie shoelaces. Can copy triangle with pencil	

population is 2% and this figure is reflected in surveys carried out in the United Kingdom. It is estimated[14] on these criteria that 2-3% of the population have a measurable IQ below 70. In practical terms this would mean that there are approximately one to one and a half million mentally handicapped people in the United Kingdom; this is termed 'true' prevalence.[14] However, this figure is impossible to validate as a large number of mildly mentally handicapped people are able to live relatively independent lives, receiving little or no official help.[14] This gives rise to the concept of 'administrative' prevalence, which indicates the number of people who receive some form of service. This in turn raises the differences in local services provided, and those services provided for specific ages and dependency levels. The prevalence of severe mental handicap is estimated to occur at the ratio of 2-3 per 1000 for adults and 4 per 1000 for children and adolescents [2] (Table 1).

A number of surveys identifying the number of mentally handicapped people either receiving or in need of health care have been carried out recently. Table 2 shows an analysis of three such surveys.[2]

The identification of incapacities associated with mental handicap, such as inability to walk, behaviour difficulties and incontinence, highlights another

ision	General understanding	Time scale
ague looking at objects	Begins to	Birth
yes fixate objects, can ollow moving person	Watch mother when she speaks. Smiles	1 month
atches own hands while ing on back	Interest in surroundings and in toys. 'Squeals' of pleasure	3 months
ood fixation n small brick	Interest in picture book. Shakes head for 'No'. Asks for objects by pointing	12 months
	Can point to or name several common objects	2 years
	Tells 'tall' stories, imaginative play with dolls	4 years
	Can give age, distinguish morning from afternoon, name four colours	5 years

Increasing ability to notice small features and to make smaller glances

aspect of mental handicap—the difference between the 'normal' and the handicapped. These factors are fundamental to the concept of mental handicap and include physical, psychological and social differences which are discussed in the next section.

DIFFERENCES CHARACTERISTIC OF MENTAL HANDICAP

There are many characteristic ways in which the mentally handicapped may be seen to differ from the 'normal' population. Perhaps the most obvious is in intellectual ability, which has already been discussed. However, intellectual ability is only one aspect of an individual's total development and differences may also be seen in a mentally handicapped person's development of motor skills, visual and manipulative skills, hearing and speech ability, and social and interpersonal skills.[15]

Normal developmental progress occurs when there is an even acquisition of skills, allowing for individual variation. These skills are sometimes called 'milestones' or more imaginatively 'stepping stones'[15] and represent the average age at which a particular skill or ability would normally be acquired. Examples of the stages in the development of normal children can be seen in Table 3.[7]

From conception an individual's development is determined by the delicate interaction of hereditary and environmental influences, with heredity determining the limit of each person's capacity and environment determining the extent to which he fulfils his capacity.[15] In mental handicap there may be either a delay in reaching the developmental 'milestones' or a failure to reach them. This may be due to a number of factors which in turn may give rise to further 'differences'.

Physical differences

The majority of mentally handicapped people are physically normal, although there may be signs of physical immaturity such as delayed physical or sexual development. The profoundly or severely mentally handicapped may in addition have severe physical handicaps brought about by genetic or chromosomal factors. An example of a chromosomal disorder is Down's syndrome, which is caused by the presence of one additional chromosome and produces characteristic physical differences. There is a close relationship between the nervous system and mental handicap and occasionally physical problems such as epilepsy, cerebral palsy, blindness or deafness may be accompanying features of a particular syndrome.[15] These points are discussed in greater detail in Chapter 2 and in Part II.

Psychological differences

A major psychological 'difference' that may be seen in the mentally handicapped is related to intellectual ability and concerns the ability to learn. The mentally handicapped person's slowness to learn may be due to a number of factors involving delay in acquiring or failure to acquire gross motor skills, fine manipulative skills, hand–eye coordination, visual discrimination and language and communication skills. These skill deficits may be aggravated by the effects of a poor learning environment resulting in a lack of opportunity to learn.

A further area of psychological 'difference' may be seen in the mentally handicapped person's emotional response to stress. This may take the form of either over-reaction to or withdrawal from an interaction, relationship or situation.

Social differences

The social differences are mainly those concerned with the mentally handicapped person's dependency on others. This dependency is, of course, quite normal in childhood but often extends throughout the individual's life and may vary from total dependence and 24-hour care, to simply need for guidance with complex social skills such as budgeting a wage or salary. The level of dependency

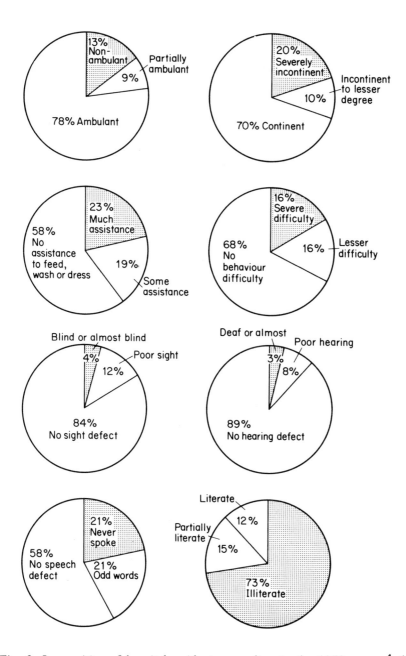

Fig. 3. Incapacities of hospital residents according to the 1970 census.[4] (*By permission of the Controller of Her Majesty's Stationery Office*)

will also determine to some extent the role that the mentally handicapped person is able to play in society. One difference may be seen in the job that the individual is able to do, which in an increasingly technical society tends to be of a simple repetitive nature. Other social differences may be seen in social relationships, an example of which is the relatively low number of marriages amongst the mentally handicapped.

Fig. 3 shows some of the incapacities of hospital residents[4] in the UK.

The above examples of physical, psychological and social differences serve to illustrate some of the special needs of the mentally handicapped. Some of these needs may be met by the different forms of service discussed in the next section.

SERVICES FOR THE MENTALLY HANDICAPPED

A wide range of services may be available to the mentally handicapped, including residential care, both long- and short-term, day care, special schools, adult training centres, advisory and research bodies and specialist treatment facilities. Tables 4 and 5 show NHS, local authority and voluntary provision in England, Scotland and Wales.[4] Before any decision is made about where a mentally handicapped person is placed and what treatment he should receive, it is essential that all

Table 4. NHS provision in England, Scotland and Wales[4]

	1970	1974	1975	1976
NHS residents, adults and children	65 326	60 154	59 119	58 516
NHS residents, children under 15	7384	5666	5295	4879
Short-stay beds*	—	701	—	1080

*England and Wales only. Some short-stay residents are also included as NHS residents.
By permission of the Controller of Her Majesty's Stationery Office.

those concerned are involved in making the decision. The decision should be influenced by, if not based on, as full an assessment as possible of the person's abilities, limitations and needs, so that he may benefit from the most appropriate form of care. An initial assessment can be carried out by using a form which summarizes a person's abilities and limitations. Fig. 4 shows such a form based on one designed by the Wessex Health Care Evaluation Team; it may be used by anyone who is familiar with the child or adult.[4]

Table 5. Local authority and voluntary provision in England and Wales[3]

	1970	1977
Places in local authority homes, adults and children	5221	10 158
Places in local authority homes, children under 16	1407	1721*
Places in local authority unstaffed homes	85	653
Places in Adult Training Centres	26 649	40 369
Places in Adult Training Centre special care units	not available	1672
Places in voluntary and private homes	1814†	3404

*Some places were 'lost' in the transfer of a number of children's homes to education authorities following the Education (Handicapped Children) Act 1970.
†England only.
By permission of the Controller of Her Majesty's Stationery Office.

Residential care

It is estimated that 80% of severely mentally handicapped children, 40% of severely mentally handicapped adults and the majority of the mildly mentally handicapped live at home.[3] However, some mentally handicapped people will require residential care.

Residential care can be considered under the headings of NHS hospitals and hostels, local authority hostels, group homes and fostering schemes, charitable and voluntary organisations.

The White Paper *Better Services for the Mentally Handicapped* recommended that there should be a move away from hospital care towards community care, for about 35 000 residents.[2] Table 7 shows planning figures for services for the mentally handicapped. A reduction in the hospital population, particularly of children, was foreseen and it was recommended that hospitals would in future care for the most severely handicapped and those with behaviour problems, whilst the local authorities would care for the less handicapped.[2] Kushlik estimated from research carried out in Wessex that it would be necessary to provide 20 residential places for children in a population of 100 000.[10] The reasoning behind this division of responsibility is that the hospital will have a greater number of trained staff and other facilities to manage and care for the most severely handicapped. The local authority provides accommodation for the less handicapped in the form of hostels and group homes.

MENTAL HANDICAP REGISTER[4]

(based on the form used by Wessex Health Care Evaluation Research Team)

CONFIDENTIAL   SWS(P)

NAME ——————————————————————— Date of Birth ☐☐☐☐☐☐

NEXT OF KIN ——————————————————— 6   11

ADDRESS OF NEXT OF KIN ————————— Grade: 1 Mentally Handicapped

————————————————— 2. Severely Mentally Handicapped ☐ 12

ADDRESS OF SUBJECT ————————————— 3. Not Known.

(if different from above) ————————————— (Please enter appropriate code in Box)

WARD (if applicable)

INCAPACITIES, PLEASE ENTER APPROPRIATE CODE (eg 1, 2, 3 or 4) IN BOXES PROVIDED

a.	WETTING (Nights)	1.	Frequently	2.	Occasionally	3.	Never	☐	13
b.	SOILING (Nights)	1.	Frequently	2.	Occasionally	3.	Never	☐	14
c.	WETTING (Days)	1.	Frequently	2.	Occasionally	3.	Never	☐	15
d.	SOILING (Days)	1.	Frequently	2.	Occasionally	3.	Never	☐	16
e.	WALK WITH HELP	1.	Not at all	2.	Not upstairs	3.	Upstairs & elsewhere	☐	17

(NOTE: If this person walks by himself upstairs and elsewhere. Please also Code '3' for walk with help)

f.	WALK BY HIMSELF	1.	Not at all	2.	Not upstairs	3.	Upstairs & elsewhere	☐	18
g.	FEED HIMSELF	1.	Not at all	2.	With help	3.	Without help	☐	19
h.	WASH HIMSELF	1.	Not at all	2.	With help	3.	Without help	☐	20
i.	DRESS HIMSELF	1.	Not at all	2.	With help	3.	Without help	☐	21
j.	VISION	1.	Blind or Almost	2.	Poor	3.	Normal	☐	22
k.	HEARING	1.	Deaf or Almost	2.	Poor	3.	Normal	☐	23
l.	SPEECH	1.	Never a word	2.	Odd words only	3.	Sentences & Normal 4. Can talk but doesn't	☐	24
m.	READS	1.	Nothing	2.	A little	3.	Newspaper & or Books	☐	25
n.	WRITES	1.	Nothing	2.	A little	3.	Own correspondence	☐	26
o.	COUNTS	1.	Nothing	2.	A little	3.	Understands money values	☐	27

SPEECH IF THIS PERSON TALKS IN SENTENCES IS THE SPEECH (Enter Appropriate code in Box).
CODE
1. Difficult to understand even by close acquaintances. Impossible for Strangers?
2. Easily understood by close acquaintances. Difficult for strangers?   ☐ 28
3. Clear enough to be understood by anyone?

BEHAVIOUR PROBLEMS (Enter appropriate Code in Box)

a.	HITS OUT OR ATTACKS OTHERS	1. Marked. 2. Lesser. 3. No.	☐	29
b.	TEARS UP PAPERS, MAGAZINES, CLOTHING OR DAMAGES FURNITURE	1. Marked. 2. Lesser. 3. No.	☐	30
c.	EXTREMELY OVER ACTIVE, PACES UP & DOWN DOES NOT SIT DOWN FOR A MINUTE	1. Marked. 2. Lesser. 3. No.	☐	31
d.	CONSTANTLY SEEKING ATTENTION—WILL NOT LEAVE ADULTS	1. Marked. 2. Lesser. 3. No.	☐	32
e.	CONTINUOUSLY INJURING HIMSELF PHYSICALLY, eg HEAD BANGING PICKING AT SORES: BEATING EYES	1. Marked. 2. Lesser. 3. No	☐	33

MEDICAL CONDITION AND TREATMENT (if any)
CRIMINAL AND OTHER PROPENSITIES NECESSITATING RESTRICTION
ANY OTHER REMARKS
COMPLETED BY ——————————————————————— DATE ————
For Notes of Guidance See Over

Fig. 4. Mental handicap evaluation form.
(See facing page for reverse side of form).

The general trend is for the mentally handicapped to be cared for in the community in small units, in existing rather than purpose-built accommodation. A reflection of this trend is an increase in short-term care provision in both hospitals and hostels.[13] This short-term care is increasingly being planned, as well as being provided as a crisis measure. Other innovations include weekly boarding and day care facilities.[13]

INSTRUCTIONS FOR COMPLETING THIS FORM

This form has been designed to collect the necessary information as accurately as possible with (we hope) the minimum of inconvenience to the person completing.
1. Please answer all questions.
2. Please write in the boxes where requested.
   eg, for a date of birth of 2nd Feb 1934 enter
   eg. for occasional wetting nights enter 2

0	2	0	2	3	4

3. Please leave boxes for Research No blank.

NOTES OF GUIDANCE

INCAPACITIES
If this person is incapacitated due to *temporary* injury etc, please code the normal ability.

a-d) *Wetting & Soiling* Frequently = more than once a week.

wetting or soiling which occurs during an epileptic fit should be recorded in the same way as wetting or soiling of any other kind.

e-f) *Walking* This question aims to assess only whether the person is ambulant and to what degree. Thus, if he or she needs help with walking because of blindness, or because of the danger of fits, this should *not* be recorded as an incapacity of walking.

g) *Feeding* A person is able to feed himself WITHOUT HELP if:
   (a) He does not cause undue disturbance by messy eating, nor take an unreasonable time to finish eating if left to himself.
   (b) He does not need to have food specially prepared after it has left the central kitchen.

h) *Washing* If a male can wash himself but ONLY has to be shaved, this should be scored WITHOUT HELP.

i) *Dressing* If a person dresses himself but is unable to tie his shoe laces, this should be scored WITH HELP.

j) *Vision* If a person wears spectacles his vision should be assessed as with spectacles.

k) *Hearing* If a person wears a hearing aid, this should be assessed as with hearing aid.

l) *Speech* This first question on speech is a measure of the ability to use language, it is NOT a measure of speech defect. Thus, if a person uses sentences he should be scored as SENTENCES AND NORMAL even though his speech is difficult to understand.

m) *Reading* Score NOTHING if this person is unable to read or recognise his own name.
   Score A LITTLE if this person can read or recognise his own name.
   Score NEWSPAPERS &/OR BOOKS if he or she is able to read and understand a newspaper or simple book. (A person who only looks at pictures should be scored as reading NOTHING.)

n) *Writing* Score NOTHING if this person is unable to write his own name or is only able to copy it.
   Score A LITTLE if this person can at least write his own name without copying.
   Score OWN CORRESPONDENCE if he is able to write brief letters to his family without help in composition or the actual process of writing.

o) *Counting* A person would score NOTHING if he is quite unable to count or, even if he can count, eg, up to 5 or 10, he cannot make use of this at all.
   A person who scores A LITTLE would be able to recognise small values, eg would be able to sort out 4 sheets or 5 pillows or 3 spoons etc.
   A person who scores UNDERSTANDS MONEY VALUES would be able to make small purchases at shop and give or receive correct change.

SPEECH
This item has been added because we think it is important to know not only if a person can use language, but also whether or not his speech can be understood.

BEHAVIOUR PROBLEMS
Please code behaviour irrespective of whether or not the person is on drugs at the time of rating.

Definitions of ratings
   MARKED   If this behaviour has occurred during the last month and continues to present problems of management.
   LESSER   If the behaviour appears to be between MARKED and NO.
   NO   If this behaviour never occurs or if it occurs so seldom that it is difficult to remember when it last occurred.

Charities often provide residential care in the form of homes or residential schools. The Spastics Society runs a number of residential schools of extremely high standard, with the curriculum and care designed to alleviate the problems of cerebral palsy.

Fostering is a service which is developing very slowly and then only in some areas.

Some residential care facilities serve a dual purpose in that they provide 24-hour care for a particular group. Two examples are the residential assessment centres and the newly proposed Regional Secure Units, for those people who require secure conditions.

In 1979 the Report of the Committee of Enquiry into Mental Handicap Nursing and Care,[4] chaired by Mrs Peggy Jay, recommended a radical revision of care for the mentally handicapped. Its proposals are based on the principle that mentally handicapped people should lead as normal a life as possible in the community. They include the provision of small living units; integration of the mentally handicapped into normal children's and old people's homes; a range of

Table 6. Estimated number of children and their presenting problems,[10] with their predicted future responsibility[2]

No. of children (per 100 000 population)	Presenting problem or incapacity [10]	Responsibility of [2]
6	Non-ambulant	Hospital
4	Severe behaviour disorder	
4	Doubly incontinent	Local authority/ Social Services
6	Continent, ambulant, no severe behaviour disorder	

staffing designed to meet particular needs, from an unstaffed group home to a staffing ratio 1:1 for the severely handicapped; and the continued use of hospital resources for those whose management requires specialized nursing and facilities.[4] The Committee's proposals are discussed in detail in Part VI.

Day care and schools

Since the Education Act 1970 every child has the right to receive an education. Normally, mentally handicapped children attend a special school (ESN(M) or (S)) which will have special facilities and trained teachers. Some children may not receive formal training in school but will be visited in their homes by a peripatetic teacher.[6] For younger children opportunity play groups and nursery schools/classes may be used. A further scheme receiving attention is 'day fostering' where a child spends the day with another family, returning to his own in the evening.[4]

Adult training

When the time comes for the child to leave school, and it is generally considered that 19 is a more realistic age than 16 for the mentally handicapped,[11] he can attend an adult training centre. There his social experiences and education may be extended and he will be able to learn craft and work skills. Work orientation and experience schemes or training at a government skills centre are possible options open to the mentally handicapped school leaver.

Day-release, evening classes and special courses at colleges of further education are now becoming more frequent for the mentally handicapped. These courses may be non-vocational and designed to stimulate interest in leisure activities and to help in the formation of community contacts.[12]

Often the mentally handicapped adult is able to work in sheltered employment or in a full-time job and may be helped in this by the Disablement Resettlement Officer (DRO).

Table 7. Planning figures for services for the mentally handicapped compared with existing provision²

Type of service	Places for children (age 0-15)			Places for adults (age 16+)		
	Required		Provided	Required		Provided
	Per 100 000 total population	Total England and Wales 1969	Total England and Wales 1969	Per 100 000 total population	Total England and Wales 1969	Total England and Wales 1969
Day care or education for children under five	8	3 900	500*	—	—	—
Education for children of school age:						
In the community						
Children with severe mental handicap living in the community	56	27 400	23 400	—	—	—
Children coming by day from hospital	6	2 900		—	—	—
In hospitals						
In-patients	7	3 400	4 600	—	—	—
Day patients	6	2 900	200	—	—	—
Occupation and training for adults:						
In the community						
Adults living in the community	—	—	—	130	63 700	24 500
Adults coming by day from hospital	—	—	—	20	9 800	100
In hospitals						
In-patients	—	—	—	35	17 200	30 000*
Day patients	—	—	—	10	4 900	200*
Residential care in the community (including short-stay)						
Local authority, voluntary or privately owned residential homes	10	4 900	1 800	60	29 400	4 300
Foster homes, lodgings, etc.	2	1 000	100	15	7 400	550
Hospital treatment						
In-patients	13	6 400	7 400†	55	27 000	52 100†
Day patients	6	2 900	200*	10	4 900	500*

* Estimated. † NHS beds allocated to mental handicap.
By permission of the Controller of Her Majesty's Stationery Office.

Research centres

There are many research centres concerned with mental handicap but because of the technical nature of the research the results may not directly benefit the mentally handicapped individual. An example of work that does have an immediate impact is the parents' workshops that are organized by a number of bodies. The Hester Adrian Research Centre in Manchester, under the direction of Professor P. Mittler, has run parents' workshops concerned with aspects of language and learning and development.

Specialist treatment facilities

The mentally handicapped may require the expert services of specialists and recently there has been an increase in both the use and the availability of these services in the community and in the hospital. Table 8 shows the number of therapists in hospitals for the mentally handicapped in England (1975).[11] The guiding principle in using the special skills of the professionals listed in the table is that they should be called in as early as possible so that they may be involved in every decision that is made about a mentally handicapped child or adult. Their unique skills are vital in helping the mentally handicapped to achieve some measure of independence, with the paediatrician advising on child health matters; the psychologist being concerned with assessment and skill development; the

Table 8. Number of specialists/therapists in hospitals for the mentally handicapped (England, 1975)[11]

Specialist	No. of qualified staff	No. of other staff
Paediatrician	4.3	—
Psychologist	114.0	—
Social worker assigned to hospital	171.0	—
Physiotherapist	77.5	49.2
Speech therapist	22.9	—
Occupational therapist	97.8	445.5
Industrial therapist	100.0	419.1

social worker in liaison with the family and other agencies affecting placement and care; the physiotherapist developing and establishing normal movement patterns; the speech therapist advising on feeding techniques and communication skills, verbal or non-verbal; and the occupational and industrial therapists teaching methods of overcoming physical handicap and acquiring work and occupational skills.

SUMMARY

This chapter has briefly discussed some aspects of mental handicap, with a view to introducing concepts that will be examined in greater depth in the remainder of the text.

Gradually as society's attitudes towards the mentally handicapped have changed, and awareness of the problems involved has increased, there have been considerable changes in the way mentally handicapped people are managed and cared for. One of these changes is in the terminology used to describe the condition. 'Mental handicap' is preferred as it carries the implication that a handicapped person can be helped to overcome his handicap. 'Mental handicap' is a social and administrative definition.[8]

Attempts have been made to define mental handicap further and traditionally an individual is classified on the basis of his intelligence quotient (IQ). It is now recognized that intelligence is only one aspect of mental handicap and criteria such as developmental age, learning and skill development and social competence are just as relevant.

The prevalence of mental handicap, particularly mild mental handicap, is difficult to assess. The prevalence of severe mental handicap is variable, depending on the area surveyed, but is thought to be in the range of 2.9–5.8 per 1000 population in children and 3.7 per 1000 in adults. This information is vital for the planning of future policies and services for the mentally handicapped.

Surveys of the mentally handicapped population have also identified some of the additional problems the mentally handicapped may experience, such as an inability to walk, severe behaviour disorders, incontinence or learning difficulties.[4] These give rise to physical, psychological and social differences which may be linked to either delay in reaching or failure to reach the normal developmental 'milestones'. Although the term 'differences' is used in the text, it is used in a descriptive sense only, and in fact the mentally handicapped are more 'like' other people than they are 'different' from them. This is reflected in the current debate about community and hospital care, with the trend for the mentally handicapped to live in the community rather than in hospital.[14]

In discussing the services that are, or should be, available for care, the comprehensive nature of mental handicap becomes apparent. All the health care professions need to be involved: nursing, psychiatry, medicine, psychology, teaching, physiotherapy, speech therapy, occupational therapy and other related professions.[11] No one discipline can meet all the varied needs of the mentally handicapped. Successive reports stress the need for all disciplines to work together as a team to provide a range of care options which allow the mentally handicapped person to enjoy a normal pattern of life, in a setting which takes account of his physical, psychological and social needs.

GLOSSARY

ATC
Adult Training Centre, organized and staffed by the local authority social service department, where the mentally handicapped may learn social, educational and work skills, on a daily basis.

Cerebral palsy
A genetic term which describes a number of disorders of movement and posture and may vary from a mild difficulty in coordination to almost total incapacity. 'Spasticity' is one form of cerebral palsy.

Chromosomal disorder
Deletion, absence or addition of chromosomal material in the cell nucleus.

Developmental age
The age which the individual has reached in normal development irrespective of chronological age.

DRO
Disablement Resettlement Officer, employed by the Employment Agency, whose job is to place disabled people in employment.

Down's syndrome
An abnormality resulting in an additional chromosome at pair 21. Sometimes called 'mongolism'.

Epilepsy
A disorder characterized by recurring loss or alteration of consciousness. Symptoms are due to paroxysmal disturbance of the electrical activity of the brain.

ESN
Educationally subnormal. ESN(M) = educationally subnormal (moderate), and ESN(S) = educationally subnormal (severe).

Eugenics Society
A society of people who believe that the mentally handicapped should be segregated from the community and be prohibited from procreation.

Incidence
The proportion of babies who are born suffering from a particular condition, such as mental handicap, compared to the number of normal births.

IQ
Intelligence Quotient. The score on an intelligence test.

Prevalence
'True' prevalence is the estimated number of mentally handicapped people in the population. 'Administrative' prevalence is the number of mentally handicapped people receiving some form of service.

Regional Secure Units
Hospital units proposed for those residents who require secure conditions but not to the degree offered by the Special State Hospitals.

BIBLIOGRAPHY

1. Clarke, A.M. & Clarke, A.D.B. (1974) *Mental Deficiency: The Changing Outlook*, 3rd ed. London: Methuen.
2. DHSS (1980) *Mental Handicap: Progress, Problems and Priorities*. London: HMSO.
3. DHSS (1980) *Mental Handicap: Progress, Problems and Priorities*. London: HMSO.
4. DHSS (1979) *Report of the Committee of Enquiry into Mental Handicap Nursing and Care*, Cmmd 7468. London: HMSO.
5. Dutton, G. (1975) *Mental Handicap*. London: Butterworths.
6. Heaton-Ward, A. (1975) *Mental Subnormality*, 4th ed. Bristol: John Wright.
7. Hegarty, J. (1973) *Educating and Training the Mentally Handicapped Patient—Workbook*. Chelmsford: Medical Recording Service Foundation.
8. Shearer, A. (1971) *Fact Sheet 1—What and Why*. London: King's Fund Centre.
9. Kirman, B. & Bicknell, J. (1975) *Mental Handicap*. London: Churchill Livingstone.
10. Kushlick, A. (1967) The Wessex Experiment—Comprehensive care for the mentally subnormal. *Br. Hosp. J. soc. Serv. Rev.*, 77.
11. National Development Group (1978) *Helping Mentally Handicapped People in Hospital*. London: DHSS.
12. National Development Group (1977) *Helping Mentally Handicapped School Leavers*, Pamphlet 3. London: DHSS.
13. National Development Group (1977) *Residential Short Term Care for Mentally Handicapped People*, Pamphlet 4. London: DHSS.
14. Office of Health Economics (1978) *Mental Handicap Ways Forward*. London: DHSS.
15. Sheridan, M.D. (1975) *Children's Developmental Progress*, 3rd ed. Windsor: National Foundation for Educational Research.

Clinical concepts of mental handicap

2

'A person who is mentally handicapped does not develop in childhood as quickly as other children nor attain the full mental capacities of a normal adult'.[1] This simple statement provides only a superficial indication of the complex factors involved in the manifestation of mental handicap. This chapter identifies some of these and explains how they produce differing degrees of handicap.

An important point to remember is that mental handicap can be caused by either single or multiple factors. Recent figures[4] estimate approximately 300 known causes; however, of the 300 000 severely mentally handicapped children and adults in Great Britain it is possible to define an exact cause in only 35%.[4] The incidence of mental handicap in the population is approximately 2–4 per 1000, although it is known that 1 in 40 babies is born with some abnormality.

Examples of some of the causes of mental handicap include genetic and chromosomal abnormalities; brain damage caused by lack of oxygen or trauma; maternal or childhood infections; food deprivation; and the absence of the right learning experiences.[2]

Children remain vulnerable to these factors until they reach their genetically predetermined level of intelligence.[2] The effects can be mild and in these cases the child is able to overcome them and lead a normal life. Conversely, they may be so severe that the child will need skilled care in order to maintain life. As well as suffering from mental handicap the child may have a condition complicated by the presence of various physical handicaps. These may include visual impairment, hearing loss, epilepsy or cerebral palsy.

GENETIC CAUSES

Once conception has taken place the fertilized ovum develops through a process of cell division called mitosis.[7] Repeated cellular division produces cells which become increasingly specialized. This specialization occurs because contained within the original cell nucleus were 23 pairs of chromosomes.[7] These carried the instructions for the development of new cells. Before cellular division occurs the chromosomes duplicate so that each daughter cell contains the full genetic complement of 46 chromosomes. These consist of 44 chromosomes which are the same in both males and females and are called autosomes. The remaining two chromosomes determine the sex of the individual and are termed XX in the female and XY in the male.[2]

Chromosomes carry the genes which, acting either individually or in combination with others, determine the person's physical and mental characteristics.[2] Therefore it follows that each pair of chromosomes carries genes for a particular characteristic, examples being hair colour, eye colour or body height.[3] Some genes are said to be dominant, for example those for curly hair, brown eyes or the Rhesus factor in the blood. In these cases the effects of the gene will always be present in the child's development. As we have seen, all the body cells contain within their nucleus 46 chromosomes and are subject to mitotic division. However, this is not so of the sex cells, which are called the ovum and spermatozoa. These contain 23 single chromosomes. The reason for this is that in the division of the sex cells the chromosomes divide in two, with each new cell containing only 23 chromosomes. This division is called meiosis or reduction division.[3] Therefore the ovum and spermatozoa do not duplicate as in mitosis so each sex cell contains only one half of the genetic information from the person's chromosomes. At conception the mother contributes the ovum containing 23 chromosomes and the father contributes the spermatozoa containing 23 chromosomes, making up the full genetic complement of 46 chromosomes in the new individual.[6]

This very brief description of genetic development is included as an introduction to the discussion of the clinical abnormalities that may occur. A more detailed explanation of genetics is included in Chapter 5.

Chromosomal abnormalities

It was in 1956 that human cells were found to contain 46 chromosomes. Since this discovery various chromosomal abnormalities have been demonstrated and their relationship to mental handicap proved. One such abnormality is the presence of an extra chromosome, called trisomy.[2] This produces a profound effect, an example of which is seen in *Down's syndrome*. This abnormality is thought to be due to a maturational defect in the mother's sex cells. This results in the presence of an extra chromosome at pair 21.

Mental handicap may also be seen where extra chromosomal material appears as an additional part of a chromosome. This is usually associated with gross physical malformation and severe mental handicap.

Conversely there may be deletions of part of a chromosome. An example is seen in the *cri du chat syndrome*, where there is partial deletion of the fifth pair of chromosomes, resulting in a severely handicapped child.[2]

Occasionally the chromosome may form a ring and this can produce severe physical malformations as well as a marked degree of mental handicap.[2]

As we have seen, the sex of the individual is determined by the two sex chromosomes which make up pair 23. It is possible for men and women to have an *extra X chromosome.* There are two common sex trisomies. Trisomy X in females, which produces XXX chromosomes, results in slight mental handicap. Trisomy X in males produces XXY chromosomes and manifests itself as Klinefelter's syndrome. The more X chromosomes that are present the greater the physical and mental handicap.[2] Occasionally some men have an additional Y chromosome, resulting in the XYY pattern. This addition may produce no symptoms or can result in mild mental handicap.

Genetic abnormalities

Genetic abnormalities may give rise to mental handicap. The affected individuals are usually severely handicapped, with various physical deformities. One such example is *microcephaly*, which is caused by a single abnormal gene. The presence of this abnormality prevents the brain from developing normally.

Another example is *tuberous sclerosis* or epiloia. This condition is caused by an abnormal dominant gene and produces severe mental handicap, multiple body tumours and facial rashes.[2] However, despite the fact that it is caused by a dominant gene, it is unusual to see the complete manifestations of this disorder.

A large group of disorders, known as *inborn errors of metabolism*, are also caused by abnormal genes. Metabolism is the process of breaking down food into elements that the body can use; if this process is interrupted the incomplete products of metabolism may affect the individual adversely. The most common form of inborn error is found in the condition of *phenylketonuria.* This is a disorder of protein metabolism. In this case there is a deficiency of an enzyme called phenylalanine hydroxylase, which is normally present in the liver. When present, this enzyme converts phenylalanine, an amino acid, to tyrosine. Without this conversion high levels of phenylalanine occurs in the blood, producing severe effects on the child's mental and physical development.[2]

A disorder of carbohydrate metabolism called *galactosaemia* is caused by abnormal genes. This abnormality results in a deficiency or absence of an enzyme vital for the effective metabolism of galactose. This produces an accumulation of harmful chemicals which damage the liver and kidneys as well as causing mental handicap. However, it is possible to treat both phenylketonuria and galactosaemia by dietary measures.[5]

In disorders of fat metabolism there is abnormal storage of fats in tissues leading to their degeneration and which can be attributed to genetic abnormalities. A rare example is *Tay-Sachs disease* which is caused by the deficiency of an enzyme which leads to the abnormal accumulation of fat which has a progressive effect leading to an early death.

The above examples are just a few of the large number of known causes of mental handicap. They serve to illustrate how defects or abnormalities of the chromosomes or genes can cause mental handicap.

ENVIRONMENTAL CAUSES

From the moment of conception the fetus develops normally in the uterus; the child is born at full term, is cared for in infancy and childhood and develops into an independent adult. Unfortunately this normal picture of development does not always occur, as environmental factors may intervene at any time from conception and may cause mental handicap.

One of the best known of these environmental factors is *maternal infection* which has been known for fifty years to affect the fetus. An example of maternal infection affecting the fetus seriously enough to cause mental handicap is rubella (German measles) where there may also be additional handicaps such as blindness and deafness. Other virus infections are known to cause mental handicap; these include varicella (chickenpox), herpes simplex, infective hepatitis, influenza, mumps and poliomyelitis. The degree of handicap varies from mild to profound and the risk is always greater if infection occurs in the first three months of pregnancy.

Childhood infections such as inflammation of the brain (encephalitis) or its coverings (meningitis) may damage the brain to the extent that there may be mental handicap, slight or severe.

Traumatic factors may intervene during pregnancy, at birth or during childhood to produce mental handicap. The mother may be excessively exposed to radiation, particularly during the first 16 weeks, which may cause microcephaly with severe mental handicap. Sometimes a mother may try to procure an abortion using substances that will damage a fertilized ovum and which may cause abnormalities and mental handicap in the child. *Incompatibility of the mother's and baby's blood* may result in the destruction of the baby's red blood cells and damage to parts of the brain. Fortunately it is possible to treat this condition in a number of ways. A further factor may occur at birth. During the second stage of labour the baby's head is compressed to allow its passage through the birth canal, but if this stage is too rapid for proper moulding of the head there may be brain damage or haemorrhage causing mental handicap.[2] Included in this group are those children who experience accidental or non-accidental violence sufficient to cause mental handicap.

Other conditions may occur when the developing fetus is denied essential nutrients as a result of *placental insufficiency*. The developing fetus is very sensitive and can be affected by a lack of protein, blood sugar or oxygen and this deprivation is particularly significant at the period when brain development is at its peak.

Mental handicap may occur as a result of the child eating *poisonous substances*. An example of this is the ingestion of lead from paint which may lead to a serious condition called lead encephalopathy causing blindness, deafness, convulsions and severe mental handicap.[2]

SUMMARY

This chapter has presented a simplified overview of the many factors which can contribute to or cause mental handicap and is designed as an introduction to the more detailed account of causation, symptomatology and treatment contained in Part II.

It should be born in mind that, although there seem to be a bewildering number of causes and contributory factors, it is still possible to diagnose only 35% of cases with any accuracy and the number of treatments available is considerably less.[4] This inevitably raises the question of whether a concern with the clinical factors in mental handicap is very important; after all, knowing a person's diagnosis may not help us to care for that person. The answer must be that continued effort is vital because as more and more advances are made in the study of genetics and in techniques of protection and prevention it may soon be possible to treat actively more and more of the conditions that render people mentally handicapped.

GLOSSARY

Autosome	Any paired chromosome other than a sex chromosome.
Chromosome	A rod-shaped dark staining body, present in all body cells and appearing within the nucleus at cell division. Chromosomes contain the genes or hereditary factors and are constant in number.
Cerebral palsy	A persisting qualitative motor disease due to non-progressive damage of the brain.
Cri-du-chat syndrome	A condition producing severe mental handicap caused by a partial deletion of one of the fifth pair of chromosomes.
Down's syndrome	Also called trisomy 21 and mongolism. An abnormality resulting in an additional chromosome at pair 21, making the total chromosome count 47.
Encephalitis	Inflammation of the brain.
Epilepsy	A disorder characterized by recurring loss or alteration of consciousness. Symptoms are due to paroxysmal disturbance of the electrical activity of the brain.
Galactose	A white crystalline carbohydrate substance. Obtained from lactose (milk sugar) during the digestive process.
Galactosaemia	An inborn error of carbohydrate metabolism, caused by the inability to convert galactose to glucose. Leads to mental handicap if untreated.

Genes	The biological units of heredity, self-reproducing and located in a definite position on a particular chromosome.
Herpes simplex	An acute viral disease characterized by groups of watery blisters on the skin and mucous membranes.
Hepatitis	Inflammation of the liver.
Klinefelter's syndrome	The commonest sex chromosome abnormality affecting males. Caused by the presence of an extra X chromosome resulting in mental handicap and female bodily proportions.
Microcephaly	Abnormal smallness of the head.
Meiosis	A special method of cell division, occurring in the maturation of the sex cells, by means of which each daughter nucleus receives half the chromosomes.
Mitosis	A method of cell division in which the two daughter nuclei normally receive identical complements of chromosomes.
Mumps	An infectious viral disease characterized by inflammation of the salivary glands, especially the parotids.
Meningitis	Inflammation of the meninges of the brain.
Ovum	The female reproductive cell.
Phenylalanine hydroxylase	An essential enzyme found in the liver which is necessary for the metabolism of the protein phenylalanine.
Phenyl-ketonuria	An inborn error of metabolism concerning phenylalanine. Untreated leads to mental handicap.
Poliomyelitis	An acute viral disease with varying degrees of severity. In severe cases it can affect the central nervous system leading to paralysis.
Rubella (German measles)	An acute contagious viral disease, lasting only a short time with mild symptoms. Serious mental and physical handicaps can result in the newborn if mothers become infected during the first 16 weeks of pregnancy.
Spermatazoon	The male reproductive cell.
Tay-Sachs disease	A progressive disorder of lipid (fat) metabolism characterized by abnormal storage of fats in the tissues leading to their degeneration.
Trisomy	The presence of an additional chromosome.
Tuberous sclerosis (epiloia)	A condition caused by an autosomal dominant gene where only partial features of the condition may be seen.

Tyrosine   An amino acid essential to the body for the production of adrenaline, thyroxine and melanin.

Varicella   An acute contagious disease of children. Various skin
(chickenpox)   eruptions occur, accompanied by a slight rise in temperature.

BIBLIOGRAPHY

1. DHSS (1971) *Better Services for the Mentally Handicapped.* London: HMSO.
2. Heaton-Ward, A. (1975) *Mental Subnormality*, 4th ed. Bristol: John Wright.
3. Heywood Jones, I. (1978) *Genetics and Inherited Diseases.* London: Nursing Times.
4. Shearer, A. (1971) *Fact Sheet 1—What and Why.* London: King's Fund Centre.
5. Kirman, B. (1972) *The Mentally Handicapped Child.* London: Thomas Nelson.
6. Mathews, D.R. (1978) *Your Fate in Your Genes.* London: Nursing Mirror.
7. Oates, J. & Floyd, A. (1976) *Course of Development.* Milton Keynes: Open University Press.

Legal concepts of mental handicap 3

History has shown that attitudes about mental handicap have been both changeable and arbitrary and are reflected in the treatment and legislation formulated to care for the mentally handicapped at different times. As early as 400 B.C. Hippocrates taught that mental disorder was of physical and not divine origin and advocated medical treatment for insanity and epilepsy. However, in Western civilizations mental handicap was viewed rather differently, with people thinking that the treatment of mental disorder was a matter more for the priest than for the physician. Treatment was carried out by exorcism and purification of the soul and when this failed witchcraft was blamed.

The law in England reflected society's attitudes in that from the time of Edward II (1284-1327) until the beginning of the 19th century the emphasis was on the protection of the property of 'idiots' and 'lunatics', rather than on the care of the people themselves. People who were so mentally disordered that they required custody were looked after by private individuals in 'madhouses'. The conditions in the madhouses were often appalling and included physical abuse, starvation and sometimes murder. As a result of a growing public awareness of these abuses and the pioneering work of William Tuke in York, Charlesworth Hill in Lincoln and Guggenbühl in Switzerland the law was changed in an attempt to regulate the care received by the mentally disordered.[9] In 1845 a Lunacy Act was passed which instituted a Board of Commissioners which had the power to licence and inspect premises where mentally disordered people were kept. In 1853 major legislation was enacted in the form of three Acts of Parliament: the Lunacy Regulation Act, the Lunacy Act and the Lunatic Asylum Act. They were repealed in 1890 and the Lunacy Act 1890 combined all the previous legislation into one legislative document. Gradually, the needs of the less handicapped became important, particularly the social problems and the need for care. Following the Report of the Royal Commission on the Care and Control of the Feeble Minded (1904-8) the Mental Deficiency Act 1913 was passed. This Act required the local authorities to provide institutions and community care facilities for the mentally handicapped.

There was a growing feeling that the mentally handicapped should be segregated from normal society and this prompted the proliferation of institutions, hospitals and colonies up and down the country. The Mental Deficiency Act, amended in 1927, also attempted a 'scientific' definition of mental deficiency.[11] By today's standards of assessment it is very inadequate but is included as an example of attitudes towards mental handicap at this time. Mental deficiency was defined as: 'A condition of arrested or incomplete development of mind existing before the age of eighteen years whether arising from inherent causes or induced by disease or injury'.

Four types of defective were recognized and defined as:

1. *'Idiots'*: persons in whose case exists mental defectiveness of such a degree that they are unable to guard themselves against common physical dangers.

2. *'Imbeciles'*: persons in whose case there exists mental defectiveness which, though not amounting to idiocy, is yet so pronounced that they are incapable of managing themselves or their affairs or in the case of children of being taught to do so.

3. *'Feeble Minded'*: persons in whose case there exists mental defectiveness which, though not amounting to imbecility, is yet so pronounced that they require care, supervision and control for their own protection or for the protection of others.

4. *'Moral defectives'*: persons in whose case there exists mental defectiveness coupled with strongly vicious or criminal propensities and who require care, supervision and control for the protection of others.

The definition and classification of mental deficiency set out in the Mental Deficiency Act 1913 and its amendments gave little or no regard to possible improvement following treatment and training and was aimed at the control and segregation of the mentally handicapped. A further aspect was that a large number of patients were 'certified' as mentally defective and compulsorily detained in hospital.

During the period from 1913 to 1958 parallel legislation was enacted in England and other countries. An attitude prevalent at the time was that unless the mentally handicapped were prevented from breeding there would be a 'dilution' of the nation's intelligence, the philosophy of the Eugenics Society.[9] In America this view was carried to the point of legislation and by 1926 sterilization laws had been enacted in 23 states.[9]

In 1944 an Education Act was passed which stated that the severely mentally handicapped were ineducable and this had the effect of further reinforcing institutional care by forcing the institutions to provide 'occupation and training'.

In 1946 the National Health Service Act transferred responsibility for providing hospital and specialist services for the mentally handicapped from the local authorities to the National Health Service.[13] Community services remained the responsibility of the local authorities.

It was during this time of change and reorientation that opinion changed regarding the suitability of the law relating to mental handicap and resulted eventually in the Mental Health Act 1959.

THE MENTAL HEALTH ACT 1959

The next part of this chapter examines some of the sections of the Mental Health Act 1959 in some detail. This is done deliberately as it is recognized that some readers may wish to use this as a form of reference. Readers who require more detailed information are advised to refer to the Bibliography at the end of this chapter.

The pressure to change the outdated 19th century legislation regarding the mentally disordered led to the Royal Commission on the Law relating to Mental Illness and Mental Deficiency which met from 1954 to 1957. Its report led to the drafting of the Mental Health Act 1959. The Act had two important aims: to provide appropriate administrative machinery to deal with the mentally disordered and to ensure that no one should be admitted to hospital if alternative care could be provided in the community.[1]

The Mental Health Act 1959 regulates the admission and discharge of both the mentally ill and the mentally handicapped under the broad term of mental disorder. This is defined in Section 4 as 'mental illness, arrested or incomplete development of mind, psychopathic disorder, and any other disorder or disability of mind'.[10] These broad classifications are illustrated in Fig. 5. It can be seen that the Act abolished the terms idiot, imbecile, feeble-minded and moral defective and redefined the mentally handicapped as either subnormal or severely subnormal. Although these terms are used in this chapter it should be remembered that they are legal terms and do not reflect the modern concept of mental handicap.

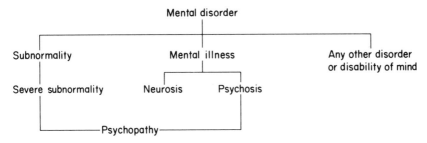

Fig. 5. The broad classification of disorders under the Mental Health Act 1959.

Severe subnormality is defined in Section 4 (2)[10] and means:

A state of arrested or incomplete development of mind which includes subnormality of intelligence and is of such a nature or degree that the patient is incapable of living an independent life or of guarding himself against serious exploitation, or will be so incapable when of an age to do so.

Subnormality is defined in Section 4(3)[10] and means:

A state of arrested or incomplete development of mind (not amounting to severe subnormality) which includes subnormality of intelligence and is of a nature or degree which requires or is susceptible to medical treatment or other special care of training of the patient.

The difference in classification centres around whether the individual is 'incapable of living an independent life', using the criterion of social incapacity; or whether he 'requires or is susceptible to medical treatment or other special care or training', using the criterion of clinical treatment.[7]

Psychopathic disorder is defined in Section 4 (4)[10] and means:

A persistent disorder or disability of mind (whether or nor including subnormality of intelligence) which results in abnormally aggressive or seriously irresponsible conduct on the part of the patient, and requires or is susceptible to medical treatment.

In defining psychopathic disorder the Mental Health Act again uses the criterion that the disorder 'requires or is susceptible to medical treatment'. The person may be admitted to hospital under this section but receive no treatment as there is none available.[8] This also applies to the admission of someone who is defined as subnormal.

The Act does not equate the categories of severe subnormality or subnormality with a score on an IQ test.[7] However, it is accepted that those with an IQ of 50 or below are termed severely subnormal and those with an IQ of 50-70 are termed subnormal. It is important that the legal classification is made separate from IQ scores and that the classification itself is regularly reviewed.

Surprisingly, the Act does not define mental illness at all, even though it is grounds for compulsory adult admission to hospital.[8]

Sections governing admission to hospital

Informal admission (Section 5)

Informal admission means that the individual comes into hospital for treatment of his own free will; no powers of detention are involved. A child under 16 years may be detained in hospital at the request of his parents or guardians regardless of the child's wishes. However, at 16 the patient can discharge himself regardless of his parent's wishes.

This section accounts for the vast majority of admissions to hospital; an overall 87% of all admissions.[5] Approximately 98% of all children are admitted to hospital under this section at the request of their parents or guardians.[5]

Comment: At first sight informal admission would seem to be in the hospital patients' interests as they are 'free' to leave at any time. However, they may not fully understand the implications of admission and, because they are unable to represent themselves, often spend a long time in hospital without other alternatives being considered. This is particularly true of children who are admitted at their parent's request and whose sixteenth birthday is passed without a review of their position.

Formal or compulsory admission

Application for formal admission is made to the hospital by either a local authority social worker or the nearest relative. This application must be supported by two medical recommendations, one from a doctor who is familiar with the person, such as his general practitioner, and one from a doctor who is approved by the Secretary of State as 'having special experience in the diagnosis and treatment of mental disorder'.[10] The social worker and the nearest relative must have seen the person within the previous two weeks. The doctors' reports must state the diagnosis and the reasons why other forms of care are inappropriate. Most often the social worker liaises with the hospital doctor before application for admission is made, so ensuring that a place is available.[8]

Admission for observation (Section 25)

This section authorizes the compulsory admission to hospital of an individual for the purpose of observation. The patient may not be detained for more than 28 days from the date of admission. The grounds for admitting someone to hospital under this section are:

1. That the person is suffering a mental disorder that warrants detention for a limited period.
2. That the person ought to be detained in the interest of his own health or safety or for the protection of others.

Comment: This section is seen to be both unfair and unnecessary. All other countries in Europe and North America have abandoned it.[5] The problems are that once a patient is admitted under Section 25 there is no appeal possible and, although the section is designed for the purpose of observation, patients are often treated against their will.

Emergency admission for observation (Section 29)

Section 29 is used in an emergency where the normal processes of section 25 would take too long. In this section only one doctor, normally the individual's general practitioner, is required to make a medical recommendation. The section allows detention in hospital for a period not exceeding 72 hours. However, if a second medical recommendation is made within this period of 72 hours the section is altered to section 25 and the period of detention becomes 28 days.

Comment: This section is open to abuse as it requires only one medical recommendation, that of the general practitioner, who may not have special experience in mental disorder. Again there is no appeal against the fact of admission and many people feel that 24 hours is adequate for a further medical opinion to be obtained.[5]

Admission for treatment (Section 26)

This section is used where admission is for a longer period of time. The person may be compulsorily admitted for one year initially, although this can be renewed for one further year and subsequent periods of two years.

The disorder must warrant detention for medical treatment and be in the patient's interest or for the protection of others. The procedure is the same as for section 25 with two important differences: age and classification. The adult patient must be suffering from either mental illness or severe subnormality in order to be admitted under section 26. However, a patient under 21 may be admitted suffering from subnormality or psychopathy. In this case the patient may not be automatically discharged at 21 but may be detained until the age of 25.

In summary, a patient suffering from mental illness or severe subnormality can be admitted at any age under section 26. An adult suffering from subnormality or psychopathy cannot be detained, but someone under 21 can be.

The patient has the right under this section to apply to a Mental Health Review Tribunal for his detention and/or release to be considered. Mental Health Review Tribunals and methods of application are considered on p. 40.

Comment: Although the patient admitted under this section has the right to apply to a Mental Health Review Tribunal this may take months to arrange and for a decision to be reached. The effect of this is that the person may be detained and treated against his will. The whole question of the rights of patients is raised by section 26. The right to refuse treatment and also the right to receive treatment are rights which we all accept as fundamental. Treatment under the Act includes 'nursing care' which should take account of the mentally handicapped person's need to acquire those behavioural skills which will enable him to live in the community. Failure to do this would seem to be a dereliction of the hospital's duty, under the Act, to the patient who is compulsorily admitted to hospital for treatment.

Admission to a 'Place of Safety' (Sections 136 and 135)

The Act defines a 'place of safety' as a hospital, a police station, a nursing home for mental disorder or any other suitable place where the occupier is willing temporarily to receive the patient.

Section 136 authorizes a police officer to detain and remove to a place of safety any person who *appears* to be suffering from mental disorder and who seems to be in need of care or control. The duration of this order is 72 hours and its purpose is to enable the patient to be examined by a medical practitioner and to be interviewed by a social worker.[8]

Section 135 allows a social worker to apply to a Justice of the Peace for a warrant to remove a person, believed to be ill-treated, neglected or unable to care for himself, to a place of safety. The police have powers under the warrant to enter, by force if necessary, the place where the person is and remove him. The duration of this section is 72 hours.

Both section 135 and 136 may be altered to either section 25 or 26 if the person's condition is serious enough.

Comment: The major problem with section 136 is that it is left to a policeman to make a decision regarding a person's apparent mental disorder. The only requirement is that the policeman acts in 'good faith' and with 'reasonable care'. If he does act in this way he is protected from possible legal proceedings by section 141 of the Mental Health Act 1959. A further problem is that a 'place of safety' can be a police station and if it is difficult to obtain a place in hospital the individual may be kept in a cell and not in a hospital ward.[5]

Detention of patients already in hospital (Section 30)

This section allows the detention in hospital of an informal patient admitted under section 5 for a period of 72 hours. This is used when an informal patient insists on discharging himself when in the opinion of the responsible doctor his condition requires further treatment in hospital. This section can be then substituted for either section 25 (observation) or section 26 (treatment).

It may also be used in the case of compulsory detention under section 25 and 29 which is being converted into section 26 (treatment).

The aim of this section is to safeguard the interests of the patient and also the general public.

Comment: This section should be used as little as possible because if it is used routinely it would undermine the spirit of the Mental Health Act which says that treatment should be on a voluntary or informal basis.

Admission from the courts: hospital orders (Sections 60 and 65)

Section 60 authorizes a person to be admitted to hospital from the Assize Court or Quarter Sessions for a period of one year. The Court needs to be satisfied from the evidence of two medical practitioners that the person is suffering from mental illness, severe subnormality, subnormality or psychopathic disorder to a degree that warrants his detention in hospital. The court must also be sure that a place in hospital will be available for the person within 28 days of the order being made.

In making a decision to substitute a hospital order for a prison sentence for people concerned in criminal proceedings the court takes into account the details of the offence, the character and antecedents of the offender and alternative methods of dealing with him.[10]

Although the section deals with the admission of patients convicted of a criminal offence the magistrate's court has the power to make a hospital order in respect of someone who is mentally ill or severely subnormal without convicting him. The Crown Court, however, cannot make a hospital order without convicting the accused.[8]

The Crown Court can impose a restriction on discharge (section 65) where it feels this is necessary for the protection of the public. This restriction can be for a specified period or it may be without time limit.[8] The effect of a restriction order is that there is no need for renewal of authority for detention in hospital as long as the restriction order is in force. Further restrictions are that the patient is unable to apply to a Mental Health Review Tribunal, and leave of absence, transfer from one hospital to another and discharge can be authorized only by the Secretary of State. The Secretary of State decides on these matters as a result of reports made on the patient by the responsible medical officer. He may refer the case to a tribunal to receive advice and approximately one-third of tribunal hearings arise in this way.[8]

Comment: One of the major difficulties imposed on the courts by section 60 is that they cannot make a hospital order unless a hospital agrees to admit the person within 28 days. The hospital authorities may not agree, on the grounds that they are unable to provide the degree of security necessary or that the nursing staff may not be prepared to look after the person. The Special Hospitals may refuse admission on the grounds that the person does not require the degree of security they provide. This often leaves the court with no other option than sending the person to prison when the real need is for treatment.

Section 65 imposes severe restrictions on a person's liberty, often disproportionate to the offence he has committed. The Home Secretary is empowered to make all decisions regarding discharge, leave of absence and transfer, with no automatic system of appeal for the patient. Even where a consultant psychiatrist who knows the patient very well recommends discharge through a tribunal the Home Secretary is not obliged to take the advice, and indeed in the period 1970-5 he rejected the advice in 40% of all cases.[5] The Home Secretary's decision gives no indication of why the application is refused.

Absence without leave (Section 40)

This section is concerned with the return and readmission of a detained patient who is absent without leave. It may be used when a patient fails to return at the end of his leave, does not stay in the place specified or leaves the hospital without permission. Under the section a social worker, nurse, police constable or any person authorized in writing by the hospital may arrest and return the patient. There are, however, differences in the provision for subnormal and psychopathic patients and those who are classified as severely subnormal or mentally ill. Subnormal and psychopathic patients who are over 21 years of age may be subject to section 40 within a period of six months. In mental illness and severe subnormality this period is 28 days. It would seem that the law is saying that if someone who is subnormal or a psychopath can live in society for six months without trouble he can be discharged from the Act. Similarly, if a person is severely subnormal or mentally ill and can survive for 28 days he too can be discharged. Once the time periods of six months and 28 days respectively have elapsed, the person can be readmitted only informally or by initiating the full procedure for compulsory admission.

Sections concerned with discharge

Informal patients should be discharged by mutual agreement between the doctor, patient and relatives. This is often not the case as the patient may simply walk out without consulting anybody or may be discharged from the hospital for administrative reasons.

A patient who is detained under section 25 (for observation) or section 29 (for emergency admission) must be discharged on expiry of the order. This is 28 days in respect of section 25 and 72 hours in respect of section 29. Only the responsible medical officer can discharge the patient earlier.

Those patients who are detained under section 26 (for treatment) can be discharged in the following ways under section 47:

1. By the patient's relatives, providing notice of discharge is given in writing 72 hours before the proposed date of discharge.
2. By the responsible medical officer (consultant).
3. By three or more managers of the hospital.

Section 43 limits the duration of detention under section 26 to one year and, providing the authority is not renewed for a further year or two years, the patient must be discharged. However, the doctor may renew the order, using section 43, if he thinks that this would be in the interests of the patient or of other people. To do this he must have seen the patient within the last two months of the detention period.

If the nearest relative applies for the discharge of a patient he must give 72 hours notice in writing. If the doctor feels that discharge at this stage is premature he may issues a barring certificate under section 48 which authorizes the continued detention of the patient regardless of the nearest relative's wishes. Section 48 has two further important functions: it prohibits the relative from ordering discharge for six months but gives the relative the opportunity to apply to a Mental Health Review Tribunal within 28 days of being informed of the barring certificate.

Patients admitted under section 60 (hospital order) can be discharged only by the responsible medical officer. The patient's nearest relative cannot order discharge under section 47 but can apply to a Mental Health Review Tribunal within the period of 12 months beginning with the date of the order and after that, once in any subsequent period of 12 months.[6] The patient himself may make an application to a Mental Health Review Tribunal within six months of the date of the order.

If restrictions are imposed on the hospital order under section 65 the only person with the power to discharge the patient is the Secretary of State, who normally takes advice either from the responsible medical officer or from a Mental Health Review Tribunal. Neither the patient nor his nearest relative may apply directly to a Mental Health Review Tribunal.

Sections 135 and 136 can be dealt with only by the responsible medical officer who may discharge the individual before 72 hours or use section 30 to further detain the person for observation.

Mental Health Review Tribunals

Frequent reference to Mental Health Review Tribunals has been made and there follows an explanation of their powers and responsibilities.

The Royal Commission of 1954-7 recognized that a medical disorder, as defined in the 1959 Mental Health Act, should be dealt with as a medical and not a legal matter.[8] It was also considered important that someone who was compulsorily admitted to hospital should be able to apply to an independent body which would review the case and make recommendations regarding discharge or continuing detention. For this reason the Mental Health Review Tribunals were recommended and set up.

The Mental Health Review Tribunals' function is to consider those applications made regarding discharge of those patients who are compulsorily detained. They also advise the Secretary of State about those patients who are subject to special restrictions under section 65.

In each of the 15 Regional Health Authorities there is a panel, appointed by the Lord Chancellor, from which each Tribunal is composed. The membership of each panel is drawn from the legal and medical professions and 'lay members'. The legal members are appointed directly by the Lord Chancellor. The medical members are appointed by the Lord Chancellor on the recommendations of the Secretary of State for Health and Social Security and in practice are consultant psychiatrists. The lay members are appointed in the same way and are people who have particular experience in 'administration, the social services or other experience considered suitable'.[10]

A tribunal consists of a minimum of three people, one from each of the three disciplines: one legal member is the President of the tribunal, a consultant psychiatrist and a lay person.

Those patients who are detained under sections 25, 29, 135 and 136 are not eligible to apply to a Mental Health Review Tribunal. Those patients compulsorily detained under sections 26 and 60 are eligible to apply within the first six months of the date of the order and if the order is renewed once during each period of renewal. Section 48 authorizes the nearest relative to apply to a Tribunal within 28 days of the issuing of a barring certificate following unsuccessful notice of discharge. Patients subject to restrictions on a hospital order (section 65) are not eligible to apply to a Tribunal. The Tribunal must decide, on a majority basis, to discharge a patient if it is satisfied that:[10]

1. 'the patient is not suffering from mental illness, psychopathic disorder, subnormality or severe subnormality'.
2. 'it is not necessary in the interests of the patient's health or safety or for the protection of others that the patient should be continued to be detained'.
3. 'if released the patient would not be likely to act in a manner dangerous to other persons or to himself'.

In 1975 the National Association for Mental Health (MIND) reported that only 3% of those compulsorily admitted under the civil provisions of the Mental Health Act were eligible to apply to a Mental Health Review Tribunal.[5] It was further estimated that only 12% of these people actually applied for a hearing.[5] This may be for a number of reasons but does not of itself invalidate the concept of independent review. Indeed, MIND goes further and recommends that there should be a system of automatic referral to a Mental Health Review Tribunal within a specified period of time, between six months and two years, for any patient detained under the Mental Health Act.[5]

Sections concerned with the management of property and affairs of patients

Sometimes 'a person is incapable, by reason of mental disorder of managing and administering his property and affairs'.[10] This eventuality is dealt with in sections 100-121 of the Mental Health Act which brings into effect the Court of Protection which is part of the Supreme Court. If a person is found to be incapable of managing his affairs through mental disorder his affairs may be placed in the hands of the Court of Protection which will manage them for him whilst he is suffering from the mental disorder. It does not matter whether the person is in hospital on a detained or informal basis or living at home.

The Court of Protection may appoint a receiver to manage the person's affairs, normally either one of the person's relatives or an officer of the local authority. The receiver is required to show annual accounts of any transactions undertaken. Often insurance against loss of monies is taken out and paid for from the person's estate.

From time to time as directed by the Court, Lord Chancellor's Visitors may visit the person to determine whether the mental disorder persists and to what degree. Lord Chancellor's Visitors are doctors who are specially trained or experienced in mental disorder.[8]

Where a person's property does not exceed £500 it is not necessary to appoint a receiver. The person's money will be placed in a fund and used to provide for the person's needs.[8]

Sections concerned with special hospitals

The provision of Special Hospitals is dealt with in sections 97 and 98 of the Mental Health Act, which authorize the Secretary of State for Health and Social Services to provide and manage Special Hospitals. The Special Hospitals are directly administered by the Department of Health and Social Security and any admission must be referred to them.

The purpose of the Special Hospitals is to provide 'treatment for people under detention orders in conditions of special security, who are dangerous, violent or have criminal propensities'.[10] There are four Special Hospitals in England and Wales: Broadmoor and Park Lane for the mentally ill and Rampton and Moss Side for the mentally handicapped and mentally ill.

In October 1975 the Committee on Mentally Abnormal Offenders chaired by Lord Butler submitted their Report in which they proposed a number of changes in the law and the provisions made for the mentally abnormal offender.[3] One of their important recommendations was that each of the Regional Health Authorities should provide facilities, which they termed Regional Secure Units, 'for those patients who do not require the security of a Special Hospital but nevertheless cannot be suitably treated in an open psychiatric ward'.[3] Although the government of the day supported the recommendation, including that of central funding, little progress seems to have been made (1981). There is no doubt that the secure units are urgently needed, in the author's opinion, so that the gross overcrowding in the Special Hospitals can be relieved and more people enabled to benefit from a less restrictive environment.

A further recommendation concerns criminal responsibility and recommends changes to the existing McNaghten's rules; these state:

> The jurors ought to be told in all cases that every man is to be presumed to be sane, and to possess a sufficient degree of reason to be responsible for his crimes, until the contrary be proved to their satisfaction; and that to establish a defence on the grounds of insanity it must be clearly proved that at the time of the committing of the act, the party accused was labouring under such a defect of reason, from disease of the mind, as not to know the nature

and quality of the act he was doing; or if he did know it, that he did not know he was doing wrong.[3]

The Committee fully accept the principle that if a person is severely mentally disordered he ought not to be held responsible for his crimes, but hold that the McNaghten rules are not a satisfactory test. They propose a new form of verdict, namely: 'not guilty on evidence of mental disorder'. In this there would be specific exemption for those people charged who were suffering at the time of the act from severe mental illness or severe subnormality.

Table 9. Summary of the provisions of the Mental Health Act 1959

Section number	Relating to
6	Functions of Local Health Authorities
12	Power to compel attendance at training centre
27	Application for admission to hospital
28	Medical recommendations for admission to hospital
31	Effect of application for admission
33	Application for guardianship
35	Regulations as to guardianship
36	Correspondence of patients
38	Re-classification of patients
39	Leave of absence from hospital
41	Regulations as to transfer of patients
42	Transfer of guardianship in case of death or incapacity of guardian
43	Duration of authority for detention
44	Special provisions as to psychopathic and subnormal patients
47	Discharge of patients
49	Definition of relative and nearest relative
57	Power of Secretary of State to refer to Tribunal
62	Requirement as to medical evidence in connection with section 60
63	Effects of hospital and guardianship orders
66	Powers of Secretary of State in respect of patients subject to restriction orders
71	Persons ordered to be kept in custody during Her Majesty's pleasure
72	Removal to hospital of persons serving prison sentences
74	Restriction on discharge of prisoners removed to hospital
99	Transfers to and from Special Hospitals
100	Judicial authorities and Court of Protection
122	Application to Mental Health Review Tribunal
123	Powers of Mental Health Review Tribunals
126	Ill treatment of patients
128	Sexual intercourse with patients
129	Assisting patients to absent themselves without leave
133	Provision of pocket money for in-patients in hospital
138	Pay, pensions, etc. of mentally disordered people
141	Protection for acts done in pursuance of the 1959 Mental Health Act

This concludes the discussion on the more important sections of the Mental Health Act 1959. There are of course many more and a number of these are set out in Table 9 for quick reference.

RELATED LEGISLATION

There are a number of aspects of every-day life that are governed by law and which affect the mentally handicapped.

Contracts

A contract made by someone who is mentally handicapped is binding on both parties. However, if it can be shown that the mentally handicapped person did not understand the terms of the contract and that the other person knew this, then the contract may be cancelled. Personal experience has shown that if the situation is explained to the other person or concern involved they are usually sympathetic and withdraw.

Making a will

The same conditions apply to the mentally handicapped as to the mentally ill,[7] in that they can legally make a will provided that at the time of doing so:

1. They know the nature and extent of their property.
2. They know those persons who might justifiably have a claim on their property.
3. Their judgement and will power are such that they can determine the relative strength of these claims.[7]

In practice very few mentally handicapped people make wills, particularly those in hospital.

Marriage

There is no law which prevents the mentally handicapped from marrying if they are over 16, provided they have parental permission, or over 18 years. However, they must understand what they are doing and if one of the persons was unaware at the time of the marriage that the partner was suffering from any of the mental disorders defined in the Mental Health Act which made them unfitted for marriage, then the marriage is voidable under the Matrimonial Causes Act 1973. Under this Act proceedings must be instituted within a year of the marriage. Mentally handicapped people are increasingly marrying and living fulfilled lives with each other. They may need and should be given as much help and support as necessary in setting up their home and in managing day-to-day difficulties.

Voting

The right to vote is protected by the Representation of the People Act 1949. For the mentally handicapped in hospital, the administrative procedures often mean that they do not vote even if they are capable of doing so. Everyone is entitled to have his name on the electoral roll or register of voters but a patient in hospital must vote in the constituency where he was registered before his admission to hospital. In common law persons of 'unsound mind' and 'idiots' are legally incapable of voting, which bars those patients classified as severely subnormal. Those patients who are legally detained under a hospital order are also ineligible to vote. Many people feel that all mentally ill and mentally handicapped people who are receiving hospital treatment for any length of time should be able to register using the hospital address.

Driving licences

If a person is classified as severely subnormal he is precluded from taking a driving test under the Road Traffic Act 1960 and its amendments. This is obviously sensible but may have implications for those mentally handicapped people who are being trained in horticulture and agriculture in view of the increasing use of machinery in these occupations.

Medical termination of pregnancy

A pregnancy may be terminated by a doctor under the Abortion Act 1967 if the following conditions are met. Two doctors must be of the opinion, formed in 'good faith', that the pregnancy would involve either risk to the life of the pregnant woman or injury to the physical or mental health of the pregnant woman or her family greater than if the pregnancy were terminated. The second clause is the one that is intimately concerned with mental handicap and says that a pregnancy may be terminated where 'there is a substantial risk that if the child were born it would suffer from such physical or mental abnormalities as to be seriously handicapped'. Many conditions in mental handicap can be identified by the procedure of amniocentesis and termination of pregnancy may then be advised by the mother's doctor or requested by the parents, as in the case of rubella contracted during the first three months of pregnancy.

CONGENITAL DISABILITIES (CIVIL LIABILITY) ACT 1976

This Act allows the child, or those acting on the child's behalf, to recover damages where it has suffered damage or injury as a result of negligence in meeting the duty of care on the part of those responsible for the care of the mother before and during pregnancy and at birth. The time period during which claims may be made extends until the child is 19 and may extend up until 21 years. The significance of this Act in relation to mental handicap is difficult to assess as yet.

SUMMARY

The law relating to mental disorder has moved steadily from an emphasis on protection of the property of 'idiots' and 'lunatics' to the present Mental Health Act 1959. At the time it was formulated, the Mental Health Act 1959 was considered to be enlightened and forward-looking.[1] Its underlying principles are:

1. That treatment both in hospital and in the community should be voluntary.
2. That if it is necessary to detain a patient compulsorily in hospital it should be for a limited period only.
3. That the mentally disordered should increasingly be cared for in the community rather than in hospital.

Since 1959 there have been many important changes in attitudes regarding the mentally handicapped and how they should be cared for. This awareness of the need to bring the Mental Health Act 1959 into line with current thinking is reflected in a Consultative Document issued by the Department of Health and Social Security in 1976.[1] This document, prompted by pressure from individuals and organizations such as the National Association for Mental Health, raises the issue of whether or not the mentally handicapped should be entirely removed from the jurisdiction of the Mental Health Act. The argument for removal of the mentally handicapped from the Mental Health Act is based on the principle that medical treatment is inappropriate as mental handicap is not a disease that can be 'cured'. The argument for retaining legislation for the mentally handicapped centres around the 'need' to provide treatment, protect from exploitation and control behaviour.

In the author's opinion the mentally handicapped should be excluded from the Act as no other group of handicapped people are subject to the same restrictions as the mentally handicapped under the Mental Health Act.

The Report[4] of the Committee of Enquiry into Mental Handicap Nursing and Care 1979 advocates a normal life style for the mentally handicapped and this philosophy should be reflected in any future legislation regarding the mentally handicapped.

GLOSSARY

Abortion Act   Allows the medical termination of pregnancy where there is
1967   substantial risk that the child would be born suffering from
                     physical and/or mental handicap.

Age limits	Refers to age limits of subnormal and psychopathic patients subject to detention.
Barring Certificate	Under section 48 of the Mental Health Act the responsible medical officer can issue a barring certificate preventing the nearest relative from discharging a patient detained under section 26.
Butler Committee	Committee under the chairmanship of Lord Butler who produced the *Report of the Committee on Abnormal Offenders.*[3]
Compulsory admission	Admission for observation or treatment against the person's wishes.
Congenital Disabilities Act 1976	An Act which allows a child up to the age of 19 to recover damages for injuries received as a result of a breach of the 'duty of care'.
Court of Protection	Set up by the Lord Chancellor to administer and safeguard the affairs of mentally disordered patients in hospital.
Eugenics Society	A society which believed that the mentally handicapped should be segregated from the community. They also believed that the mentally handicapped should in no circumstances be allowed to procreate as this would 'lower the level of the nation's intelligence'.
Feeble-minded	A classification under the 1913 Mental Deficiency Act which equates with the category of the subnormal under the Mental Health Act 1959.
Hospital Order	An order made by the Assize Court, Quarter Sessions or Crown Court for a person to be detained in hospital for initially one year, under section 26 or 60 of the Mental Health Act 1959.
Idiot/Imbecile	Classifications under the Mental Deficiency Act 1913 which equate approximately with category of the severely subnormal under the Mental Health Act 1959.
Informal admission	Admission of a patient to hospital without any power of detention.
IQ	Intelligence quotient. The score achieved on an intelligence test.
Medical recommendation	Formal written recommendation made by a doctor in support of an application for compulsory admission or hospital order.

Mental Health Act 1959	The legislative Act which governs the admission, discharge and related aspects of the law as it relates to mental disorder. It contains nine parts, 154 sections and schedules.
Mental Health Review Tribunals	A panel of experts in mental disorder who review the necessity for continued detention of patients under some sections of the Mental Health Act 1959.
McNaghten's Rules	The rules used to establish a defence on grounds of insanity in a court of law.
Moral defective	Classification under the 1913 Mental Deficiency Act which equates approximately with the definition of psychopathy in section 4 (4) Mental Health Act 1959.
Place of Safety	Defined in the Mental Health Act 1959 as a hospital a police station, a nursing home for mental disorder or any other suitable place. Used in sections 135 and 136.
Psychopath	Defined in section 4 (4) of the Mental Health Act 1959 relating to abnormally aggressive or seriously irresponsible conduct on the part of the individual.
Regional Secure Unit	Hospital unit proposed by the Butler Committee for those patients who require secure conditions but not to the degree offered by the Special Hospitals.
Responsible Medical Officer	Doctor, usually a consultant psychiatrist, in charge of the treatment of a detained patient.
Representation of the People Act 1949	An Act of Parliament which regulates arrangements for voting. Under this Act there are restrictions on the voting rights of the mentally handicapped.
Restriction Order	Order imposed by the Court in addition to a hospital order which has the effect of requiring the Home Secretary's consent to leave, transfer and discharge.
Royal Commission	There have been two Royal Commissions on Mental Health since 1900. The first 1904-8 led to the formulation of the 1913 Mental Deficiency Act, and the second led to the formulation of the 1959 Mental Health Act.
Sections	See text for explanation of individual sections.
Severe subnormality	Defined in section 4 (2) of the Mental Health Act 1959, where the individual is incapable of living an independent life.
Subnormality	Defined in section 4 (3) of the Mental Health Act 1959 where the individual's condition requires or is susceptible to medical treatment or training.

Special Hospitals Hospitals provided for the treatment of detained patients who in the opinion of the Secretary of State require conditions of special security because of their dangerous, violent or criminal propensities.

BIBLIOGRAPHY

1. DHSS (1976) *A Review of the Mental Health Act 1959.* London: HMSO.
2. DHSS (1971) *Better Services for the Mentally Handicapped*, Cmmd 4683. London: HMSO.
3. DHSS/Home Office (1975) *Report of the Committee on Mentally Abnormal Offenders*, Cmmd 6244. London: HMSO.
4. DHSS (1979) *Report of the Committee of Enquiry into Mental Handicap Nursing and Care*, Cmmd 7468. London: HMSO.
5. Gostin, L.O. (1978) *Is it Fair?* London: NAMH.
6. Hargrove, A. (1961) *NAMH Guide to the Mental Health Act 1959.* London: NAMH.
7. Heaton-Ward, W.A. (1975) *Mental Subnormality*, 4th ed. Bristol: John Wright.
8. Jacobs, J. (undated) *The Mental Health Act Explained.* London: NAMH.
9. Kanner, L. (1964) *A History of the Care and Study of the Mentally Retarded.* Springfield, Ill.: Charles C. Thomas.
10. Mental Health Act 1959. London: HMSO.
11. NAMH (1956) *Notes on Legislation relating to Mental Defectives.* London: NAMH.

Educational concepts of mental handicap

4

All over the developed world children attend some form of educational activity. The age at which they commence or finish this activity will vary, but it is estimated that most will have received upwards of 10 000 hours of education during this time.[8] They will have been taught by teachers whose aim is to promote optimum learning through a vast number of interpersonal transactions, multi-media techniques and scientifically based programmes involving a bewildering variety of teaching methods. However, in spite of this provision, some children either experience difficulty or fail and are in need of special educational intervention.[8] These children fall into many groups: maladjusted, socially deprived, autistic, delicate, epileptic or educationally subnormal.[8] We are concerned with both children and adults who experience learning difficulties as a result of mental handicap. It is now recognized that the mentally handicapped can and do learn, but may need special techniques and methods to help them over a longer period. This recognition was not always apparent and is reflected in the succeeding acts of parliament which governed the residential and educational provision for the mentally handicapped from 1800 to the present day.

HISTORICAL ASPECTS

In 1799 a boy of 12 years of age was found living in a wild state in some woods in southern France.[6] He was a 'disgustingly dirty child affected with spasmodic movements and often convulsions who swayed back and forth ceaselessly like certain animals in the menagerie, who bit and scratched those who attended him, was in short, indifferent to everything and attentive to nothing'.[6] This was Itard's description of the famous Wild Boy of Aveyron. He believed that with suitable training Victor, as he called him, could be helped. Itard spent five years teaching Victor, who made considerable progress in acquiring some speech and comprehension. Victor never became normal and Itard considered he had failed.[6] However, Eduard Séguin, who had been Itard's pupil, devised a 'physiological method of teaching based on the premise that there was a link between the senses and learning. His method was to develop the senses systematically through training.[6]

Gradually small schools for 'idiots' grew in France, Switzerland, Germany and America. Saxony was the first state to make training for the mentally handicapped compulsory by law.[4] In England the Lunacy Act 1845 made no distinction between the mentally ill and the mentally handicapped although in 1847 the Asylum for Idiots at Park House, Highgate, was opened. Eight years later Park House became Earlswood Asylum, England's first large institution for the mentally handicapped.[4]

The Education Acts of 1870, 1876 and 1880 saw the introduction of compulsory education and this meant that mentally handicapped children had to attend normal schools. This development convinced the authorities that these children needed special facilities. The first school for the mentally handicapped opened in Leicester in 1892 and by 1896 there were 24 special schools in London catering for over 900 pupils.[6] In 1899 a further Education Act was passed specifically for defective and epileptic children which *permitted* authorities to provide facilities for the mentally handicapped.[6] Faced with astronomical costs for building, most authorities did very little. This led to mounting concern over the lack of provision for children of school age and older, and this concern, coupled with a growing belief that the severely handicapped would never become part of normal society, led to the Report of the Royal Commission on the Care and Control of the Feeble Minded in 1908. Their report resulted in the 1913 Mental Deficiency Act and because of this many mentally handicapped children were excluded from the state educational system. The 1913 Mental Deficiency Act favoured segregation and institutional care and this view was reinforced by the influential Wood Committee in 1929 which saw the institution providing training and rehabilitation.[1] In 1944 another Education Act was passed which said that the severely mentally handicapped were ineducable and in practice this meant that any education received took place in the hospital with largely untrained teachers who 'occupied' rather than taught.

The 1959 Mental Health Act redefined the classification of mental handicap into two major classes. The 'idiots' and 'imbeciles' were redefined as severely subnormal and the 'feeble-minded' and 'moral defectives' were redefined as subnormal. Considering the background against which it was written the 1959 Mental Health Act was an enlightened step forward. It placed emphasis on community care and also stated that the severely subnormal were no longer to be regarded as ineducable but that they were 'unsuitable for education at school'.[7]

At last the 1970 Education Act recognized that no child was so handicapped that he could not benefit from education. The Act described those children with an IQ of 50-70 as being moderately educational subnormal or ESN(M) and those with an IQ of less than 50 as being severely educationally subnormal or

ESN(S). The responsibility for the education of the severely mentally handicapped was taken over by the Department of Education from the National Health Service.[1]

This brief review of some of the factors which influenced the education of the mentally handicapped is certainly not exhaustive, there were many Reports and developments in many countries, but they represent the most significant events in the author's opinion.

INTELLIGENCE AND INTELLIGENCE TESTING

Central to the debate regarding the most suitable form of educational provision for the mentally handicapped was the concept of intellectual ability. In 1904, Alfred Binet, a Parisian psychologist, was asked by the authorities if it was possible to predict which children would do well and which children would do badly in terms of school performance.[2] As a result of this Binet and Simon in 1905 published a series of tests whose aim was to separate the intelligent from the dull. Although earlier workers, such as Charles Darwin and Sir Francis Galton, had recognized that intelligence was measurable, it was not until the work of Binet and Simon that accurate measurement of intellectual ability was made possible. The tests measured the child's intellectual ability or mental age in relation to his chronological age. Thus a child of ten years who was only able to complete the tasks that an average five-year-old was able to do would be five years behind for his age, and a ten-year-old child functioning at a ten-year-old level would be average for his age.[3] This fraction was converted into a single number by multiplying it by a hundred and this number became known as the intelligence quotient or IQ. The formula for calculating the intelligence quotient can be represented as $MA/CA \times 100 = IQ$.[2] However, it is generally assumed that the genetically determined limits of intelligence are reached by the age of 16 and when measuring an older person's IQ the 'chronological age' remains 16 years.

As progress was made in the development of intelligence testing it was recognized that there were verbal factors and performance factors in intelligence.[3] Tests were devised to measure these different abilities. This was an important development for the handicapped child in that the mentally handicapped had problems in communication and understanding - the verbal component - and the physically handicapped had problems with the practical skills - the performance component. One test which was developed to overcome these problems and is used extensively is the Weschler test. There is a Weschler Scale of Intelligence for adults, children and pre-school children. They are designed to include a battery of verbal and performance tests (Table 10). The Weschler Test has the advantage of providing three kinds of IQ: the verbal, the performance and the full score obtained by combining verbal and performance scores.

A further attempt to test the mentally handicapped adequately, allowing for their poor levels of communication, was a test devised by S.D. Porteus (1952)

Table 10. Tests in the Wechsler
Intelligence Scale for children[3]

Verbal tests	Performance tests
Information	Picture arrangement
Comprehension	Picture completion
Arithmetical reasoning	Block design
Memory span for digits	Digit symbol test
Similarities	Object assembly
Vocabulary	

called the Porteus maze. The mazes are of increasing difficulty and there is one for each year from three to 15. The child is asked to draw a line through the maze without crossing lines or lifting pencil from paper. It is useful as an additional test.[3]

There are some negative aspects of intelligence testing. Too often an intelligence quotient leads to the labelling of a child and, worse, becomes the basis for a definitive diagnosis of 'educational subnormality'. When this occurs the resulting expectations of poor performance may become self-fulfilling, as those caring for and teaching the child will not expect him to be capable of improving his performance. The IQ should be regarded as a means of expressing a child's overall rate of development in relation to others of the same age. It will tell us only how an individual child performed doing a specific test on a particular day. The IQ test will not predict learning ability, social behaviour or future performance.

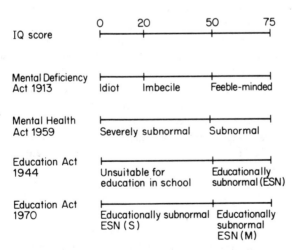

Fig. 6. How the concept of 'educability' was linked to legislation.[2] (*By permission of the Controller of Her Majesty's Stationery Office*)

The sections on historical aspects and intelligence and intelligence testing so far discussed in this chapter can be linked as shown in Fig. 6.

SOCIALIZATION AND LEARNING

The changes in thinking which led to the 1970 Education Act and the recognition that no child was so handicapped that he could not benefit from education were stimulated by developments in normal child care.

With the emphasis placed on the normal, increasing attention was paid to the process of socialization and the role of the environment in the education of the mentally handicapped. This was seen particularly in residential care, with moves towards reducing the number of children living in hospital wards, forming family groupings and creating a more normal environment.

Socialization is a life-long process and describes the ways in which the individual learns the rules and behaviour required by the society he lives in. It commences in the family and broadens over a variable period of time to include experience with peers, at school and work and in social settings. This process is in turn modified by the effect of the environment on the individual, which can act to facilitate or to reduce learning. The mentally handicapped either may be unable to benefit from normal socialization experiences or, if they live in an institutional environment, may simply not experience them.

King, Raynes and Tizard[5] describe how different environments and care practices can affect the learning of mentally handicapped children. They were interested in the ways in which different residential homes for mentally handicapped children were organized. In the course of their research they identified two contrasting types of care. The first of these they termed 'institutionally oriented care', which ignored individual differences in the children, exercised a rigid routine, denied expression of individuality and emphasized the differences between staff and patients. In contrast, 'child-oriented care' recognized individual differences in children, had a flexible routine and encouraged personal possession of belongings; interaction between staff and patients was warmer and more frequent. The institutionally oriented wards or units were geared to the efficient running of the institution and the convenience of the staff, whereas the child-oriented units were geared to the needs of individual children.[5] There were four patterns of care which showed whether the unit or ward was institutionally or child oriented. The first of these was termed 'block treatment' and meant that all the children did the same thing at the same time which resulted in individual children spending a large part of their day queuing and waiting for something to happen. A 'rigid routine' meant that there would be very little variation from day to day, and this may have the effect of precluding individual programming. Sometimes children were denied the opportunity to express their individuality, which was termed 'depersonalization' and was seen where the children were all dressed in the same way with few personal possessions and little opportunity for privacy. Finally, it was noticed that there was a difference in the frequency and warmth of the interaction between staff and children, which was termed 'social distance', and was demonstrated by a separation of the roles of the staff and those for whom they were caring. An example of social distance is where the staff never eat with the children or sit down with them to watch television.

The effect of these negative care practices is to reduce the number of opportunities available to the mentally handicapped to learn the vital skills necessary for greater independence.

INTEGRATION

The effect that the environment can have on learning has been recognized for a long time by all those who teach and care for children. In 1978 the Department of Education and Science published the *Report of the Committee into the Education of Handicapped Children and Young People*[1] (the Warnock Committee), which makes recommendations covering the whole range of special educational provision in Great Britain from the earliest years to adulthood. One of the committee's fundamental proposals is that handicapped children and adults should be integrated into the normal school system. This will mean that handicapped children will have the advantage of a more normal learning environment, a concept which has existed in Sweden for several years. The committee affirms its belief in the importance of handicapped children receiving education as early as possible and continuing for as long as possible, rather than adherence to age linked school attendance, which as far as the mentally handicapped are concerned is totally unrealistic.

These developments, coupled with a firm resolve on the part of authorities to provide alternatives to hospital admission, will help to ensure that mentally handicapped children receive the education they need in as normal an environment as possible.

CONTINUING EDUCATION

The National Development Group[7] estimate that approximately 2000 mentally handicapped young people leave school each year. They stress the importance of a comprehensive assessment before the child is due to leave school and also that the assessment leads to a statement of the child's future needs.

This theme is reiterated in the Warnock Committee's proposals[1] and recommendations that schools and colleges of further education should conduct courses for the mentally handicapped. They also recommend further education provisions in Adult Training Centres (ATC) and day centres, which are the traditional extensions of the special schools for the mentally handicapped.

The importance of the concept of continuing education is already recognized in some Adult Training Centre which devote an increasingly large part of their programme to social education rather than repetitive work skills.

Other developments include a bridging course into further education, day-release to colleges, full- and part-time courses at colleges of education, evening classes, work orientation and work experience schemes and non-vocational courses which help the mentally handicapped to broaden interests, develop skills and make contacts in the community.[7]

No mentally handicapped person, whatever his age, should be denied the opportunity to learn the skills that make for a full and satisfying life.

SUMMARY

Education is concerned with helping people gain and use experience and knowledge and with developing their personality and self-confidence. It should be intellectually stimulating, emotionally satisfying, socially valuable and related to the needs of the individual.

The mentally handicapped often experience failure or difficulty in learning but they can and do learn, a fact which has finally been accepted in recent legislation after nearly 200 years of segregation and indifference. They will need help in areas such as motor ability and coordination, sensory education and perception, communication, social education, work experience and knowledge of the world around them.

The mentally handicapped need to learn in an environment which is stimulating and supportive and to be taught by people who understand their special educational needs.

Education should be seen as a continuing process which starts from birth and continues through life.

GLOSSARY

Adult Training Centre (ATC)	A department run by the social services which provides education and work experience for mentally handicapped people over 16 years.
Binet/Simon	French psychologists who worked together to produce the first intelligence test in 1904-5.
Block treatment	A pattern of care characterized by treating a group of people as one.
Chronological age	Age in years.
Depersonalization	A pattern of care in which the individual is denied expression of his individuality.
ESN(M)	Educationally subnormal (moderate).
ESN(S)	Educationally subnormal (severe).

Feeble-minded	1913 Mental Deficiency Act classification of a person with an IQ of 50-75.
Idiot	1913 Mental Deficiency Act classification of a person with an IQ of 0-20.
Imbecile	1913 Mental Deficiency Act classification of a person with an IQ of 20-50.
IQ	Intelligence quotient.
Itard (1774-1838)	Doctor in Paris who described the Wild Boy of Aveyron and designed first teaching programme for individual.
Mental age	Age at which individual is functioning mentally, either advanced or retarded.
Moral defective	1913 Mental Deficiency Act classification of a mentally defective person with vicious or criminal propensities.
National Development Group	An independent advisory body set up in 1975 by the Secretary of State for Social Services to advise on development and implementation of better services for the mentally handicapped.
Porteus Maze	A test designed by S. Porteus to try to predict how an individual will progress; it tests ability to plan.
Rigid routine	A pattern of care characterized by an inflexible routine which does not allow consideration of individual children's needs.
Séguin (1812-80)	Itard's pupil and successor devised sense training programmes for the mentally handicapped.
Social distance	A pattern of care characterized by a low level of interaction and warmth between staff and children.
Warnock Committee	A committee chaired by Mrs H.M. Warnock which produced the *Report of the Committee of Enquiry into the Education of Handicapped Children and Young People* in 1978. Concerns Special Education.
WISC	Weschler Intelligence Scale for Children.
Wood Committee	A committee which investigated the incidence of feeble-minded children and their education in 1929.

BIBLIOGRAPHY

1. DHSS (1978) *Report of the Committee of Enquiry into the Education of Handicapped Children and Young People*, Cmmd 7212. London: HMSO.
2. Hegarty, J. (1976) *Educating and Training the Mentally Handicapped Patient —Workbook.* Chelmsfort: Medical Recording Service Foundation.
3. Jackson, S. (1974) *A Teacher's Guide to Tests and Testing*, 3rd ed. London: Longman.
4. Shearer, A. (1971) *Fact Sheet 3—The Story of Services for the Mentally Handicapped.* London: King's Fund Centre.
5. King, R.D., Raynes, N.V. & Tizard, J. (1971) *Patterns of Residential Care.* London: Routledge & Kegan Paul.
6. McMaster, J. McG. (1973) *Toward an Educiational Theory for the Mentally Handicapped.* London: Edward Arnold.
7. Segal, S.S. (1974) *No Child is Ineducable*, 2nd ed. Oxford: Pergamon Press.
8. Wragg, E., Oates, J. & Gump, F. (1976) *Classroom Interaction.* Milton Keynes: Open University Press.

PART II
Causation of Mental Handicap

Introduction

This part of the book attempts to explain some of the reasons why mental handicap may occur.

In most cases, a knowledge of causation will not directly help someone in the daily care of a mentally handicapped child or adult. Indeed, this clinical emphasis has often been the root cause of inappropriate patterns of care, based as they are on a theoretical expertise incapable of practical application in the care setting. However, it is recognized that many people involved in the care process may need information about the causation of mental handicap out of interest, to pass examinations or for specific information regarding individuals in their care.

Chapter 5 introduces the concept of inheritance and starts by discussing cell structure and division. The material contained in the cell nucleus, the chromosomes and genes, is shown to be responsible for the physical and mental characteristics of the individual. The mechanism of inheritance is explained through the process of meiosis, dominant and recessive gene inheritance and sex linkage.

Chapter 6 continues this theme with an explanation of the causation of chromosomal and genetic abnormalities. This is achieved through a discussion of the chromosomal abnormalities of trisomy, translocation, chromosome absence and deletion and their effects. The mechanism of dominant, recessive and sex-linked inheritance is explained and provides an explanatory framework for the latter part of the chapter which gives detailed information in the form of a checklist related to selected syndromes.

Chapter 7 is concerned with those environmental factors that may affect physical and mental development sufficiently to cause mental handicap at any time after conception, during pregnancy, at birth and during childhood. It discusses the ways in which the various environmental factors operate to cause mental handicap. These factors include maternal and childhood infections and malnutrition; anoxia; direct and indirect violence; maternal–fetal incompatibility; prematurity; birth injury; and sensory and social deprivation. As in

Chapter 5, the second part of the chapter is devoted to a descriptive checklist of a number of selected abnormalities.

Chapters 8 and 9 are concerned with epilepsy and cerebral palsy respectively and are included as they frequently accompany mental handicap and a theoretical knowledge can be applied to the management of both conditions with positive benefits.

Chapter 8 discusses epilepsy from the view of causation, diagnosis and management. The principal types of fit seen in *grand mal, petit mal,* focal epilepsy and myoclonus are described and related to the specific care required in each case. The important aspects of observation and recording are linked to the prescription and administration of drugs in the overall management of the person with epilepsy. Finally, a normal lifestyle is advocated within the constraints of employment, accommodation and legislation.

Chapter 9 follows the same pattern by discussing cerebral palsy in relation to causation, incidence, classification, associated handicaps, behavioural problems and the management of the individual child or adult.

This part of the book concentrates on the clinical aspects of the handicapped individual's condition. It should be remembered that each handicapped person has the same physical, psychological and social needs as the non-handicapped person and that clinical labelling is often limiting in terms of low expectations and self-fulfilling prophecies.

Inheritance 5

The cell is the basic unit of all living material. The human body is composed of fifty thousand billion cells, all of which have a particular function.[1,4] Cells which have a similar function are grouped together to form tissues and organs which make up the systems of the body.[4] Although there are many cells with different functions they all have a similar structure which can be seen in Fig. 7.

The ability of each cell to behave in a specific way is determined by the coded instructions contained in the genetic material of the cell nucleus. These instructions determine the type of cell, its function, its life span and its reproduction.[6]

GENETIC MATERIAL

The cell nuclei contain the hereditary material called chromosomes. The number of chromosomes is constant for a given species; in human cells there are 46.[4] The chromosomes are very long fine strands composed of deoxyribonucleic acid (DNA) and protein. The DNA, composed of four chemicals called adenine, thymine, guanine and cytosine, is arranged in the form of two spiral strands of sugar and phosphate linked by the four chemicals. Adenine always links with thymine and guanine always links with cytosine.[2] A useful analogy for understanding the structure of DNA is that it resembles a ladder that has been twisted (Fig. 8). The sides of the ladder are composed of sugar and phosphate molecules and the rungs of the ladder are adenine and thymine and guanine and cytosine.[2]

The sequence of the nucleotide bases carries the coded instructions for the cell. A sequence of three bases is the code for a single instruction and is called a gene.[2] Each cell carries approximately 100 000 genes on the 46 chromosomes, and a sequence of several hundred paired units is usually needed to code each complete instruction.[6] All cellular activity is governed by the action of the genes, which remain constant in their effect. This is because during cell division the double-spiral strands of DNA separate and a new matching strand is built up by the original strand and so two new molecules of DNA are formed.[2]

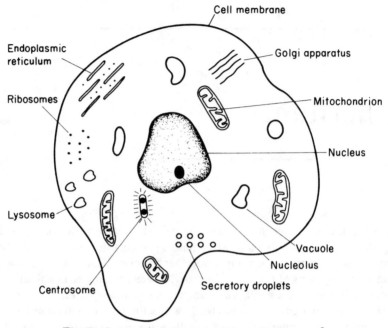

Fig. 7. A simplified diagram of the cell structure.[8]

Cytoplasm	Cell structure less nucleus
Protoplasm	Cell structure plus nucleus
Cell membrane	Acts as protective barrier keeping out harmful substances but allowing beneficial ones to enter
Vacuole	Excretory mechanism of cell
Golgi apparatus	Stores substances made by the cell and distributes them
Centrosome	Necessary for cell division
Mitochondria	Cell's energy source as a result of chemical reactions. The more active the cell the more mitochondria there are
Secretory droplets	Storage areas for proteins, carbohydrates and fats
Endoplasmic reticulum	Network of membranous sacs which divide the cell into functional areas. May be attached to ribosomes
Ribosomes	Manufacture protein; may be either free or attached to endoplasmic reticulum
Lysosome	Contains enzymes capable of digesting dead or harmful material
Nucleolus	Composed of RNA
Nucleus	Composed of DNA and protein; provides the blueprint for the cell. Controls reproduction

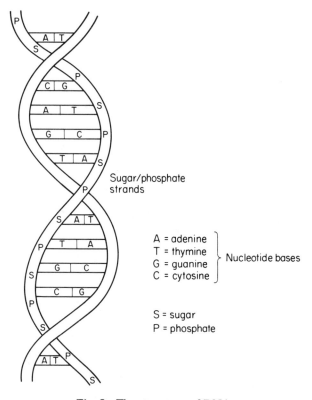

Fig. 8. The structure of DNA.

Because adenine combines only with thymine and guanine combines only with cytosine, an exact copy is reproduced, ensuring that the new cells receive precisely the same coded instructions or genes as in the original cell.[2]

The DNA exerts its effect through an intermediary substance called ribonucleic acid or RNA. An example of this may be seen in the way the cell manufactures protein. The instructions for making proteins are stored in the DNA and when it is necessary for more of a particular protein to be made special 'messenger' RNA is copied and passes from the nucleus to the cytoplasm. It then passes to the ribosome responsible for making protein and acts as a 'template' for the manufacture of new proteins.[1]

CELL DIVISION

Human cells normally have 46 chromosomes, 44 of these being the same in both sexes and called autosomes.[3] The two remaining chromosomes are called sex chromosomes as they determine the sex of the individual. The female has two X (XX) chromosomes and the male has an X and a Y (XY) chromosome. Fig. 9 shows a karyotype which is how the chromosomes are identified and catalogued.[2]

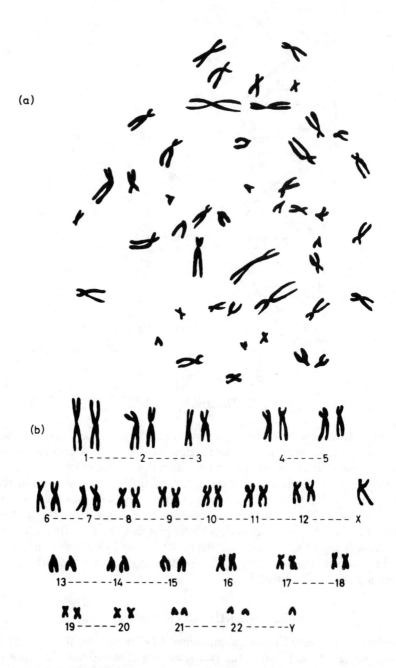

Fig. 9. *Above*, The human chromosomes at one stage of division. *Below*, A normal male karyotype.

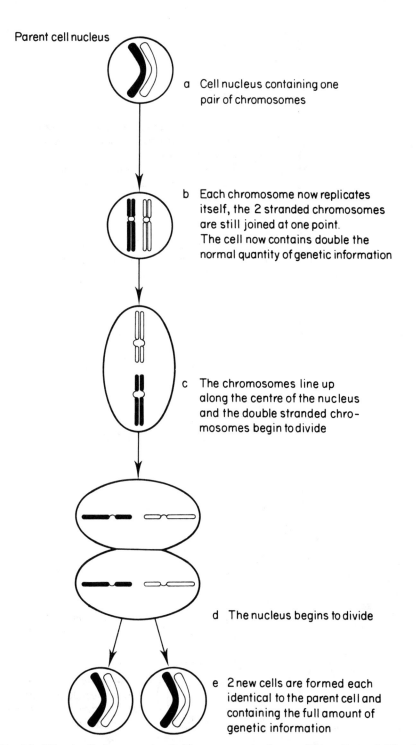

Parent cell nucleus

a Cell nucleus containing one pair of chromosomes

b Each chromosome now replicates itself, the 2 stranded chromosomes are still joined at one point. The cell now contains double the normal quantity of genetic information

c The chromosomes line up along the centre of the nucleus and the double stranded chromosomes begin to divide

d The nucleus begins to divide

e 2 new cells are formed each identical to the parent cell and containing the full amount of genetic information

Fig. 10. Mitosis. Only one pair of chromosomes is shown. (*From Oates & Floyd (1976) The Course of Development, E201, Block 4, Open University Press*)

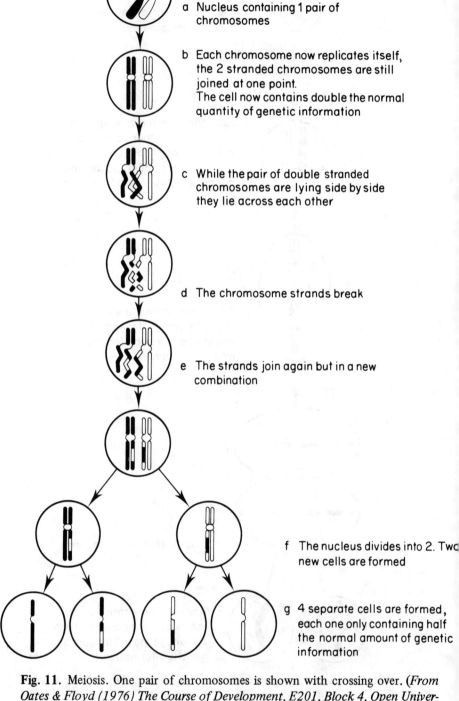

a Nucleus containing 1 pair of chromosomes

b Each chromosome now replicates itself, the 2 stranded chromosomes are still joined at one point.
The cell now contains double the normal quantity of genetic information

c While the pair of double stranded chromosomes are lying side by side they lie across each other

d The chromosome strands break

e The strands join again but in a new combination

f The nucleus divides into 2. Two new cells are formed

g 4 separate cells are formed, each one only containing half the normal amount of genetic information

Fig. 11. Meiosis. One pair of chromosomes is shown with crossing over. (*From Oates & Floyd (1976) The Course of Development, E201, Block 4, Open University Press*)

A photograph is taken of the cell at a particular moment in cell division when it is easy to see the chromosomes. This is enlarged and the photographed chromosomes paired in order of decreasing size from pair 1 to pair 22, with pair 23 being the sex chromosomes.[6]

All cells, with the exception of the sex cells, the ovum and spermatozoa, reproduce themselves by a process of cell division called mitosis. It can be seen from Fig. 10 that each cell doubles the normal quantity of genetic material and at the subsequent division forms two new cells each identical to the parent cell and containing the full amount of genetic material of 46 chromosomes.[7]

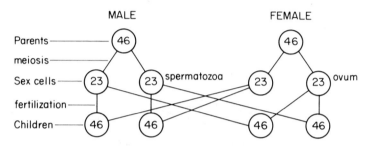

Fig. 12. Autosomal meiosis.

The ovum and spermatozoa, the sex cells, reproduce themselves by a process of cell division called meiosis or reduction division. Fig. 11 shows how the original cell divides in two stages to produce four cells, each containing 23 single chromosomes.[7] However, following duplication of the genetic material the chromosomes lie across each other, break and rejoin in a different combination. This means that every ovum and spermatozoa carries a unique combination of genetic material and in this way sexual reproduction results in each individual inheriting different characteristics.[7] At conception the spermatozoon and the ovum come together to form a new individual with the full genetic complement of 46 chromosomes. This mechanism can be seen in Fig. 12.

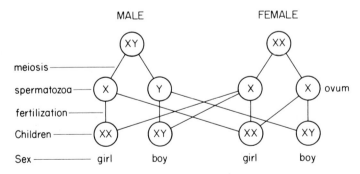

Fig. 13. Sex chromosome meiosis.

The sex of a child is decided by the male sex cell, the spermatozoon. During meiosis every ovum receives one X chromosome but the spermatozoon may receive either an X or a Y chromosome, which means that sex determination is a random process dependent on which type of spermatozoon fertilizes the ovum.[1] This mechanism can be seen in Fig. 13.

DOMINANT AND RECESSIVE GENES

The genes are arranged in linear formation on the chromosomes at a specific site, and on each pair of chromosomes there are corresponding genes for a particular characteristic.[6] Some genes are said to be dominant and others recessive in their expression.

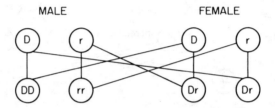

Fig. 14. Dominant and recessive gene inheritance. D = dominant gene; r = recessive gene.

The dominant form of gene expression occurs where a particular characteristic is due to the influence of a single gene. Recessive genes are able to express their effect only when two recessive genes for the same characteristic are present.[3] It can be seen from Fig. 14 that the chance of two recessive genes combining is one in four and that in the remaining three instances the effect of the dominant gene will be produced.[3] Both dominant and recessive genes may be abnormal and produce a clinical disease or abnormality. Theoretically, in dominant inheritance one child in two will be affected and in recessive inheritance one in four will be affected.[2]

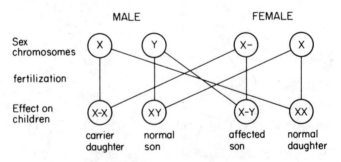

Fig. 15. X-linked inheritance.

A different form of inheritance is termed sex-linked, as the genes responsible are carried on either the X or the Y chromosomes. If the gene on the X chromosome is abnormal it acts in a recessive way in the female and in a dominant way in the male.[2] Fig. 15 shows how a female who carries an abnormal gene on the X chromosome but does not suffer its effects can pass this on to her children. Her daughter will carry the abnormal gene but not suffer from it as she has a normal X chromosome from her father which counteracts the effect of the abnormal gene. Her son is affected because the abnormal X chromosome is able to act unopposed by the Y chromosome.

SUMMARY

From conception the fertilized ovum rapidly develops by cell division or mitosis. The cells become increasingly specialized to form tissues, organs and body systems.[4] The information which is necessary for normal cell development is contained in chromosomes in the cell nucleus. The 46 chromosomes in human cells are composed of DNA which is a complex double-spiral strand composed of chemicals which when arranged in a particular sequence contain the coded instructions for cell activity and characteristics called genes.

Transmission of genetic material from one generation to another occurs through the sex cells. For the fertilized ovum to contain 23 pairs of chromosomes the spermatozoon and ovum must contain only 23 single chromosomes. This process is termed meiosis or reduction division.[7] The sex of a child is determined on a random basis by the spermatozoon which may carry an X chromosome or a Y chromosome and will join with an ovum which always carries an X chromosome at fertilization.[1]

Some characteristics are inherited in a dominant, recessive or sex-linked manner.[2,3] Dominant genes are able to produce their effect in isolation whereas recessive genes are able to produce their effect only in combination with another recessive gene for the same characteristic.

This first chapter is intended to provide an introduction to Chapter 6 by discussing some aspects of cell division and inheritance. It is not intended to be a comprehensive account of a very complex subject.

GLOSSARY

Adenine   One of the chemical constituents of DNA.

Autosome   Any paired chromosome other than a sex chromosome.

Carrier   A person who carries an abnormal gene on the X chromosome but does not suffer from its effect.

Cell	The following terms are described in Fig. 7, p. 64: cytoplasm, protoplasm, nucleus, nucleolus, cell membrane, vacuole, Golgi apparatus, centrosome, mitochrondria, secretory droplets, endoplasmic reticulum, ribosomes, lysosome.
Chromosomes	Rod-shaped bodies in the cell nucleus composed of DNA and protein. They contain the genes or hereditary factors and in human cells normally number 46.
Cytosine	One of the chemical constituents of DNA.
Deoxyribonucleic acid (DNA)	Long spiral molecules composed of sugar and phosphate linked with adenine and thymine, guanine and cytosine which make up the chromosomes.
Dominant gene	A gene which is able to produce its effect in isolation from its paired corresponding gene.
Genes	The biological unit of inheritance, self-producing and located in a definite position on a specific chromosome.
Guanine	One of the chemical constituents of DNA.
Karyotype	The method of classifying the chromosomes in order to identify abnormalities.
Meiosis	Cell division occurring in the maturation of the sex cells resulting in a halving of the chromosome complement.
Mitosis	Cell division occurring in body cells resulting in the duplication of identical cells.
Nucleotide bases	The four paired chemials of the DNA molecule: adenine, thymine, guanine and cytosine.
Ovum	The female sex cell.
Recessive gene	A gene that can produce its effect only in combination with another recessive gene for the same characteristic.
Spermatozoon	The male sex cell.

BIBLIOGRAPHY

1. British Museum (1977) *Human Biology—An Exhibition of Ourselves.* Cambridge: Cambridge University Press.
2. Dutton, G. (1975) *Mental Handicap.* London: Butterworths.
3. Heaton-Ward, A. (1975) *Mental Subnormality*, 4th ed. Bristol: John Wright.
4. Heywood Jones, I. (1978) *Genetics and Inherited Diseases.* London: Nursing Times.

5. Mackean, D.G. (1971) *Introduction to Genetics*, 2nd ed. London: John Murray.
6. Mathews, D.R. (1978) *Your Fate in Your Genes.* London: Nursing Mirror.
7. Oates, J. & Floyd, A. (1976) *The Course of Development.* Milton Keynes: Open University Press.
8. Richards, R. & Chapman, D. (1977) Introduction and the Reproductive system. *Anatomy and Physiology, A Self-instructional Course.* London: Churchill Livingstone.

Chromosomal and genetic abnormalities

6

CHROMOSOMAL ABNORMALITIES

It is now possible to identify a large number of chromosomal abnormalities. These abnormalities include extra chromosomes, absence of chromosomes, deletion of parts of a chromosome or addition of chromosomal material and alterations to the form of chromosomes. The incidence of chromosomal abnormalities in live births is approximately 1 in 200.[3]

The method used to classify the chromosomes and identify abnormalities is to stain the cultured chromosomes with special dyes such as quinacrine, heterochromatin and Giemsa. In combination the dyes allow the identification of each pair of chromosomes by comparison of their banding patterns.[3] This method will also show minor variations in the chromosome material such as deletions.

The presence of an extra chromosome is termed a 'trisomy' and is due to an error in meiosis.[2] At an early stage in meiotic cell division the chromosomes separate to produce four cells, each containing 23 chromosomes. If they fail to separate correctly, one of the cells will have an additional chromosome which on fertilization would make a total complement of 47 instead of 46. This failure to separate during meiosis is called non-disjunction. The presence of an extra large chromosome from pair 1 to pair 12 appears to be incompatible with life and may be seen in aborted material.[2] Even where the trisomy occurs from pair 13 the fetus will show gross physical abnormality. Occasionally a child may be born with less severe abnormalities caused by the presence of additional chromosomal material called a partial trisomy.

Trisomy of the sex chromosomes occurs and is associated with an increased risk of intellectual impairment and characteristic physical symptoms. In the male the presence of up to four extra X chromosomes (XXXXY) is possible, but the affected person is severely mentally and physically handicapped.[2] Females may have a karyotype showing XXX (trisomy X) or XXXX. The general rule is that the greater the number of extra X chromosomes the more profound the mental and physical effects.[1]

A further anomaly is seen where two chromosomes become attached to each other, giving an apparent total chromosome count of 45 instead of the normal 46. This is called a 'translocation' and usually occurs during meiosis.[2] As there is the full complement of genetic material, although arranged in a different form, there is often no physical or mental abnormality. However, subsequent cell division may not be normal and on fertilization may give rise to a trisomy, resulting in both physical and intellectual impairment.

Absence of one of the autosomes appears to be incompatible with life, but absence of one of the sex chromosomes is not. However, all cells must have at least one X chromosome to be viable and so the karyotype OY would be lethal. Turner's syndrome shows a karyotype of XO, absence of one X chromosome, and although there may be physical anomalies there is no increased risk of the person being mentally handicapped.[1]

Occasionally there may be 'deletions' of part of a chromosome which can have profound effects. The deletion results in loss of genetic material from either the short or the long arms of one of the autosomal pairs.[2]

Chromosomal 'mosaicism' is a condition which occurs after fertilization. During subsequent cell division (mitosis) the chromosomes may fail to separate properly. The effect of this non-disjunction is that some cells will contain excess chromosomes and others will show a corresponding deficit. The proportion of abnormal cells to normal cells will determine the extent of physical and mental abnormality.[1]

Almost all chromosomal abnormalities, of both the autosomes and the sex chromosomes, can be detected in utero by the technique of amniocentesis.[2] A small amount of amniotic fluid (the fluid which surrounds the fetus whilst in the uterus) is drawn off between the fourteenth and sixteenth weeks of pregnancy. The cells can then be cultured and the karyotypes identified to reveal any abnormalities of the chromosomes. If an abnormality is revealed the decision can then be made about the possible termination of the pregnancy.[2]

GENETIC ABNORMALITIES

Whilst it is possible to identify most of the chromosomal abnormalities through techniques such as amniocentesis, use of dyes and karyotyping, the presence of genetic abnormalities can in most cases only be inferred from their observed effects. These effects can be produced by the presence of abnormal dominant or recessive genes, or by the absence of genes responsible for essential enzymes.

In Chapter 5 normal cell division was discussed and it was seen that the fertilized ovum contains 23 pairs of chromosomes. Arranged in linear formation on the chromosomes are sequences of nucleotide bases, containing the coded instructions for the cell. A sequence of three nucleotide bases is the code for a single instruction and is called a gene.[1] Each chromosome pair carries genes responsible for specific characteristics. Any alteration to the genetic code may produce an abnormality severe enough to cause physical and mental handicap. Dominant inheritance of a disease (Fig. 16) occurs when one abnormal gene

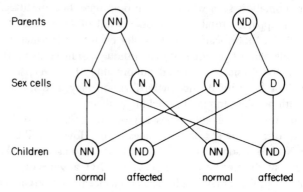

Fig. 16. Dominant inheritance of an abnormal gene. N = normal gene; D = abnormal dominant gene.

for a particular characteristic expresses itself, over-riding the effect of the corresponding normal gene.[1] A feature of dominant inheritance is the variations in the effect that the abnormal gene may have, and so partial features of a condition may be seen in different members of a family. There is a one in two chance that a child will inherit a dominant gene defect if one of the parents has the abnormal dominant gene.

Sometimes both parents carry the same abnormal dominant gene and in this case the fetus will have two abnormal dominant genes for the same characteristic. The effect of this is usually so severe as to be incompatible with life.[1]

Dominantly inherited diseases which cause mental handicap are rare, as the conditions are usually so severe as to reduce fertility or make it unlikely that the sufferer will be able to reproduce - a process of natural selection.[4]

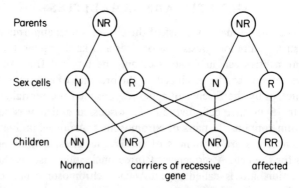

Fig. 17. Recessive inheritance of an abnormal gene. N = normal gene; R = abnormal recessive gene.

Recessive inheritance of a disease (Fig. 17) depends on two abnormal recessive genes for the same characteristic occurring on both the chromosomes of a pair. Although rare, recessive defects have an incidence of approximately 1 in 50 000 of the population; they occur more frequently than dominant defects.[3] This is particularly true of the children of parents who are blood relatives. Marriage between blood relatives is termed consanguineous marriage; the risk of producing an affected child is significantly increased as first cousins have one-eighth of their genes in common.[1]

An important group of disorders, called inborn errors of metabolism, are most often caused by autosomal recessive genes, although some are X-linked.[2] There are about 80 known inborn errors of metabolism which cause mental handicap.[2] Food is taken into the body and broken down (metabolized) into a form which the body can use. The process of metabolism is carried out by the action of enzymes which in turn is determined by the coded instructions in the genes. If the genes responsible for a specific enzyme are abnormal or missing then there is a block in the 'metabolic pathway'.[1] The results of this incomplete metabolism may cause an accumulation of harmful toxins in the blood or lead to the deposition of harmful material in the tissues, resulting in varying degrees of intellectual impairment, usually severe.[1] It is encouraging that as more progress is made in understanding the biochemistry of the inborn errors of metabolism it is possible to treat them actively by dietary means.

A further group of disorders are inherited as a result of abnormal genes on the X chromosome and this type of inheritance is termed sex-linked. The affected individuals will be males and the disorder will be passed on by carrier females.[1] In the male the abnormal gene acts in a dominant way as the X chromosome is able to exert its effect without opposition from the Y chromosome.[1] In the female the abnormal gene acts in a recessive way and, although she will be a carrier of the disorder, she will not suffer from it, as the normal X chromosome is able to oppose the effects of the abnormal X chromosome.[1] However, she will pass the abnormal gene to her sons who will be affected, and to her daughters who will be carriers.

SUMMARY

This brief introduction has discussed chromosomal abnormalities such as trisomy, translocation and absence or deletion of genetic material, occurring in the autosomes and the sex chromosomes. Disorders brought about by the presence of abnormal genes have been discussed according to their mode of inheritance. This has been seen to be dominant, recessive or sex-linked inheritance.

It is intended that the above discussion of the ways in which mental handicap is caused will provide an explanatory framework for the next part of the chapter. This provides more detailed information about a number of selected syndromes arranged in the form of a checklist. The syndromes are arranged in alphabetical order for quick and easy reference, based on the format used by Holmes et al.[3]

CHECKLIST OF SYNDROMES

Down's syndrome (trisomy 21)

Condition

First described by Dr Langdon Down in 1866; an auto-somal abnormality with a karyotype of 47 chromosomes. Has a variable effect but a characteristic physical appearance evident from birth.[2] It is the commonest chromosomal abnormality.[3]

Cause

Meiotic non-disjunction in maternal sex cells resulting in an an extra chromosome at pair 21.

Incidence

1 in 600 or 700 live births, occurring in most races.[2] There is an association between maternal age and Down's syndrome. The risk rates at different maternal ages are estimated:

Maternal age	Risk
20 years	1 : 2000
40 years	1 : 100
45 years	1 : 46

Physical features

These will be described under specific headings.

Head: Small and round with the back of the skull flattened; cranial capacity reduced.

Neck: Short and thick with a lower hairline than normal.

Hair: Smooth and soft in children becoming more coarse in adulthood. Recurrent focal alopecia common in adulthood.[3]

Eyes: Fine white speckling of the iris called 'Brushfield spots'.[2] There may also be strabismus, nystagmus and cataracts. Epicanthic folds are often present.

Nose: Small with flattened bridge of nose due to under-development or absence of nasal bones.

Ears: Low set and small with a simple pattern, ear lobes are small or absent.[2]

Mouth, teeth and tongue: Mouth small with high arched palate.[2] Tongue often protruded and appears large but this may be due to the small mouth. There is delayed dental development which may be abnormal.

Hands and feet: Square palm with short stubby fingers and an incurving little finger. Single palmar crease. There may be webbing of the fingers (syndactly). Fingerprints are said to be typical and diagnostic of Down's syndrome.[2] Toes are shorter than normal and there may be a wide gap between the great toe and the others which may extend onto the sole of the foot.[2]

Muscles: Hypotonic.[1]
Skin: Hands and feet have mottled cyanotic appearance. Rough, dry skin increasingly evident with advancing age.[3]
Growth and development: Smaller than normal from birth.

Congenital abnormalities   Cardiac abnormalities may be present. Peripheral circutory disturbances are common and cyanosis of lips, hands and feet frequent.[2] Umbilical hernia frequently present.[3] Epilepsy and cerebral palsy are rare.[2]

Abilities and limitations   Variation in ability is very wide with good progress being made until three years with a slowing down after this. Said to be mimics and to like rhythmic music and to be lovable and demonstrative.[2] However, all Down's syndrome children and adults are individuals and need to be treated as such.

Care points   (1) Down's syndrome children are 'mouth breathers' and are therefore susceptible to severe respiratory infections.
(2) There is a congenital absence of the enzyme lysozyme, normally present in the tears, which helps to prevent infection.[2] As a result these children may suffer from blepharitis (inflammation of the eyelid).
(3) Because of disturbances in the peripheral circulation their hands and feet need to be kept warm in cold weather.

Genetic note   95% of all cases of Down's syndrome are inherited as an autosomal trisomy with an extra chromosome at pair 21.[3] Most of the remainder occur as a result of translocation; the commonest form being a 15/21 translocation.[2] In this case the chromosome count will be apparently 46, because the extra chromosome 21 becomes attached to one of the fifteenth pair, forming a compound chromosome. Translocated forms of Down's syndrome are not linked to maternal age.

Edwards' syndrome (trisomy 17–18)

Condition   First described in 1960 by Edwards and associates; characterized by abnormal facial features, webbing of the neck, congenital heart abnormalities.[3]

Cause   Meiotic disjunction related to increasing maternal age, causing the presence of an extra chromosome at pair 18.[3]

Incidence   Estimates vary from 1 in 2000[2] live births to 1 in 6800 live births.[3] The majority of those affected are female (70%) and there may be additional X chromosomes.[3]

Physical features   *Head*: There is an elongation of the skull with a receding chin.
Face: Widely set eyes (hypertelorism) with under-developed supraorbital ridges, eyebrows and eyelashes.
Ears: Small, low-set and malformed.[3]
Neck: Short neck with redundant folds of skin or webbing.
Limbs: The hands are unusual with flexed and overlapping fingers. They may have 'rocker bottom' feet, limited hip movement and spasticity.[3]
Fingerprints: These show a particular pattern in over 80% of children suffering from this syndrome.[2]
Nervous system: The frontal lobes of the cerebral hemispheres may not separate normally.[2] Seizures are common. There may be abnormalities in muscle tone which may vary from hypertonia to hypotonia.

Congenital abnormalities   These are usually severe and wide ranging with abnormalities of the heart, nervous system, abdominal organs, the kidneys and the ears.

Abilities   All these children are profoundly mentally and physically handicapped.

Prognosis   The prognosis is poor with average survival being less than three years.[1]

Patau's syndrome (trisomy 13–15)

Condition   First described by Patau and associates in 1960; characterized by hare lip, cleft palate, eye defects and extra fingers.[1]

Cause   Meiotic non-disjunction associated with an increase in maternal age, causing the presence of an extra chromosome at pair 13.[3]

Incidence   The incidence has been estimated at 1 in 10 000 live births.[2]

Physical features   *Head*: Microcephaly is common with a small receding chin.[2,3]
Mouth and lips: There is often a hare lip and cleft palate although cases have been seen that have a bulbous nose and no cleft lip or palate.[3]
Eyes: A common defect is that of microphthalmia (small eyes) and occasionally unilateral anophthalmia (lack of one eye).[3]
Ears: Small, low-set and malformed.[2]

Neck: Short with redundant skin, but webbing is rare.
Height and weight: Always below the average for their age.
Limbs: There may be polydactyly (extra fingers and toes).

Congenital abnormalities

There are specific abnormalities of the brain which include a simplified gyral pattern and absence of the olfactory bulb and tract (concerned with sense of smell).[3] Almost all children have some heart defect, the most common being septal defects.

Abilities

All children suffering from this condition are profoundly physically and mentally handicapped.

Prognosis

The prognosis is poor with most children not surviving beyond the first few months of life.[1]

'Cri du chat' syndrome (deletion of short arm of chromosome 5)

Condition

First described by Lejeune and associates in 1963.[3] The condition is characterized by a cat-like cry in infancy, multiple deformities and severe mental handicap.

Cause

Partial deletion of the short arm of one of the fifth pair of chromosomes.[2]

Incidence

Overall incidence is not known although it is known that females are affected more than males.[2]

Physical features

Head: Always small and usually microcephalic.[3]
Face: Typically small with hypertelorism (wide-set eyes).[3]
Eyes: Almond-shaped, with strabismus (squint) being the most common defect.
Larynx: Underdeveloped and narrow which, combined with a flaccid (floppy) epiglottis, produces the characteristic cat-like cry in infancy. This cry disappears a few weeks after birth.[3]
Hair: There is premature greying of the hair.[2]
Limbs: The fingers and toes may be shortened and in some cases there may be increasing spasticity with exaggerated reflexes.[2]
Growth and development: There appears to be an intra-uterine malnutrition which results in babies with a low birth weight. There is often failure to thrive in the neo-natal period (first 28 days).[1] They remain retarded in physical development throughout their lives.

Abilities

The degree of mental handicap is severe with associated delayed motor development.

Triple X syndrome (trisomy X)

Condition	A condition where there is an extra X chromosome which may produce no obvious physical or sexual abnormality.[2]
Cause	Meiotic non-disjunction resulting in the presence of an extra X chromosome.
Incidence	Overall incidence 1 in 1000 live births and is estimated to occur in 1 in 100 mentally handicapped females.[2]
Physical features	No obvious physical features. This may lead to failure to recognize the condition.
Menstruation	This varies from amenorrhoea (no menstruation) to normal menstruation.
Fertility	The more severely affected are infertile while the less severely affected are fertile and may give birth to normal children.[2]
Abilities	The degree of mental handicap is usually slight and so with planned skill development they may achieve high levels of performance.

Other X chromosome anomalies in females

It is possible for two and rarely three extra X chromosomes to be present giving karyotypes of 48 and 49 chromosomes respectively. The affected person is severely mentally handicapped, infertile with poorly developed sexual organs, and suffering a number of severe skeletal deformities.[2]

Klinefelter's syndrome (trisomy XY)

Condition	First described by Klinefelter and associates in 1942,[3] it is the most common sex chromosome abnormality in males and is characterized by development of female secondary sex characteristics.[1]
Cause	Meiotic non-disjunction resulting in the presence of an extra X chromosome in males.
Incidence	1 in 500; estimated to occur in slightly over 1 in 100 mentally handicapped males who are slightly less handicapped.[2]
Physical features	*Breasts*: Development of breast tissue (gynaecomastia) following puberty, either unilateral or bilateral.[3] *Genitalia*: Although the penis appears normal in size the testes are small and underdeveloped.[3]

Hair: Pubic hair may be feminine in distribution and there is a lack of facial hair.

Growth and development: Development is usually normal until puberty when the body develops female characteristics.[2] The individuals are usually tall and slender.

Abilities

Klinefelter's syndrome does not usually cause severe mental handicap. Those affected score better on performance tests than on verbal tests. However, it is thought that emotional instability is associated with this condition possibly leading to schizoid psychosis.[1]

Treatment

Treatment in adolescence with testosterone was reported to have produced a more masculine appearance and more purposeful behaviour.[3]

Other X chromosome anomalies in males

Klinefelter's syndrome may be associated with Down's syndrome producing a karyotype of 48 chromosomes. In other conditions there may be two or three extra chromosomes which produce severe mental handicap, increase in height and failure of the secondary sex characteristics to develop.[2]

XYY syndrome (trisomy Y)

Condition

First described by Sandberg and associates in 1961;[1] characterized by tallness, normal physical and sexual development and a tendency towards antisocial behaviour.[2]

Cause

The presence of an extra Y chromosome.

Incidence

Estimated incidence of 1 in 700 males.[2]

Physical features

Although there is normal physical and sexual development in the majority of cases, some differences have been consistently reported.

Height: Affected males are over 2 m (6 ft) tall.[2]

Skeletal system: A number of bone abnormalities have been reported although there is no evidence that this is due to the extra Y chromosome.[2]

Personality and behaviour

It has been suggested that the presence of an extra Y chromosome is linked to antisocial or criminal behaviour. This stemmed from the discovery of the syndrome in patients in special maximum security hospitals.[1] Since this time males with an XYY karyotype have been identified living normally in the community and not exhibiting antisocial tendencies. However, it appears that there may be a predisposition towards antisocial or violent behaviour in those people with XYY syndrome which is modified by environmental circumstances.[1,2]

Abilities   There is a variation from mild mental handicap to normality.

Other Y chromosome anomalies in males

Occasionally males may have an extra X as well as an extra Y chromosome producing a karyotype of 48 chromosomes. Those suffering from this condition showed features of Klinefelter's syndrome as well as antisocial behaviour.

Microcephaly ('true')

Condition   Characterized by a small cranial circumference of 43 cm (17 in) or less in an adult, but with facial features of normal size.[2]

Cause   Autosomal recessive genes which do not allow normal development of the brain.

Incidence   1 in 1000 live births. Several members of the same generation and family may be affected.[2]

Physical features   *Head*: Small head (43 cm (17 in) or less in adult) with tiny cranial vault.[2]
Face: Face and features are of normal size which gives rise to a striking disproportion between the facial features and the tiny cranial vault.[2] Profile is characteristic with receding chin and forehead.
Limbs: There is often spasticity of all four limbs, especially the legs.[3]
Height: Usually short and below normal.
Nervous system: There may be abnormalities in the brain such as small, narrow gyri (microgyria) or large cyst-like spaces (porencephaly). Epilepsy may occur.[2]

Abilities   Almost all are severely mentally handicapped.

Tuberous sclerosis (epiloia)

Condition   First described in 1880 as a syndrome characterized by severe mental handicap, epilepsy and a facial rash (adenoma sebaceum).[1]

Cause	Autosomal dominant gene of poor penetrance, which may result in only partial features of the syndrome being evident.
Incidence	Estimates vary from 1 in 20 000[3] to 1 in 30 000.[2]
Physical features	*Skin*: First visible signs are white macules sometimes called *café-au-lait* patches.[3] The most distinctive feature is the facial rash called adenoma sebaceum. This appears about the fourth or fifth year of life and spreads over the nose, cheeks and skin (butterfly rash) and is due to an overgrowth of the sebaceous glands.[2] Other skin lesions include 'shagreen patches' which are raised thickened areas of skin on the back and loins, and fibromata (benign tumours) of the finger nails.
	Eyes: Flat, oval, greyish white patches occur on the retina called 'phakoma' (benign tumour of the retina).[3]
	Nervous system: Multiple sclerotic nodules in the brain substance particularly around the ventricles. Epilepsy is common.
Congenital abnormalities	There may be tumours of the heart, lungs, spleen and kidneys which may become malignant.[1]
Abilities	These vary considerably as a result of the irregular effects of the responsible dominant gene. Even though an individual has the physical signs he may be of normal intelli-, gence, but more usually is severely mentally handicapped.[1]

Lesch-Nyhan syndrome (infantile hyperuricaemia)

Condition	First described in 1964 by Lesch and Nyhan. An inborn error of purine metabolism characterized by severe mental handicap, athetosis and self-multilation.[3]
Cause	X-linked recessive gene resulting in the deficiency of an enzyme concerned with purine metabolism leading to the accumulation of excess amounts of uric acid in the blood.[2]
Incidence	Unknown, but believed to be very rare.
Physical features	*Face*: Normal at birth but there may be severe mutilation of the lower lip.
	Ears: Those children who survive for ten years or more may have uric acid tophi (deposits in the external ear).[3]
	Limbs: There may be choreoathetosis and sometimes spasticity which is progressive. Further self-mutilation occurs with the child biting the fingertips.[2]

Height and weight: Usually below normal.

Nervous system: The distressing feature of self-mutilation is thought to be due to excessive thirst caused by the excess uric acid in the blood.[1] Pain perception appears to be normal and the children appear relieved when restrained from biting themselves.[3]

Abilities

All are severely or moderately mentally handicapped and although there may be normal motor development during the first six months there is progressive spasticity.

Diagnosis

It is possible to diagnose the condition by carrying out amniocentesis and estimating enzyme concentrations.[2]

Treatment and prognosis

Allopurinol is used to lower the uric acid levels, but does not prevent or reduce the brain damage. The prognosis is said to be poor with affected children rarely surviving beyond puberty.[3]

Care points

Considerable effort should be made to prevent painful self-mutilation by use of mechanical restraints or tooth extraction.

Lawrence-Moon-Bardet-Biedl syndrome

Condition

First described by Lawrence and Moon in 1866 with further symptomatology reported on by Bardet (1920) and Biedl (1933). It is characterized by obesity, retinal degeneration and underdevelopment of the genitalia.[3]

Cause

Autosomal recessive gene.

Incidence

Not known.

Physical features

Face: Some individuals show a degree of hypertelorism.[3]

Eyes: Progressive degeneration of the retina called retinitis pigmentosa.[1] Other disorders of vision include night blindness, nystagmus and poor vision with the occasional appearance of cataracts.[3]

Genitalia: The external genitalia are usually underdeveloped.

Limbs: There may be polydactyly (extra fingers and toes), usually bilateral.

Height and weight: The height is usually unaffected but occasionally affected individuals may be shorter than normal. There is obesity of the Frölich type, which is obvious in infancy, and is seen on the chest, abdomen and hips.[2,3]

Nervous system: Where the degree of mental handicap is severe there may be an associated hearing loss and epilepsy.[1,3]

Galactosaemia

Condition

First reported by Reuss in 1908. A disorder of carbohydrate metabolism characterized by failure to thrive, enlargement of the liver and spleen, development of cataracts and mental handicap in those cases which are not diagnosed and treated.[3]

Cause

An autosomal recessive gene causing a deficiency or absence of the enzyme necessary for the conversion of galactose in the blood and urine.[2]

Incidence

Estimated at 1 in 70 000 live births.[3]

Physical features

Present in those children who are not treated.

Eyes: Cataracts may develop during the first year of life.[3]

Abdomen: There may be enlargement of the liver and spleen. The child who is severely affected will start to show signs of this in the first two weeks of life, with vomiting, lethargy and severe loss of weight.[2]

Skin: There may be either jaundice as a result of liver involvement or pallor associated with anaemia.[3]

Diagnosis

It is possible to diagnose the condition following amniocentesis and estimation of the enzyme concentrations.

Treatment and prognosis

Treatment is achieved by giving a galactose-restricted or galactose-free diet. This treatment will result in normal body function and a lessening or prevention of mental handicap.[2]

Abilities

In untreated cases there is profound mental handicap. However, early treatment can result in nearly normal intellectual development.

Phenylketonuria

Condition

First described by Fölling in 1934. A disorder of protein metabolism characterized by fair complexion and hair, skin disorders and manneristic behaviour.[2]

Cause

An autosomal recessive gene causing a deficiency of the enzyme, normally present in the liver, which converts phenylalanine (a normal constituent of dietary protein) to tyrosine. This results in raised blood levels of phenylalanine which is toxic to the developing brain, causing brain damage.[1]

Incidence

Approximately 1 in 12 000 live births.[2]

Physical features   *Head*: Microcephaly occurs in about half the untreated cases.[3]
Eyes: Iris pigmentation is lighter and is characteristically blue in European races.[2]
Skin: Infantile eczema occurs in about one-third of affected individuals and may persist into adolescence and adulthood.[3] The skin is fair in complexion due to an absence of melanin (the skin-colouring pigment).
Nervous system: There is motor retardation with delay in learning to walk. Approximately one-third never learn to talk. Approximately one-quarter suffer from epilepsy, with three-quarters demonstrating an abnormal EEG reading.[2] Post-mortems have revealed that there is a slight to moderate deficiency of myelin.[1]

Diagnosis   The most reliable method is Guthrie's test which is a blood test carried out six to 14 days after birth.[2] The normal serum level of phenylalanine is 2–4 mg/100 ml but in phenylketonuria this can be as high as 20–30 mg/100 ml.[3] Urine tests such as the ferric chloride test or Phenistix test can be used but are less reliable.

Treatment   This is aimed at maintaining the serum phenylalanine levels at 2.5–10 mg/100 ml.[2] This is achieved by feeding the child a phenylalanine-restricted diet with the addition of tyrosine and vitamin supplements. It should be remembered that excessive phenylalanine restriction can be as harmful, since phenylalanine is essential to life. The child will fail to thrive, and vomit and progressive apathy will lead to death.[2]

Abilities and behaviour   Untreated individuals are profoundly mentally handicapped and may show disturbances in behaviour. These take the form of 'autistic' behaviour, with reluctance or inability to form relationships with others. They may also show typical manneristic behaviour in rocking backwards and forwards and posturing with hands.[2] If the diet is given early in infancy (in the first two months) then the physical symptoms and mental handicap can be avoided.

Note: Phenylketonuria may be transmitted to a fetus in other ways. Successfully treated women may have high blood levels of phenylalanine which may affect the fetus and these women will need to resume a phenylalanine-restricted diet during pregnancy to avoid damage to the fetus.[2] Those women who are carriers of the abnormal gene may have phenylalanine blood levels high enough to damage the fetus and these women will also need to take a phenylalanine-restricted diet during pregnancy.[2]

Tay-Sachs disease

Condition	First described by Tay (1881) and Sachs (1886). A condition of abnormal storage of lipid (fat) material in tissues which leads to their degeneration. It is characterized by progressive deterioration of intellect and vision.[3]
Cause	An autosomal recessive gene defect, resulting in the deficiency of an enzyme essential for normal lipid metabolism.[2]
Incidence	It occurs most frequently in the Jewish race, with a carrier rate as high as 1 in 25.[2] In American Jews it is estimated to occur in 1 in 6000 live births.[3] It is very rare in the non-Jewish population.
Physical features	*Head*: In infancy the head is normal in size but in those children who survive to two years there is generalized head enlargement.[2] *Eyes*: There is a 'cherry red spot' at the macula lutea (part of the retina) which can be seen from approximately two and a half months; this progressively enlarges so that after nine months vision deteriorates rapidly to blindness by the fifteenth month.[3] *Limbs*: From the sixth month there is progressive spastic paralysis affecting all muscles.[3] *Nervous system*: There may be an exaggerated motor response to sound, excessive drooling, shrill cries and laughter for no apparent reason.[3] After the first year there are almost always generalized convulsions. Hearing remains acute until the terminal stages.[2]
Treatment and prognosis	The prognosis is poor, with progressive deterioration leading to death in two to four years. Death often occurs as a result of aspiration pneumonia.[3]
Prevention	It is possible to detect the abnormality through amniocentesis. This shows an absence or deficiency of the essential enzyme. Where there is a high risk, as in the Jewish population, amniocentesis can be carried out with a view to termination in affected cases.

Note: There is a juvenile form of the disease where the children develop normally until the fifth or seventh year of life. The disease follows the same course as the infantile form but is slower, with the prognosis of death before 18 years of age.[2]

GLOSSARY

Adenoma sebaceum	An overgrowth of the sebaceous glands of the cheeks, nose and chin seen in the condition of tuberous sclerosis.

Allopurinol	A drug used to lower the level of uric acid in the blood given in cases of Lesch-Nyhan syndrome.
Alopecia	Loss of hair which may be focal or complete.
Amenorrhoea	Absence or abnormal cessation of menstruation.
Amniocentesis	The aspiration of amniotic fluid from the pregnant uterus, normally carried out between the 14th and 16th weeks, with a view to detecting fetal abnormality.
Anophthalmia	Congenital absence of one or both eyes.
Athetosis	A particular form of cerebral palsy caused by damage to the basal ganglia.
Blepharitis	Inflammation of the eyelids, seen frequently in Down's syndrome.
Cataract	Loss of transparency of the lens of the eye.
Consanguinity	Blood relationship. This is significant when first cousins marry as the risk of abnormality to the children of the marriage is 1 in 8.
Dominance	The mechanism by which a dominant gene expresses itself over a recessive gene.
Epicanthic fold	A fold of skin extending from the nose to inner termination of the eyebrow. Often seen in Down's syndrome.
Fibromata	Benign growths derived from fibrous connective tissue seen in tuberous sclerosis.
Flaccid	Relaxed and without tone.
Frölich obesity	Increase in fat over chest, abdomen and hips seen in Lawrence-Moon-Bardet-Biedl syndrome.
Giemsa	Dye used to identify chromosomes in karyotype.
Gynaecomastia	Development of breast tissue in males, typically seen in Klinefelter's syndrome (XXY).
Gyri	Convolutions on the surface of the brain which may be abnormal in their narrowness or absence.
Heterochromatin	Dye used to identify chromosomes in karyotype.
Hypertonia	Extreme tension of the muscles.
Hypertelorism	Abnormal distance between paired organs, usually applied to the eyes; this sign may accompany syndromes causing mental handicap.

Hypotonia	Reduced muscle tension, as seen in Down's syndrome.
Karyotype	The chromosome characteristics of an individual, photographed at a particular stage of cell division and arranged in order of decreasing size.
Lipid	A comprehensive term used to describe water-insoluble fats and oils. A disorder of lipid metabolism occurs in Tay-Sachs disease.
Macula lutea	A small orange-yellow area on the inner surface of the retina. This is altered in Tay–Sachs disease when there is a cherry-red spot at the macula lutea.
Meiosis	The process of cell division occurring in the sex cells.
Melanin	The colouring pigment in the body which is reduced in the condition of phenylketonuria.
Metabolism	The process by which the body utilizes food stuffs. It consists of anabolism, which is the process of building proteins for growth and repair of body tissue, and catabolism, where the body breaks down complex substances so that they can be used.
Microcephaly	Abnormal smallness of the cranial vault with facial features of normal size. The head circumference is 43 cm (17 in) or less in the adult.
Microphthalmia	The presence of one or both eyes of abnormally small size.
Mosaicism	May occur after fertilization when the chromosomes fail to separate properly so that some cells contain excess chromosomes with others showing a corresponding deficit.
Non-disjunction	Failure of chromosomes to separate properly during mitotic or meiotic cell division.
Nystagmus	Involuntary flicking of the eyeball.
Olfactory bulb	The organ concerned with the sense of smell which may be congenitally absent in Patau's syndrome.
Phakoma	Greyish-white 'patches' seen in the retina in those suffering from tuberous sclerosis.
Polydactyly	The presence of more than five fingers or toes on the hand or foot.
Porencephaly	The presence of cyst-like spaces or cavities in the brain substance, may be seen in tuberous sclerosis.
Prognosis	A forecast of the outcome of a disease.

Quinacrine	Dye used to identify chromosomes in karyotype.
Recessive gene	A gene which can produce its effect only in combination with another recessive gene for the same characteristic.
Retinitis pigmentosa	A degenerative process affecting the retina of the eye which may be seen in the Lawrence-Mood-Bardet-Biedl syndrome.
Schizoid psychosis	A form of mental illness characterized by a tendency to avoid close interpersonal relationships.
Sex linkage	A mechanism of inheritance where an abnormal gene is carried by the female on one X chromosome. Classically the sons will be affected and the daughters will be carriers.
Shagreen patches	Raised, flat, thickened areas of skin seen on the back in tuberous sclerosis.
Strabismus	A squint.
Supraorbital ridge	The bony ridge over the eye socket.
Syndactyly	Webbing of the fingers or toes.
Testosterone	Male sex hormone.
Tophi	Deposits of sodium urate in joints or the cartilage of the external ear. They may be seen in children over 10 years suffering from Lesch–Nyhan syndrome.
Translocation	The process in which two chromosomes become attached to each other and form a compound chromosome as a result of failure to separate properly during cell division.
Trisomy	An additional chromosome occurring as a result of an error in meiotic cell division.
Tyrosine	An amino acid present in most proteins which is not metabolized in the condition of phenylketonuria.

BIBLIOGRAPHY

1. Dutton, G. (1975) *Mental Handicap*. London: Butterworths.
2. Heaton-Ward, W.A. (1975) *Mental Subnormality*, 4th ed. Bristol: John Wright.
3. Holmes, L.B., Moser, H.W., Halldorsson, S., Mack, C., Pant, S. & Matzilevich, B. (1972) *Mental Retardation–An Atlas of Diseases with Associated Physical Abnormalities*. New York: Macmillan.
4. Penrose, L.S. (1972) *The Biology of Mental Defect*, 4th ed. London: Sidgwick and Jackson.

Environmental causes

7

A fetus is a promise of normality but there are many factors which may affect its physical and mental development sufficiently to cause mental handicap. These factors may exert their influence at any time after conception, during pregnancy, birth or childhood. They include maternal and childhood infections; acute or chronic lack of oxygen to the developing brain; direct or indirect violence ranging from accidental irradiation to non-accidental injury; maternal-fetal incompatibility; prematurity; birth injury; the ingestion of chemicals in pregnancy and childhood; maternal and childhood malnutrition; and sensory and social deprivation.

The severity of their effects varies from severe mental and physical abnormality to mild mental handicap with no physical handicap. Generally the earlier the damage occurs the more severe is the outcome, as the developing brain is particularly susceptible to adverse conditions.[3]

It is useful to consider the environmental causes of mental handicap in groups that relate to the stage of development that the fetus or child has reached.

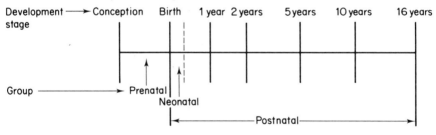

Fig. 18. Groups of environmental causes of mental handicap related to developmental stage.

PRENATAL CAUSES

Following conception the fetus develops rapidly from the fertilized ovum to the normal full-term baby. One of the more complex aspects of fetal development is the formation and maturation of the brain and central nervous system, with 'spurts' of growth occurring during the fifteenth and twentieth weeks and from the twenty-fifth week onwards.[3] The developing brain is particularly vulnerable to any adverse conditions and a number of factors are known to cause mental handicap at this time. These are described under the major headings of physical, chemical and infective factors.

Physical factors

Radiation

It has been known for some time that maternal irradiation may affect the fetus, particularly during the first three months of pregnancy. As early as 1931 X-rays were given in the second month of pregnancy to produce abortions.[5] There was further evidence that therapeutic doses of irradiation might not affect the mother but would still affect the developing fetus.[5] Following the atomic radiation at Hiroshima and Nagasaki in Japan it was found that those women who survived and were pregnant (fifth to fifteenth week) gave birth either to stillborn children or to children suffering from microcephaly.[3]

Excessive irradiation has also been shown to cause genetic mutation in the parents of the affected fetus so that subsequent children may be affected.[3] It is also thought that the X-rays can affect the sex glands (testes and ovaries) of the fetus; although apparently normal at birth these babies' future children may suffer genetic disease.[2]

It is estimated that the amount of irradiation required to produce malformations in the fetus is one hundred times that required for normal diagnostic X-ray purposes.[5] Even so, the use of diagnostic ultrasound techniques during pregnancy is thought to be much safer.[3]

Direct violence

Direct violence severe enough to affect the fetus will usually result in a stillbirth.[3] One form of 'violence' that can affect the fetus is where an unsuccessful attempt is made to procure an abortion. Although the usual method of procuring an abortion is to administer chemicals, direct physical injury to the fetus has been reported.[5]

Anoxia

All living cells require an adequate amount of oxygen to survive. This is particularly true of brain cells and the brain of the developing fetus can withstand a lack of oxygen only for very brief periods without permanent damage occurring.[3] The fetus receives oxygen from the mother through the placenta and umbilical cord. It is thought that anoxia may occur as a result of the mother suffering from chronic mitral valve stenosis causing poor oxygenation of the maternal and subsequently the fetal blood.[5] A further cause of anoxia is seen in the mother who suffers from epilepsy with the fetus at risk from the repeated effects of maternal anoxia, although this is thought to be quite rare.[5] Maternal anoxia would seem to affect the fetus towards the end of pregnancy and typically results in cerebral palsy.

The placenta may be abnormal or may separate from the wall of the uterus prematurely, causing fetal anoxia which may result in mental handicap. Compression of the umbilical cord may occur if it coils around the neck or becomes knotted and this may give rise to anoxia.[5]

Maternal–fetal incompatibility

The most widely known maternal–fetal incompatibility is Rhesus factor incompatibility. This arises when a Rhesus-negative mother is pregnant with a Rhesus-positive fetus. During the birth of the first child Rhesus-positive cells 'leak' into the mother's circulation. In response the mother becomes immunized and develops antibodies, which in subsequent pregnancies pass across the placenta and haemolyse (break down) the fetal red blood cells. This may cause a combination of spastic paralysis of the limbs and athetosis, associated with deafness and mental handicap.[5] The damage is due to the high concentrations of bile pigments, present in the blood as a result of red blood cell destruction, which affect the basal ganglia and auditory centres.

Other blood group incompatibilities involving the ABO blood groups are known to occur but these are less common.[1]

Maternal–fetal incompatibility, particularly the Rhesus factor, may become less significant as a cause of mental handicap as diagnosis and treatment become more widely available. Rhesus-factor incompatibility may be diagnosed by amniocentesis with an estimation of the level of bilirubin. Exchange transfusions may be given in utero or after birth. Rhesus-negative mothers who have not become immunized may be given anti-D gammaglobulin within 48 hours of delivery to prevent the development of antibodies.[3]

Chemical factors

Maternal nutrition

Maternal health and level of nutrition are important during pregnancy, particularly in the early stages. Specific dietary excess or deficiency may have little or no effect on the mother but may be sufficient to cause abnormality in the fetus. This had been demonstrated by an imbalance, either an excess or a deficiency, of vitamin A.[5] Deficiency of vitamins B, C and D has also been known to produce fetal abnormalities. Other more general deficiencies of diet, such as lack of protein, may cause stunting of physical development and also a degree of mental handicap if the deficiency coincides with a period of rapid growth of the central nervous system.[3] It has been suggested that other dietary factors may affect the fetus, including green potatoes, artificial sweeteners, excessive amounts of tea in early pregnancy, food additives and the hardness of the water supply.[5]

Sometimes the level of maternal nutrition is adequate but the fetus suffers a nutritional lack brought about by placental insufficiency. This may be due to abnormalities of the placenta itself or to maternal disorders. The effect is to deprive the fetus of essential nutrients and oxygen with the risk of malformation and intellectual impairment.

Drugs

Drugs taken during pregnancy may affect the fetus and a dramatic example of this was seen in the tragic after-effects of thalidomide which caused deformities in children. Other drugs have been shown to affect the fetus and some in particular have caused mental handicap. Some antibiotics have been seen to have an anti-mitotic effect which can affect normal fetal development, particularly during periods of rapid growth.[5] Insulin used to treat maternal diabetes mellitus may induce fetal hypoglycaemia (low blood sugar) which may be severe enough to cause brain damage and mental handicap.[2] Anticonvulsant drugs used in the treatment of epilepsy may affect the fetus. Adequate serum levels of folate (a salt of folic acid) seem important in the prevention of abnormalities, and these levels are reduced in those taking anticonvulsants.[2]

Smoking during pregnancy has been shown to cause fetal underdevelopment, probably by reducing the placental blood flow, resulting in fetal anoxia, and also by depleting the amount of maternal vitamin B12 available to the fetus.[3]

Recent research has shown that alcohol can damage the fetus and cause physical and mental abnormalities. This is more widely recognized in America where the term 'fetal alcohol syndrome' was coined in 1973. In America it is thought by some researchers to be the third most frequent cause of mental handicap. Excessive levels of alcohol are believed to disrupt the maternal digestive processes, causing a lack of fetal oxygen and glucose. Evidence would suggest that the damage is caused during the period between the twenty-fourth and the fortieth days of pregnancy, which is often too early for the mother to know that she is pregnant. Research in England shows that whilst chronic alcoholism affects the fetus, more damaging effects may be produced by episodes of drinking, the 'binge drinking' theory. Abnormalities reported include microcephaly, cleft palate and malformed ears.

Infective factors

A number of maternal infections are known to cause physical and mental abnormalities.[3] The causative organism may be a virus such as the rubella virus, cytomegalovirus, infectious hepatitis virus, influenza virus, chickenpox (varicella), herpes virus and the poliomyelitis virus. Other causative organisms include the spirochaete *Treponema pallidum*, responsible for syphilis, and the protozoon *Toxoplasma gondii*, responsible for toxoplasmosis.

A feature of intrauterine infections is the variability of their effects on the fetus. Some may obviously be severely affected from birth, others are unaffected and some may seem normal at birth but show evidence of damage months or even years later. Similarly the effect on the mother is variable and she may not experience any symptoms at all or may experience a vague feeling of being unwell which is attributed to being pregnant.

The infecting organisms pass across the placenta to exert their effect in the child, usually by attacking developing nervous tissue. Generally the earlier the infection the greater the effect;[3] however, this is not always true, as in the case of cytometalovirus infection which may exert its effect late in pregnancy.[3]

Diagnosis is often difficult and in many cases impossible as the maternal infection may not be recognized clinically. Where maternal infection is known to have occurred termination of the pregnancy may be considered in view of the possible consequences. Efforts are being made to reduce the risk of congenital abnormalities caused by the rubella virus by immunizing adolescent girls who have not acquired active immunity.[3] At present it is only possible to treat congenital syphilis actively.

The above remarks are concerned with the direct effects of maternal infection in the fetus and illustrative examples of these are included later in this chapter. The fetus may also be affected indirectly as a result of maternal infection. This can occur as a consequence of a raised body temperature in the mother, when damage to the fetus is caused by the elevated temperature and not by the organism causing the disease.[2]

PERINATAL CAUSES

Perinatal causes have their effect at or about the time of birth and include such conditions as prematurity, birth injury and difficult or abnormal labour.

Prematurity

Prematurity is not in itself a cause of mental handicap, but premature babies are predisposed towards injury at birth as a result of their relative immaturity.[3] They are more prone to damage and tearing of delicate cerebral arteries which leads to haemorrhage into the brain substance; this causes compression which may result in physical and mental handicap. They are also more at risk from the effects of anoxia. Studies have shown a correlation between prematurity and intellectual impairment.[2]

Birth injury

Birth injury is thought to be the cause of mental handicap in 1% of all cases.[5] The fetus is protected from trauma and injury during intrauterine life by the amniotic fluid which surrounds it.[2] However, at birth the baby is subject to risk from anoxia, cerebral trauma and haemorrhage, mechanical injury and the chemical effects of drugs given during labour. These risks are increased in difficult or abnormal births. Statistically, injury is most likely to occur at the first birth, although other factors may be important, such as anoxia resulting from compression of the umbilical cord during a prolonged second stage of labour.[3] Sometimes the second stage may be too rapid (precipitate labour), resulting in cerebral haemorrhage.[3] The baby's head is rapidly compressed to allow its passage through the birth canal and there follows a rapid decompression, tearing delicate cerebral blood vessels. Mechanical injury may occur as a result of a forceps delivery and mental handicap, spastic paralysis or epilepsy may be the consequence. There is said to be a significant increase of breech deliveries in mothers who suffer from epilepsy.[2] A breech delivery may cause cerebral haemorrhage in the baby, by stretching and tearing blood vessels.

POSTNATAL CAUSES

Postnatal causes have their effect from birth to the time the genetically determined limits of intelligence have been reached, approximately 15-16 years of age.[3] They include blood chemistry imbalance, malnutrition, infection, cerebral trauma, ingestion of toxins and sensory and social deprivation. The child is particularly susceptible to these factors during the neonatal period, the first 28 days following birth.[2]

Blood chemistry imbalance

The developing brain is particularly susceptible to anoxia during 'spurts' of development, which occur from the twenty-fifth week of the pregnancy until the second year of life.[3] Anoxia may occur in the neonatal period as a result of depression of the baby's respiratory centre following heavy maternal sedation during pregnancy.[2] Early childhood respiratory infection may cause anoxia and subsequent brain damage.

The optimum level of oxygen is a fine balance between anoxia and hyperoxia. Hyperoxia, or too much oxygen, is sometimes associated with mental handicap as the baby's brain is particularly sensitive to high concentrations of oxygen.[5]

A further condition which may occur in the neonatal period is hypoglycaemia or low levels of blood sugar. Following birth the baby's blood sugar level falls to around 2.8 mmol/litre (50 mg/100 ml) of blood and then slowly rises over the next 72 hours.[2] In some babies, particularly those with low birth weights, the blood sugar level may fall to 1.1 mmol/litre (20 mg/100 ml) of blood or less.[2] If this continues death or permanent brain damage may occur. It is estimated to occur in 2 in 1000 live births, boys being affected twice as frequently as girls.[2] The symptoms include periods of apnoea (not breathing), tremors and convulsions. Treatment is aimed at maintaining blood sugar levels above 1.1 mmol/litre (20 mg/100 ml) of blood.[3]

Malnutrition

The effects of maternal malnutrition on the fetus have already been described. The major factor in postnatal malnutrition appears to be lack of protein and even when affected children are given high-protein diets intellectual impairment may still persist.[2] Interestingly, one study shows that there was a reduction in the amount of DNA in the brains of children who had died of malnutrition compared to a control group of children who had died of other causes.[2]

Children who suffer malnutrition during the period of accelerated nervous system development will be physically underdeveloped, with a small head circumference and associated mental handicap.

Childhood infection

Many childhood infections have been associated with mental handicap. The most important are those diseases which have a direct effect on the nervous system, such as encephalitis or meningitis.[2] Infection may be either primary or a complication of one of the common virus infections seen in childhood: measles, whooping cough, scarlet fever or mumps. The course of encephalitis (inflammation of the brain) is variable, with complete recovery in some cases and permanent brain damage in others.[3] Where brain damage does occur there may be cerebral palsy, epilepsy and varying degrees of mental handicap.[3] There may also be changes in behaviour and personality, generally of an antisocial nature.[3] In encephalitis lethargica, a form of encephalitis occurring in epidemics, there may be damage to the basal ganglia. This may result in a condition called post-encephalitic parkinsonism, which is characterized by a slowing of movement, muscle rigidity and a mask-like expression with tremors. Although the individual's appearance would suggest quite a severe handicap, it is usually slight.

Vaccination-induced encephalitis following routine vaccination for whooping cough or smallpox has been known to occur and in these instances the degree of brain damage and subsequent mental handicap is usually severe.[3]

Meningitis (inflammation of the coverings of the brain), either viral or bacterial, may cause brain damage and personality changes in the same way as encephalitis.[3]

A serious complication of meningitis may be hydrocephalus. The brain is surrounded by cerebrospinal fluid which protects it from injury. Hydrocephalus is due to overproduction of cerebrospinal fluid, to interference in the process of its absorption or to a blockage in its normal circulation. The special cells in the ventricles of the brain which make cerebrospinal fluid produce it at a constant rate. As a result of the blockage, the cerebrospinal fluid builds up and compresses the brain substance. Gradually in untreated cases the skull expands to a grossly enlarged size.[3] This may result in varying degrees of spastic paralysis and possibly other signs of brain damage such as defects of vision and hearing.[3] The degree of mental handicap is also variable, depending on the severity of the brain damage. Somewhat surprisingly, in view of their grossly handicapped appearance, these children and adults often have verbal IQs of 50 or more.

Recently treatment has been possible with the insertion of a shunt (Spitz-Holter or Pudenz-Heyer) which bypasses the obstruction.[3]

Severe childhood illness may lead to a degree of mental handicap. This may be seen in severe dehydration following acute gastroenteritis which may give rise to abnormally high levels of sodium in the blood causing brain damage.[2]

Hyperpyrexia (very high body temperature) may cause severe brain damage and subsequent mental handicap.

Cerebral trauma

Cerebral trauma in childhood may be divided into accidental and non-accidental injury.

A major cause of *accidental injury* is the increase in the number of road traffic accidents.[2] If the injury is severe enough to cause brain damage there may be residual hemiplegia, epilepsy and mental handicap. The degree of mental handicap may be slight but there may be associated behaviour problems and personality changes which limit the child's ability to learn from his environment.[2]

Brain damage may occur in whooping cough as a result of capillary haemor-rhages caused by prolonged and severe coughing.[3]

Non-accidental injury to children has given rise to the term 'battered baby syndrome' and would seem to be increasing. Injuries include depressed fractures of the skull, haematomas and damage to the blood vessels in the brain.[2] These injuries may lead to severe brain damage causing mental handicap. Many reasons are given for non-accidental injury to children, which range from family rows to immaturity in parents. There are as many reasons as there are battered children and all the problems are very difficult to resolve.

Ingestion of poisonous chemicals

A number of poisonous substances have been known to cause brain damage and mental handicap, including mercury, copper, manganese, strontium and lead.[3] Once again, the earlier the brain is subjected to adverse influences the greater the effect.

The most common form of poisoning is *lead poisoning*, although this is declining as legislation controls the lead levels of substances such as paint and petrol. In childhood the source of lead is usually lead paint from old houses or old toys.[3] Severely affected children may show signs of lead encephalopathy, such as convulsions, neck stiffness and coma. There is permanent brain damage which may be associated with residual cerebral palsy, serious visual impairment and mental handicap.[3] A further feature may be the appearance of behaviour changes, including withdrawal, hyperactivity or negativism.[2]

Treatment is aimed at reducing the lead levels in the body to below 40 mg/ 100 ml.[2] This may be achieved by giving a chelating agent such as calcium versenate or D-penicillamine.[3]

Sensory and social deprivation

The child learns and develops intellectual skills by using his special senses of sight, hearing, touch, taste and smell to interpret the environmental stimuli he experiences. Impairment of any of the special senses can have an effect on normal development. Impairment of sight and hearing are especially important and frequent accurate physical assessments should be carried out to avoid an erroneous diagnosis of mental handicap and to provide help for the child. Social deprivation has the effect of limiting opportunities to learn and in extreme instances had been known to be a direct cause of mental handicap. More often the child suffering social deprivation shows poor performance on IQ tests, in school work and in social relationships.[2]

SUMMARY

The first part of this chapter has discussed the concept of the intrauterine environment and those environmental factors which may cause mental handicap during the periods of fetal development, birth and childhood. These factors have been discussed in relation to the stage of development that the fetus or child has reached. The prenatal causes were the effects of radiation, direct violence, anoxia, maternal–fetal incompatibility, drugs and maternal infection. Perinatal causes include the effects of prematurity and birth injury. Postnatal causes include blood chemistry imbalance (anoxia, hypoglycaemia), maternal and childhood malnutrition, childhood infection, the effects of cerebral trauma, ingestion of poisons and sensory and social deprivation.

CHECKLIST OF SYNDROMES[4]

The second part of the chapter provides more detailed information about a small number of selected conditions, in the form of a checklist.[4] These conditions are arranged in alphabetical order for quick and easy reference. Included in this section is a description of childhood autism which defies clear-cut classification, but is nonetheless an important cause of mental handicap.

Autism

Condition   First described by Kanner in 1943.[2] A condition arising in early childhood characterized by a complicated pattern of abnormal behaviour.

Cause   Uncertain, but there are a number of theories. Environmental theories suggest that the abnormal behaviour is in some way conditioned by parents or others. Organic theories blame either under- or over-arousal of the reticular formation of the brain or impairment or absence of the inbuilt mechanism which facilitates acquisition of language.

Incidence   4–5 in 10 000 births. For 'classic' autism it is 2 in 10 000 and autistic features occur in 2.5 in 10 000. Three boys are affected for one girl.

Physical features	Children are said to be graceful and good-looking, but this does not persist into adulthood. They are often said to be unnaturally 'good' as babies.
Behaviour	*Basic impairments*[6] : (*a*) Language problems* both verbal and non-verbal, characterized by severe impairment of comprehension and use of language. (*b*) Perceptual problems seen in unusual responses to sound, visual stimuli, touch and pain. A tendency to use peripheral fields of vision with inability to maintain eye contact. (*c*) Problems of motor control,* particularly difficulty in copying skilled movement.

Special skills:[6] (*a*) Skills which do not involve use of language,* such as music, arithmetic, manual dexterity. (*b*) Particular form of long-term memory* for lists, poems, complicated visual patterns.

Secondary behaviour problems:[6] (*a*) Difficulty in social relationships* characterized by indifference and reluctance to interact with other children. Gradually diminishes as they become older. (*b*) Intense resistance to change* includ-an attachment to and skillful manipulation of objects. (*c*) Inability to play creatively* with others.

Diagnosis	Extremely difficult in the absence of demonstrable organic damage. Relies on identification of autistic behaviour patterns and differential diagnosis. If all those items marked * are present a diagnosis of classic early childhood autism may be made.[6]
Abilities	All autistic children are handicapped in language development. Approximately 20% may be of normal or above normal intelligence; the remaining 80% vary from mild to severe mental handicap.
Treatment	No specific treatment except intensive educational programmes. Behaviour modification techniques have proved successful in the management of 'autistic' behaviour and in teaching verbal and non-verbal means of communication.

Battered baby syndrome

Condition	Arising from direct violence to the child sufficient to cause injury from bruising to mental handicap.
Cause	Direct violence, usually assault, but may be through physical restraint.

Incidence   Usually babies and preschool children. Occurs in all socio-economic groups.[4]

Physical features   The physical signs reflect the form of abuse.
                           Skin: Abrasions, scars, bleeding commonly on trunk and buttocks, less often on head and limbs.
                           Height and weight: Children who are generally neglected tend to be retarded in normal height and weight for their age.[4]
                           Nervous system: May be brain damage as a result of cerebral haemorrhage. There may be associated hydrocephalus or microcephaly or spinal cord injury.[4]
                           Limbs and skull: The most common finding is fractures of the limbs and skull as a result of a direct blow or bending.

Diagnosis   Often missed but multiple injuries or a history of recent injury should alert the examining doctor.

Treatment   Symptomatic for child's injuries and possibly psychiatric treatment for the individual responsible.

Cytomegalovirus inclusion body disease

Condition   A maternal infection which is passed to the fetus during pregnancy. A feature of the condition is that it may not give rise to symptoms in the mother and may affect the fetus either early or late in pregnancy.[2]

Cause   Cytomegalovirus infection.

Incidence   Widespread in the environment with a high proportion of the normal population affected before middle age.[1] Of the children who suffer the effects of maternal infection approximately 10-20% become mentally handicapped.[1]

Physical features   *Head*: Microcephaly.
                           Eyes: Chorioretinitis is common and occasionally the eyes may be much smaller than normal (microphthalmia).[4]
                           Abdomen: There may be enlargement of the liver and spleen which may persist for months.[4]
                           Skin: Jaundice may be present as a result of the liver involvement.
                           Weight: The babies are frequently premature with a low birth weight.[4]
                           Nervous system: Epilepsy is a common finding and there may be other neurological signs such as cerebral palsy, deafness, hyperactivity or motor retardation.[4]

Treatment and prognosis	Some babies die within a few days of birth. Those who survive may be only mildly affected whilst others may be profoundly physically and mentally handicapped.

Herpes virus infection (perinatal)

Condition	An intrauterine infection with a wide variation in symptoms and effects which is transmitted from the infected mother at or about the time of birth.
Cause	The disease can be transmitted in three ways:[4] from the mother's infected genitalia; by an ascending infection during passage through an affected birth canal; or through the placenta. The responsible organism is the herpes virus.
Incidence	Estimates vary from 1 in 3500 to 1 in 30 000.[4]
Physical features	These are usually not seen until a few days after birth, vary widely and the child may not show any physical signs of infection.
	Eyes: Symptoms may involve simple conjunctivitis, keratitis or a slowly developing chorioretinitis, which may leave residual scarring and cataracts. Some children may be blind.[4]
	Mouth: Herpetic infection of the mouth may be seen.
	Abdomen: There may be an enlarged liver and/or jaundice.
	Skin: Primary vesicles are seen either at birth or within the first two weeks, with recurrent secondary vesicles occurring up to the second year.[4]
	Weight: A low birth weight is common.
	Nervous system: General involvement of the brain and its coverings (meningoencephalitis) is common and there may be either hydrocephaly or microcephaly.[4]
Diagnosis	Evidence of the infection is found in the tissues.
Treatment and prognosis	Those babies with severe infection often do not survive. Those with localized infections recover fully. Caesarean section avoids the risk of infection from an infected genital tract.[4]

Rhesus factor incompatibility (kernicterus)

Condition	A state of incompatibility between the blood of a Rhesus-negative mother and her Rhesus-positive child which leads to the mother producing antibodies which pass across the placenta and break down the fetal red blood cells.

Cause   Haemolysis of fetal red blood cells by maternal antibodies releasing bilirubin which when deposited in neural tissue may lead to deafness, cerebral palsy and mental handicap.[3]

Incidence   Unknown, but is becoming less common as a result of routine maternal and paternal blood typing and active treatment.

Physical features Mouth: There may be staining or discoloration of the teeth.[4]
                    Nervous system: In untreated cases there may be involvement of the basal ganglia which will give rise to athetoid cerebral palsy. Involvement of the auditory centres will result in deafness. The degree of mental handicap is variable from mild to profound.[3]

Treatment   This may be achieved by exchange transfusion which can be carried out either in utero or after birth. A further form of treatment is the administration of anti-D (Rhesus factor) gammaglobulin to the mother 48 hours after delivery, to prevent the formation of antibodies which may affect subsequent children.[3]

Rubella syndrome

Condition   First described by Gregg in 1941 and characterized by a number of severe defects which include cataracts, deafness, congenital heart defects and mental handicap.[4]

Cause   Transplacental infection with the rubella virus which attacks developing nervous tissue. Infection is often subclinical in the mother.[3]

Incidence   Unknown, but declining as immunization programmes for adolescent school girls become commonplace.[3] The risk rates have been calculated as 60% if the mother contracts rubella 3–4 weeks from last menstrual period; 35% at 5–8 weeks; 15% at 9–12 weeks; and 7% at 13–16 weeks. The overall risk is 21%.[3]

Physical features Head: There is often microcephaly.
                    Eyes: There may be cataracts and glaucoma which may be associated with microphthalmia. There may also be abnormalities of the retina which do not have any effect on visual acuity.[4]
                    Abdomen: There may be enlargement of the liver and spleen. There is also increase in the incidence of inguinal hernias.[4]

Skin: Skin lesions known to occur are macules distributed on the face, trunk and arms within 48 hours of birth.
Weight and height: There is usually a low birth weight with general underdevelopment.[1]
Nervous system: These signs are widely variable in severity and range from minor intellectual deficit to severe physical and mental handicap. Cerebral palsy may be severe (spastic quadriplegia). Deafness is found in a high proportion of children with rubella syndrome.[1]

Treatment   There is no treatment available for the condition and any treatment must be aimed at reducing the effects of the syndrome.

Syphilis

Condition   A venereal disease which may be passed from the mother to the fetus usually after the fourth month of pregnancy. It characteristically produces differing symptoms depending on the age of the person affected.[4]

Cause   Maternal transmission of the organism *Treponema pallidum* to the fetus. The more recent the maternal infection the more severe the effects.[4]

Incidence   The incidence of maternal syphilis is increasing and inevitably more children are being affected. However, blood tests and screening should lead to a reduction in the numbers suffering from congenital syphilis.

Physical features   Vary in infancy, childhood and adulthood.
Infancy   *Prematurity*: Prematurity is likely, with the child showing a withered skin and protuberant abdomen.[4]
Nose: Mucoid nasal discharge one to two weeks after birth which may become infected and blood-stained.[4]
Skin: Red round macules appear around the mouth, anus and genitalia.[4]
Other: There may be an enlarged liver and spleen, or meningitis.
Childhood   *Nose*: A 'saddle back' deformity of the bridge of the nose.[3]
Teeth: Underdevelopment of the milk teeth.
Nervous system: Mental handicap with associated behaviour problems and possibly epilepsy.
Adulthood   *Head*: Frontal bossing of the skull due to overgrowth of bone.[4]
Eyes: There are many eye signs which include unequal and

responsive pupils, interstitial keratitis, chorioretinitis and optic atrophy and blindness.[4]
Nose: The 'saddle back' deformity persists.
Teeth: The development of crescentic notches on the widely spaced incisor teeth, called Hutchinson's teeth.[3]
Skeletal system: There may be a deformity of the shin, called sabre shin, and involvement of the joints, especially the knee joints, called Clutton's joints.[4]
Nervous system: There will be varying degrees of mental impairment. Neurosyphilis may be evident from adolescence or at any time during adulthood.

Diagnosis

The most widely used are tests of the blood serum of the fetus—the VDRL.[4]

Treatment

Intensive treatment of both the pregnant mother and the newborn child with penicillin will be effective. The penicillin is given either in the last few weeks of pregnancy or in the first months of life. It is claimed that treatment of children and adults is helpful, but the degree of mental handicap is not altered.

Toxoplasmosis

Condition

First described in 1939[4] as a condition arising from infection by an organism acquired from farm and domestic animals.[3] The symptoms range from an apparently normal child at birth (the symptoms appearing a few months later) to obvious severe physical and mental handicap at birth.[3]

Cause

Infection by the organism *Toxoplasma gondii*. Many women are infected at some time in their lives but the infection has to occur during pregnancy in order for it to be transmitted to the fetus.[3]

Incidence

Unknown, although in France the estimated incidence is 1 in 1000 live births.[4]

Physical features

Head: There may be either microcephaly or mild hydrocephalus.[4]
Eyes: The most common symptom is chorioretinitis which may be bilateral. Other eye signs include microphthalmia (small eye).[3]
Abdomen: There may be enlargement of the liver and spleen at birth which persists for several weeks or months.[4]
Nervous system: The infection may cause inflammation of

the brain and its coverings which may give rise to cerebral palsy and epilepsy. The degree of mental handicap is variable.[3]

Diagnosis   This is done by blood tests leading to the identification of the toxoplasmosis organism.

Treatment   None has so far been found.

GLOSSARY

Amniocentesis   Aspiration of amniotic fluid from the pregnant uterus, normally carried out between the 14th and 16th weeks, with a view to detecting fetal abnormality.

Amniotic fluid   The protective fluid surrounding the fetus.

Anoxia   Lack of oxygen.

Antimitotic   A substance which may interrupt normal mitotic cell division. Antibiotics have been known to have this effect.

Apnoea   Cessation of breathing.

Autism   Severe emotional disturbance of childhood characterized by abnormal behaviour and difficulty with interpersonal relationships.

Basal ganglia   A collection of nerve cells in the cerebrum concerned with coordinated movement. Damage may result in athetoid cerebral palsy.

Battered baby syndrome   Non-accidental injury to children.

Calcium versenate   A drug used to neutralize the effects of abnormal levels of lead in the blood.

Cataract   Loss of transparency of the lens of the eye.

Cerebrospinal fluid   The protective fluid which surrounds the brain and spinal cord. Blockage will result in hydrocephalus.

Chelating agent   A substance which neutralizes the effect of a metal ion by forming a chemical bond.

Chorioretinitis   A particular form of inflammation of the retina, the inner lining of nerves in the eye.

Conjunctivitis   Inflammation of the mucous membrane covering the outer surface of the eyeball.

Cytomegalovirus	A virus causing maternal infection which can pass across the placenta and cause widespread symptoms in the fetus.
Diabetes mellitus	A disorder of carbohydrate metabolism caused by a lack of insulin.
DNA	Deoxyribonucleic acid which forms the chromosomal material.
D-*Penicillamine*	A chelating agent used in the management of lead poisoning.
Encephalitis	Inflammation of the brain substance.
Encephalitis lethargica	A particular form of encephalitis which occurs in epidemics; it is characterized by muscle rigidity.
Encephalopathy	Any disease of the brain.
Fetal alcohol syndrome	A syndrome occurring as a result of raised maternal alcohol levels affecting the fetus and causing mental handicap.
Fetus	The unborn baby.
Folate levels	Folate is the salt of folic acid and adequate maternal serum levels are essential. These levels may be reduced in mothers taking anticonvulsant drugs for epilepsy.
Gammaglobulin	One of the serum proteins which store antibodies.
Genitalia	The external reproductive organs.
Glaucoma	A disease of the eyes, characterized by a raised intraocular pressure. May be progressive leading to blindness.
Haematoma	Bleeding into the tissues; bruising.
Haemolysis	Destruction of red blood cells which may be seen in Rhesus factor incompatibility.
Hemiplegia	Paralysis of one side of the body.
Hydrocephalus	A condition which may be an accompaniment of mental handicap, marked by an excessive accumulation of cerebrospinal fluid causing a gross enlargement of the skull.
Hyperoxia	Excess oxygen in the tissues.
Hyperpyrexia	High body temperature over 39.4°C (103°F).
Inguinal hernia	A protrusion of the small intestine through the inguinal canal presenting as a lump in the groin.
Interstitial keratitis	A chronic inflammation of the middle and inner layers of the cornea of the eye.

IQ	Intelligence quotient.
Irradiation	The bombardment of tissues with X-rays.
Kernicterus	A condition characterized by jaundice, rigidity and athetosis as a result of damage to the basal ganglia caused by the presence of bile pigments. May be seen in Rhesus factor incompatibility.
Macule	A small discoloured spot on the skin not elevated above the general surface.
Meningitis	Inflammation of the meninges, the three coverings of the brain and spinal cord.
Microcephaly	Abnormal smallness of the cranial vault with facial features of normal size. The head circumference is 43 cm (17 in) or less in the adult.
Microphthalmia	The presence of one or both eyes of abnormally small size.
Mitral valve stenosis	A narrowing of the mitral valve in the heart causing a reduced maternal blood flow which may result in fetal anoxia.
Ovary	The female reproductive glands containing the ova.
Optic atrophy	A diminution, through wasting, of the size of the eye.
Perinatal	At or about the time of birth.
Placenta	The organ through which the fetus receives oxygen and nourishment from its mother.
Postencephalitic parkinsonism	Sometimes a sequel of encephalitis characterized by muscle rigidity, pill rolling tremor and excessive salivation.
Postnatal	After birth.
Prenatal	Before birth.
Pudenz–Heyer shunt	A device to drain excess cerebrospinal fluid from the ventricles of the brain to prevent hydrocephalus.
Reticular formation	A network of nerve cells running through the brain stem from the medulla to the cortex which convey sensory information. The function of the reticular formation is to arouse the cerebral cortex.
Rhesus factor incompatibility	A condition of blood incompatibility between mother and fetus. The mother is Rhesus-negative and the fetus Rhesus-positive.

Spitz-Holter valve	A device used to drain excess cerebrospinal fluid from the ventricles of the brain to prevent hydrocephalus.
Testes	The male reproductive glands containing the spermatozoa.
Thalidomide	A drug prescribed as a sedative which caused deformities in babies.
Toxoplasma gondii	An organism found in domestic and farm animals which causes the condition of toxoplasmosis in humans. It may be transmitted across the placenta and cause abnormalities and mental handicap.
Trauma	Violence, direct or indirect.
Treponema pallidum	The causative organism of syphilis.
Ultrasound scanning	A technique of using ultrasonic vibrations to investigate the pregnant uterus for fetal abnormalities avoiding the risk of irradiation.
Umbilical cord	The cord extending from the placenta to the umbilicus of the fetus.
Vaccination-induced encephalitis	Encephalitis incurred as a result of vaccination against a childhood disease such as whooping cough.
Ventricles	Small cavities in the brain. The two lateral ventricles produce cerebrospinal fluid.
Vesicle	A small circumscribed elevation on the skin containing serum.

BIBLIOGRAPHY

1. Clayton, B.E. (1973) *Mental Retardation: Environmental Hazards.* London: Butterworths.
2. Dutton, G. (1975) *Mental Handicap.* London: Butterworths.
3. Heaton-Ward, W.A. (1975) *Mental Subnormality*, 4th ed. Bristol: John Wright.
4. Holmes, L.B., Moser, H.W., Halldorsson, S., Mack, C., Pant, S. & Matzilevich, B. (1972) *Mental Retardation—An Atlas of Diseases with Associated Physical Abnormalities.* New York: Macmillan.
5. Penrose, L.S. (1972) *The Biology of Mental Defect*, 4th ed. London: Sidgwick and Jackson.
6. Wing, L. & Wing, J.K. (1971) Multiple impairments in early childhood autism. *J. Autism Childh. Schizophr., 1*, 256.

Epilepsy

8

Epilepsy is as old as history; the first recorded references attributed to Hammurabi, King of Babylon, in 2080 B.C., who published laws regarding marriages of people suffering from epilepsy and their status as witnesses in court. There have also been references in the Bible and the writings of Hippocrates.[2] Since that time epilepsy has been feared and has been associated with possession by demons, madness and witchcraft. There have been many well known sufferers including Alexander the Great, St Paul, Mohammed, Julius Caesar, Napoleon, Lord Byron and Tchaikovsky. Epilepsy is no respecter of class or creed and today there are many people in public life who suffer from the disability.[2] The word epilepsy is derived from the Greek *epi lambano* which means 'a taking hold of' and it is from this translation that the term seizure or fit comes.[6]

Epilepsy has been defined as a 'recurrent disturbance in the chemico-electrical activity of the brain, which manifests itself in a symptom-complex of which impairment of consciousness, perturbation of the autonomic nervous system, convulsive movements, sensory abnormalities, or psychic disturbances are the essential components'.[3] This is an operational definition which encompasses all the forms that epilepsy may take and which may vary from convulsion and coma to a brief interruption of consciousness.

The incidence of epilepsy is thought to be 1 in 200 of the population, which amounts to 300 000 sufferers in the United Kingdom;[2] interestingly, this equates with the estimated number of severely mentally handicapped people, but it should be pointed out that this is a coincidence and it does not follow that a person who has epilepsy will be mentally handicapped. However, because of the link between mental handicap and brain malfunction as a result of prenatal, perinatal or postnatal factors, epilepsy may sometimes accompany mental handicap.

AETIOLOGY

Traditionally the aetiology of epilepsy has been classified into either symptomatic or idiopathic causes. Epilepsy is said to be symptomatic or acquired when the seizures are associated with a known cause which may include tumours, head injury, cerebral arteriosclerosis, brain disease such as encephalitis and meningitis, or associated conditions like phenylketonuria or microcephaly.[6] Where the cause is not known the epilepsy is termed genuine or idiopathic.[2] The significance of heredity is not agreed, as some experts say that it is minimal and others that there is a demonstrably higher incidence in the relatives of epileptic people, put at five or six times the figure for the general population.[6] This traditional way of classifying epilepsy has been questioned in the light of more recent work, which suggests that in each person suffering from epilepsy there are predisposing and precipitating causes.[3] These factors are shown in Table 11. The implication of this theory is that where a person is predisposed towards epilepsy as a result of any of the causes listed above an epileptic seizure may be 'triggered' by one or more of the precipitating causes depending on the individual's seizure threshold.[3]

Table 11. Predisposing and precipitating causes of epilepsy

Predisposing causes	Precipitating causes
Pre-natal disorders	Exhaustion
Birth injuries	Psychological stress
Trauma	Overhydration
Inflammation	Acute cerebral anoxia
Neoplasm	Hypoglycaemia
Vascular lesion	Hypocalcaemia

The abnormal electrical discharge which initiates the epileptic seizure may have a number of different causes and it is because of this that the diagnosis of epilepsy involves a number of investigations.[6] One of these investigations is the electroencephalogram (EEG), which is a recording of the electrical activity of the brain using electrodes attached to the scalp. The recording is shown in a trace and it is from this information that the type or form of epilepsy may be classified. Examples of EEG rhythms may be seen in Figs 19 and 20, which show normal developmental changes, and in Figs 21 and 22 which show typical abnormal rhythms.[4,6] However, the EEG cannot be used on its own to diagnose epilepsy as surveys have shown that people who do not suffer from epilepsy may have brain rhythms characteristic of epilepsy and *vice versa*. The judgement of whether a person is suffering from epilepsy is a clinical one and therefore other tests are indicated, including blood and urine analysis, radiography of the chest and skull and examination of the cerebrospinal fluid.[5] The results of these investigations, combined with the history, will enable the doctor to diagnose the type of epilepsy the person is suffering from, although a doctor is usually cautious about making a definitive diagnosis, particularly when a seizure occurs

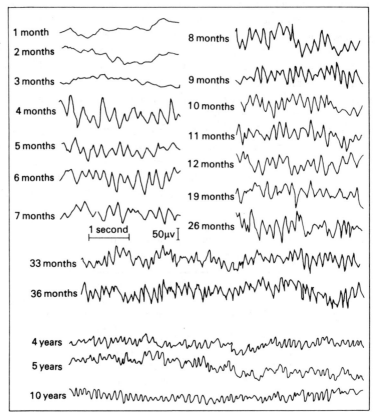

Fig. 19. Developmental changes in EEG rhythms.[4]

in isolation. A recent advance in recording EEG rhythms will greatly aid diagnosis, although at present it is available only in specialist centres. It is called 24-hour EEG monitoring and involves the use of a computer and split-screen monitor.[7] The technique allows the patient to move around and this is shown on one half of the screen; the other half shows the EEG rhythms as they occur and can be checked by a constant-time read-out. Diagnosis is facilitated by the ability to play back the recording and link events with an EEG recording.[7]

MAJOR EPILEPSY

Major epilepsy or *grand mal* is characterized by a sequence of events which are very different from each other; sometimes one or more of the events may be absent or not apparent, perhaps due to the masking effect of medication. The first stage is the aura, which is thought to serve as a warning that a seizure is going to occur and may take the form of a cry, giddiness, auditory stimuli or

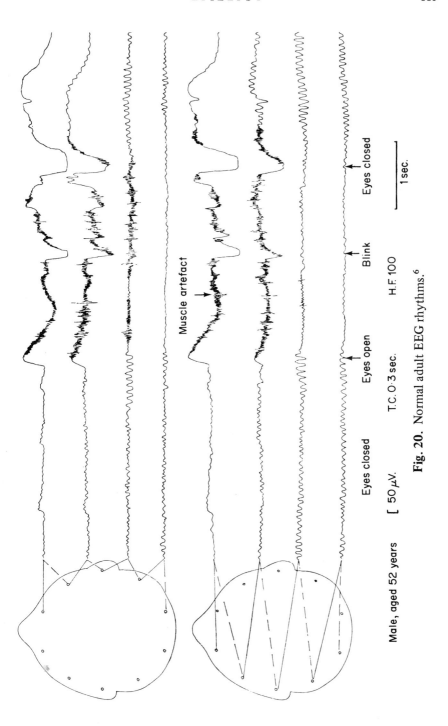

Fig. 20. Normal adult EEG rhythms.[6]

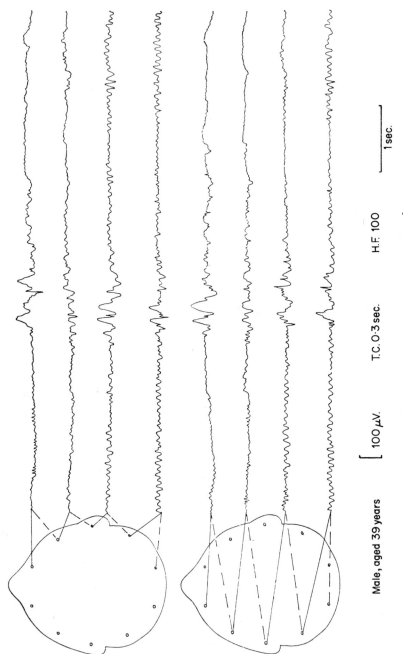

Male, aged 39 years   100 μV.   T.C. 0·3 sec.   H.F. 100

Fig. 21. *Grand mal* interseizure pattern.[6]

1 sec.

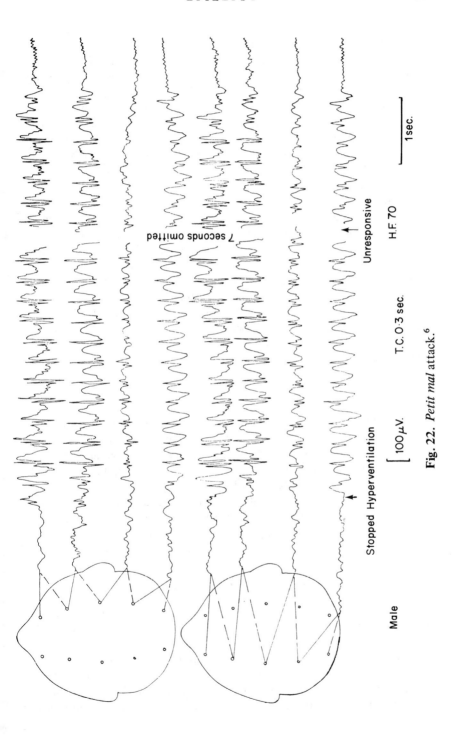

Fig. 22. *Petit mal* attack.[6]

tingling sensations. This is brief, often absent, and its occurrence is particularly difficult to establish with the mentally handicapped who are unable to communicate their feelings to others. Often the first visible sign of the seizure is when the person falls to the ground, loses consciousness and becomes rigid. This stage which lasts about a minute is called the tonic stage because all the muscles are in tonic spasm. It is for this reason that the person may appear cyanosed as the respiratory muscles are in a state of rigidity. After this period of rigidity there follows a series of convulsive movements which last for approximately one to three minutes. During this stage the tongue may be bitten; there may be frothing at the mouth; the person may be incontinent of urine and more rarely faeces. At the same time air is being drawn into the lungs and expelled rapidly to compensate for the period of apnoea during the tonic stage.[6] Gradually the convulsions stop and the cyanosis lessens. The fourth and final stage is the coma where the person sleeps for either a few minutes or hours; on waking he may appear confused and disoriented. Occasionally during this period of confusion the person may unknowingly behave in an aggressive antisocial manner, which is termed post-epileptic automatism and describes the automatic behaviour following an epileptic seizure.[3]

It should be stressed that the full pattern of the seizure with the stages of aura, tonic, clonic and coma as described above may often not be seen owing either to the effect of drugs or to the idiosyncratic form that the person's epilepsy takes.

MINOR EPILEPSY

Minor epilepsy or *petit mal* more often occurs in childhood but can also be seen in adults.[6] The attack consists of a brief interruption of consciousness where the child may stop doing something for a few seconds before resuming the activity. Apart from this blankness there are very few other signs, although the child's eyes may move upwards or to one side, and he may fall to the ground, immediately picking himself up.[3] Generally speaking there is no coma or confusion, although the child may have forgotten what he was doing before the attack.[3] *Petit mal* epilepsy varies in frequency and may be severely limiting as up to 1000 attacks may occur in a day; if this occurs it is termed pyknolepsy.[6]

FOCAL EPILEPSY

The term focal epilepsy is used to describe other forms of seizure which may occur due to an abnormal electrical discharge from a specific area or focus in the brain. Two types which may be seen are temporal lobe or psychomotor epilepsy and jacksonian epilepsy.[9] The focus is believed to be the temporal lobe and may take the form of automatic repetition of complicated behaviour such as writhing movements of the limbs, picking at clothes and even undressing; intense feelings of pleasure or fear, blushing or sweating; or psychic disturbances such as *déjà vu*, which literally translated means 'already seen', and gives the sufferer the impression he has been through the current experience before.[3] During an attack the person remains conscious but retains no memory of the events. Jacksonian epilepsy is named after Dr John Hughlings Jackson (1834–1911), an English neurologist, who first described the typical onset and course which may begin with local muscle spasms which spread to neighbouring muscles and typically involves one side of the body. If the muscle spasms spread to the other side of the body the person will suffer a *grand mal* seizure.[5]

Focal epilepsy may be characterized by periods of irritable excitement, confusion, violence, dreamy states or fugal wanderings, of which the person is quite unaware.[9]

MYOCLONUS

Myoclonic contractions take the form of a brief involuntary jerking of the body without loss of consciousness, the force of the contraction sometimes being severe enough to cause the person to fall to the ground.[6] This form of epilepsy is associated with severe mental handicap but may be caused by organic brain disease such as encephalitis or meningitis.

STATUS EPILEPTICUS

Status epilepticus occurs when a series of *grand mal* seizures follow one after the other without the person regaining consciousness. It is a serious condition which may be caused by the sudden withdrawal of an anticonvulsant drug or the onset of a febrile illness.[6] If untreated it may lead to death from exhaustion, heart failure or hyperpyrexia, which is caused by the massive increase in muscular activity. Brain damage may also occur and is thought to be due to continuous stimulation of brain cells accompanied by a severe lack of oxygen.[6]

CARING FOR THE EPILEPTIC PERSON

The care of the mentally handicapped person suffering from epilepsy centres around four major areas: specific care during a seizure; observation and recording; the administration of drugs; and the social aspects of living with the disability of epilepsy, which include placement and activities. The guiding principle should be that the care and management should enable the child or adult to live as independent a life as possible.[3] Apart from the special care that may be required, the epileptic mentally handicapped person should be treated in the same way as his peers, as failure to do so will lead to deprivation of experience and have the effect of further limiting the person's opportunity to learn.

Specific care during a major seizure

It is almost impossible to prevent the person from injuring himself at the onset of a seizure, but occasionally someone may be near enough to help him to the floor or move furniture out of the way. The care staff should then make sure that there is no further environmental danger from nearby furniture, from a cramped space or from hazards such as a crowd, traffic or fire. During the tonic stage he should be gently turned onto his side, tight clothing at neck or waist should be loosened and a firm pillow should be placed under the head. These actions are taken in preparation for the onset of the clonic stage, when muscle rigidity is replaced by convulsions. Turning the person on to his side maintains a clear airway which may otherwise be obstructed during the convulsive stage. Loosening tight clothing helps breathing to become rapid and easy, as during the tonic stage the respiratory muscles would have been paralysed and the patient unable to breathe. The pillow prevents possible injury during convulsions as a result of the head repeatedly striking the floor or ground; if not available the care staff can use their hands to support the head.

Part of the folklore surrounding epilepsy is the misconception that something solid, such as a spoon or wooden peg, should be placed between the teeth during a seizure, as it is believed that this action prevents the person biting his tongue. However, injury of this kind seldom occurs and therefore any attempt to insert anything solid between the teeth is not justified as it increases the risk of injury by damaging teeth and gums, with the added possibility of inhalation of tooth fragments. During the convulsions the limbs should not be forcibly restrained as this may result in fractures; rather the movements should be gently guided to avoid injury. Slowly the convulsions, cyanosis and rapid breathing will lessen and become more normal and sleep will follow for a few minutes. The care staff should stay with the person until he is capable of being roused. To avoid the possibility of the airway becoming obstructed, the patient may be placed in the semi-prone position. Depending on the pattern that the individual's epilepsy follows, he may be either left where he is, if not in danger and suitably covered, or put to bed so that he may recover over a longer period. If incontinence has occurred during the seizure he should be helped to wash himself and change his clothing, or it should be done for him. It is important for the care staff to remember that he may be confused and disoriented.

The person may have injured himself at the onset of or during the seizure, and cuts around the eyes or chin commonly occur from striking furniture or the floor in falling. Any injuries that have occurred can be treated on recovery from the seizure.

In the rare event of *status epilepticus*, more sophisticated care is required. Apart from urgent drug treatment, which is discussed later in this chapter, the maintenance of a clear airway is all-important: this may be aided by the use of oropharyngeal suction. The care that should be given is the same as for someone who is deeply unconscious and is aimed as supplementing the vital reflexes that protect the person when conscious. It is a serious condition and the person should always receive medical attention in hospital as speedily as possible.[2]

Specific care of minor and focal epilepsy

Minor and focal epilepsy may take many forms, from an interruption of activity to confused wandering in potentially dangerous situations; the care required is accurate observation and knowledge of the individual's particular pattern of seizure. It involves being with the person, sympathetically helping him cope with any confusion and guarding him from danger.

Observation and recording

Accurate observation and recording of the events before, during and after a seizure will aid diagnosis, facilitate management and indicate treatment.

As has been said earlier in this chapter, in a person predisposed towards epilepsy, a seizure may be 'triggered' by a precipitating cause (see Table 11) and it is important that any precipitating factor in the environment should be recorded. The care staff should look for events which regularly precede the onset of seizures such as irritability, a sudden noise or psychological stress induced by a quarrel, a change in mood or a particular activity. Other more general factors such as tiredness, constipation or premenstrual tension should also be noted, so that any precipitating factor can be identified and possible anticipated or avoided.

At the onset of the seizure the time should be noted as it is important that a record be made of the duration and the time of day. The care staff should time the stages of the seizure so that a pattern can be built up which will aid the general management of the person and indicate possible changes in the type or time of medication. A particularly important phase to note accurately is the length of time the person remains confused or experiences post-epileptic automatism, as he may be in danger from his environment and will need continuing help and supervision. The second aspect of timing which should be noted is whether the seizure occurs during the day or night. Some people with epilepsy have seizures only at night (nocturnal epilepsy) or at particular times during the day. This information may be used to increase medication at a particular time and decrease it at others. The recovery time, if known, will indicate whether the person may be left to recover where the seizure occurred or if he will need to be put to bed.

The form that the seizure takes is noted. These notes may vary from observing the time and recovery rate in minor epilepsy to describing the automatic acts seen in temporal lobe seizures or the presence or absence of rigidity and convulsions in major epilepsy. Assumptions should not be made about the type of seizure that has occurred and, until experienced, care staff should report exactly the events that took place. The check-list[1] which follows is a guide to the observations that should be made.

1. *Level of consciousness*
   a. Did the person lose consciousness?
   b. Was consciousness altered in any way?
   c. For how long was he unconscious?
   d. Did he appear confused and disoriented?
   e. Was he rousable?
   f. Did he respond to his name being called?
   g. Did he say anything?
2. *Muscle tone*
   a. Did he fall?
   b. In which direction was the fall?
   c. Was there any rigidity?
   d. Was the rigidity bilateral or unilateral?
   e. Were there convulsive movements?
   f. Were these convulsive movements generalized or localized?
   g. Did they start in one place and spread?
   h. Were there any other forms of movements?
   i. Was he incontinent of urine or faeces?
3. *Time*
   a. What time did the seizure occur?
   b. How long did the seizure last?
   c. For how long did the tonic stage last?
   d. For how long did the clonic stage last?
   e. For how long was he confused or disoriented?
   f. How long was it before he was rousable?
4. *Eye signs*
   a. Were any eye movements noted?
   b. Did the pupils react to light?
   c. Were corneal reflexes present?

The above information should be written down, preferably in the notes, as soon as possible after the seizure and also recorded on a special chart (Fig. 23).

Finally, any injury that has been sustained, such as a bitten tongue, cuts or bruising, should be noted and recorded and where appropriate an accident report should be made.

As we have seen, the accurate observation and recording of seizures is essential in providing information about the form that an individual's epilepsy takes. This is even more important when caring for mentally handicapped people who are often unable to discuss their disability or its effects. Information of the sort described above will enable the care staff to plan more realistic programmes for the individual. It will also give the doctor valuable help in deciding on the most desirable form of drug therapy.

EPILEPTIC CHART   ....19........

SURNAME					OTHER NAMES							NUMBER			

	JAN.		FEB.		MAR.		APR.		MAY		JUNE		JULY		AUG.		SEPT.		OCT.		NOV.		DEC.	
	D	N	D	N	D	N	D	N	D	N	D	N	D	N	D	N	D	N	D	N	D	N	D	N
1																								
2																								
3																								
4																								
5																								
6																								
7																								
8																								
9																								
10																								
11																								
12																								
13																								
14																								
15																								
16																								
17																								
18																								
19																								
20																								
21																								
22																								
23																								
24																								
25																								
26																								
27																								
28																								
29																								
30																								
31																								
Total																								

Fig. 23. An epilepsy chart.

DRUG TREATMENT IN EPILEPSY

The choice of drug will be made by the doctor. In the past five years rapid advances have been made in the number of drugs available and in their effectiveness. Becuase of this some of the more familiar drugs have been superseded and generally the aim of the treatment should be towards controlling epilepsy with as few drugs in as low a dosage as possible. The oral anticonvulsant drugs are absorbed in the villi of the small intestine and transported to the liver where they are metabolized and passed into the blood stream. The optimum blood serum level of the drug (Fig. 24) is that which controls the seizures but does not produce unwanted side effects.[6]

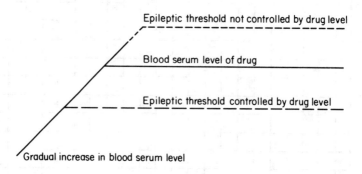

Epileptic threshold not controlled by drug level

Blood serum level of drug

Epileptic threshold controlled by drug level

Gradual increase in blood serum level

Fig. 24. Optimum blood serum levels in epilepsy.

Drugs are often used in combination as one drug may enhance or potentiate the effect of another, as is the case with ethosuximide and phenobarbitone. However, some drug interactions are not helpful, as seen in the interaction of anticonvulsant drugs and oral contraceptive drugs, with the anticonvulsants interfering with the effect of the oral contraceptives.

Some drugs have side-effects that may be so severe as to limit or prohibit their use. Each doctor has his individual drug preferences for each type of epilepsy and this is further modified by the individual needs of the patient. The patient should receive drug treatment until he has been free of attacks for three to five years; the withdrawal of drug treatment is a gradual process over a period of weeks. A comprehensive list of anticonvulsant drugs, the route of administration, the indications for their use and their daily dosage is given in Table 12. Table 13 lists some common side-effects.

One further point should be made regarding drugs and the mentally handicapped: the mentally handicapped start with the handicaps of intellectual and perceptual deficit which may be so increased by heavy doses of anticonvulsants that meaningful learning cannot take place.

Administration of drugs

In hospital the doctor will record the drug to be given on a prescription sheet with instructions regarding the dosage and the time of administration. It is important that the care staff ensure that these instructions are carried out if the drug treatment is to be successful. Dosages should be checked against the patient's prescription sheet to ensure that the correct drug is given to the correct patient at the correct time.[1] Occasionally a drug may be withdrawn too quickly, which results in a sudden fall in the blood serum level of the drug and may precipitate a seizure. The same effect can be observed if the drug is either not given by the care staff or not taken; if this should occur it should be reported to the person in charge of the ward, hostel or home.

Just as doctors rely on accurate reports from care staff to aid diagnosis they also rely on accurate observation of the effect of prescribed drugs and also the occurrence of side-effects. These reports may well influence the continuing use of a particular drug and so are very important.[1]

Emergency administration of drugs

The doctor may prescribe a drug to be given 'as and when necessary' in an emergency such as status epilepticus. Although the treatment of choice for status epilepticus is intravenous diazepam (see Table 12), this may not always be possible and so intramuscular injections of drugs such as sodium phenobarbitone or paraldehyde may be ordered. If a drug is given in an emergency such as status epilepticus it should be recorded as given and the doctor should be informed. Whatever procedure is recommended it must not be delayed as status epilepticus is a serious condition with a mortality of 20-50%.[6]

SURGICAL TREATMENT OF EPILEPSY

Brief mention should be made of possible surgical intervention in epilepsy. There are very few people whose epilepsy is suitable for surgery but in a few patients with well localized unilateral foci it may be justified.[6] However, any operation that involves the brain carries the risk of residual paralysis and the new, specific anticonvulsant drugs have largely obviated the need for surgery.

SOCIAL ASPECTS OF EPILEPSY

It has been said that social attitudes often cause more distress than epilepsy itself and this is especially applicable to mentally handicapped people with epilepsy.[2] This social stigma has been described by Dr Denis Williams, consultant physician to the National Hospital for Nervous Diseases, London: 'to have epilepsy is to be different from one's fellows as a result of a persistent intangible and recalcitrant disorder which even in the most enlightened society carries with it the stigma of the unusual'.[6] In residental care the fact that a person

Table 12. Drugs used in epilepsy

Approved name	Brand names	Route	Indications in epilepsy	Dosage
Major drugs				
ACTH	Actuar	Oral	Infantile spasms	30–60 units/day
Carbamazepine	Tegretol	Oral	Tonic-clonic Focal motor/sensory Temporal lobe psychomotor	Initial dose 100 mg/day in children, 200 mg/day in adults; then 20 mg/kg/day in two or three doses
Clonazepam	Rivotril	Oral	Myoclonic Myoclonic astatic Photosensitive Status epilepticus	0.01–0.02 mg/kg/day in children; 2.5–20 mg/day in adults
Diazepam	Valium	Intravenous Oral	Status epilepticus Prevention of anxiety	0.15–0.25 mg/kg/day 4–20 mg/kg/day
Ethosuximide	Zarontin	Oral	*Petit mal*	20–60 mg/kg for children; 500–200 mg/kg/day for adults
Nitrazepam	Mogadon	Oral	Myoclonic Myoclonic astatic Infantile spasms	0.5–1.0 mg/kg/day
Phenobarbitone	Gardenal Luminal	Oral Intravenous	Neonatal fits Symptomatic tonic-clonic fits in old age	up to 8 mg/kg/day 30 mg at night
Phenytoin	Epanutin	Oral Intravenous	*Grand mal* in men Status epilepticus Temporal lobe	300 mg/day 150–250 mg/day 50 mg/min
Primidone	Mysoline		Converted to phenobarbitone in the body within approximately one hour of ingestion	

Sodium valproate	Epilim	Oral	Myoclonic astatic Febrile convulsions *Petit mal* Myoclonic Tonic–clonic Photosensitive Temporal lobe Focal motor/sensory	Adults 600 mg initially, add 200 mg every three days up to 1000–1200 mg/day; occasionally up to 2600 mg/day Children over 20 kg, 20–30 mg/kg/day; under 20 kg, 20–50 mg/kg/day
Other drugs				
Acetazolamide	Diamox			Used as an adjuvant in myoclonic epilepsy of childhood. Has some diuretic action and has been used in catamenial (menstrual) epilepsy
Corticosteroids				Sometimes given with ACTH (see above) to potentiate their effect
Ethytoin	Peganone			Similar to phenytoin (see above) but less effective
Mepacrine	Quinacrine			No longer used
Methasuximide	Celontin			Similar to ethosuximide (see above)
Methylphenobarbitone	Prominal			Similar to troxidone (see below)
Paraldehyde				Sometimes used as third choice in febrile convulsions if prolonged
Paramethadione	Paradione			Similar to troxidone (see below)
Phenyturide	Benuride			Mainly for tonic–clonic and psychomotor epilepsy; usually given with phenytoin
Sulthiame	Ospolot			For all types of epilepsy except *petit mal*, but less good with *grand mal*. Best given with phenytoin as it inhibits that drug's metabolism
Troxidone	Trodione			A reserve treatment for *petit mal*. Sometimes given with phenytoin and/or phenobarbitone

Drug Information Service, Southampton General Hospital.

Table 13. Side-effects of drugs given for epilepsy[5]

Approved name	Intolerance and overdosage	Hypersensitivity reactions	Long-term effects
ACTH	Disturbance of electrolyte balance	General allergic reactions	Increased secretion corticosteroids
Carbamazepine	Blurred vision Dizziness Sedation (rarely)	Skin rashes Stevens-Johnson syndrome SLE	Possible teratogenicity
Diazepam	Drowsiness Dizziness Dysarthria Ataxia	Skin rash (rare)	None known
Clonazepam	Drowsiness Dizziness Fatigue Muscular hypotonia Ataxia Mucus and saliva in infants	Diplopia	None known
Ethosuximide	Vomiting Dizziness Drowsiness Ataxia	Skin rashes Stevens-Johnson syndrome	Possible mental changes
Nitrazepam	Drowsiness Ataxia Increased mucus in the young	Skin rashes (very rare)	None known
Phenobarbitone and primidone	Drowsiness Giddiness Blurred vision Dysarthria	Skin rashes Stevens-Johnson syndrome General allergic reactions	Folate deficiency Enzyme induction effects
Phenytoin	Giddiness Dysarthria Ataxia Blurred vision Confusion	Skin rashes Stevens-Johnson syndrome Liver damage Bone damage General allergic reactions SLE	Gum hypertrophy Folate deficiency Hirsutism in young women Possible teratogenic drug interactions
Sodium valproate	Nausea Vomiting Abdominal cramp Indigestion Diarrhoea Drowsiness	Coma Hair loss (usually temporary)	Not yet known

suffers from epilepsy is accepted more easily and does not give rise to fearful comment, but it may mean that the person is treated differently. This difference in treatment usually takes the form of restricting the activities that can be undertaken, with consequent overprotection, and deprivation of vital experience. The task of care staff responsible for people with epilepsy is to ensure that they are able to live as normal a life as possible, within the limits of their disability, and not be restricted by a blanket policy governing all epileptic people in care. However, the policy of encouraging independence should not place the individual in danger and certain precautions may need to be taken. They should be supervised in potentially dangerous activities such as bathing, swimming and climbing.[1] A special precaution may be the wearing of protective helmets by those who frequently injure themselves falling.[9] If home is the hospital, meaningful work may be found in one of the departments such as occupational or industrial therapy and the patient should participate as fully as possible in the social life of the ward and the hospital.

If the person is capable of living in the community he must receive help, advice and training on how to cope with his epilepsy. There are several aspects of life in the community that may cause concern with regard to his epilepsy and these should be explained to him before discharge.

Accommodation will be the first and possibly most difficult area to manage although the social worker will help. It should be explained to the prospective landlord that the intending tenant has epilepsy and what this will mean.

Employment may also be difficult as the person has two handicaps but the Disablement Resettlement Officer will assist in finding suitable employment.[6] Most jobs can be done except those where a seizure would put other people in danger. Some jobs are obviously not suitable: driving a public service vehicle, operating dangerous machinery, working at heights, jobs where balance is important.[2] The person may be put onto the Register of Disabled which could help him to find employment under the provisions of the Disabled Persons Act.[6] If he is unsuited to work in industry or commerce as a result of frequent seizures, or behavioural problems, he may be placed in sheltered employment such as Remploy where 10% of the work force suffer from epilepsy.

Driving is a frequent problem and in 1970 and 1971 legislation was passed which clarified the position for the epileptic person.[2] This states that 'a driving liecence may be granted to an applicant who has suffered from epilepsy if he can satisfy these conditions:

'1. he shall have been free from any epileptic attack whilst awake for at least three years from the date when the licence is to have effect,
'2. in the case of an applicant who has had such attacks whilst asleep during that period he shall have been subject to such attacks whilst sleeping but not whilst awake since before the beginning of that period,
'3. the driving by him in pursuance of the licence is not likely to be a source of danger to the public.'

However, there are also regulations which govern heavy goods vehicles and public service vehicles and these state 'an applicant shall not at any time since he attained the age of three have had an epileptic attack'.[2] In all cases the person would be wise to take the advice of his doctor on his suitability to drive and the risks involved.

There have been descriptions of an epileptic 'personality' which is said to be surly, bad-tempered and aggressive.[8] Experience has shown that where the environment is understanding and tolerant these personality traits may be modified so that the person becomes more amenable, making his management easier. This needs to be taken into account especially in hospital where the individual has to cope with the environmental stresses of group living. The surprising thing is that the mentally handicapped who suffer from epilepsy cope as well as they do, and care staff should not make their situation worse by an unsympathetic suspicious attitude; rather they should support and help the person towards greater personal fulfilment and independence, so that the limiting effects of his epilepsy are reduced.

GLOSSARY

Epilepsy
A disorder which produces seizures that are characterized by an altered level of consciousness and local or generalized muscular spasms. Seizures are due to paroxysmal disturbances of the electrical activity of the brain.

Aura
A subjective sensation that precedes and marks the onset of an epileptic seizure.

Automatism
Performance of actions without independent consciousness or intention.

Apnoea
Absence of respiration.

Jacksonian epilepsy
A disorder characterized by epileptic seizures due to a lesion of the cerebral motor cortex, starting in (and sometimes confined to) the region of the body related to the irritated cortical area.

Petit mal
A minor attack of epilepsy consisting of a momentary more or less partial loss of consciousness.

Pyknolepsy
Frequent, almost continual *petit mal* attacks.

Electro-encephalogram
A recording of the electrical activity of the brain using electrodes attached to the scalp.

BIBLIOGRAPHY

1. Altschul, A. (1973) *Psychiatric Nursing*. London: Baillière Tindall.
2. British Epilepsy Association (1975) *Project Notes*. London: BEA.

3. Houston, J.C., Joiner, C.L. & Trounce, J.R. (1966) *A Short Textbook of Medicine*. London: English Universities Press.
4. Oates, J. & Floyd, A. (1976) *The Course of Development*. Milton Keynes: Open University Press.
5. Parsonage, M. (1973) Anti-epileptics. *Br. J. Hosp. Med., 9,* 613.
6. Pryse-Phillips, W. (1969) *Epilepsy*, Bristol: John Wright.
7. Rich, V. (1978) Come to the (Poznam) Fair. *Nursing Times, 7,* 781.
8. Walshe-Brennan, K.S. (1976) Epileptic personality. *Nursing Mirror, 75,* 56.
9. Whitfield, W. (1977) The epilepsies. *Nursing Times, 73,* 1251.

Cerebral palsy

9

Cerebral palsy is a generic term for a number of disorders of movement and posture which may be caused by a variety of factors. It may take many forms and vary considerably in its effects, from a mild difficulty in coordination to almost total physical incapacity. The term literally means paralysis of cerebral origin and the condition was first described by Dr J. Little in 1853.[14] Since this first description enormous progress has been made in the diagnosis, treatment and management of cerebral palsy. It occurs as a result of brain damage or developmental failure of those parts of the brain which initiate, control and modify physical movement. In some cases this damage may extend to other parts of the brain and give rise to more widespread effects which may lead to varying degrees of intellectual functioning. This association between brain damage and cerebral palsy is linked to mental handicap; an estimated '55% of cerebral palsied children have an IQ of less than 70'.[14] Conversely, there are numerous examples of very intelligent people who suffer from cerebral palsy, such as the author Christy Brown who, despite enormous physical difficulties, typed the manuscripts for his books. A further problem is that the child or adult may have additional handicaps caused by involvement of those muscles which control speech, facial expression and eye focussing. This has the effect of further limiting the ability to interact with the environment and also gives the impression that they are more intellectually handicapped than they are. The inability to communicate, to take part or to withdraw voluntarily from a situation may in turn lead to emotional stress which is often not recognized by those who care for the cerebral palsied child or adult. Joey Deacon in his autobiography *Tongue Tied* gives an insight into the difficulties of the person who has cerebral palsy;[3] an imposed dependency on other people and a reduction in every-day normal experiences has the effect of limiting opportunities to learn.

PHYSIOLOGICAL AND DEVELOPMENTAL ASPECTS

The normal child learns through interaction with his environment and develops motor, visual and manipulative skills; competence in the use of speech and

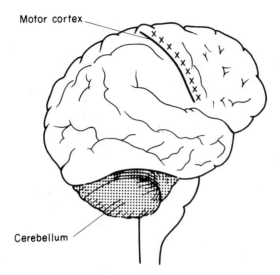

Fig. 25. The motor cortex and the cerebellum.

language; and an ability to behave in a socially acceptable way over a period of time[16] (see Table 3, pp. 10-11). This pattern of normal development is altered in cerebral palsy so that the child may show varying motor disorders, delayed language development or inability to play normally. The result of this abnormal development is a child who either fails to reach the developmental milestones for his age or who achieves them in a random 'scattered' way. The cerebral palsied

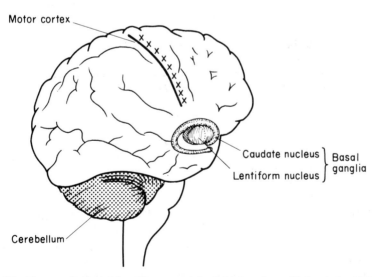

Fig. 26. The caudate and lentiform nuclei of the basal ganglia buried within the brain.

baby may often have difficulty in basic responses such as sucking, feeding and swallowing and will need to be fed in the correct way.[4] The correct feeding pattern is also important in the development of speech as this will help the child control the muscles of his tongue and lips which are important to articulation.

The most distinctive feature of cerebral palsy is the abnormal motor movement which may vary from general clumsiness to gross incoordination. These difficulties are brought about as a result of injury or damage to the cortex, the basal ganglia or the cerebellum.[6] Each of these important areas of the brain has a part in initiating, controlling or modifying movement and in order to understand how this happens and is changed in cerebral palsy it is necessary to consider normal motor movement.

The areas of the brain concerned with motor movement are the motor cortex, the basal ganglia and the cerebellum (Figs 25 and 26). Injury to the motor cortex may result in the condition of 'spastic' paralysis, characterized by disordered control of movement and muscle weakness, which occasionally affects physical growth and development. The limbs are stiff and rigid, which is termed tonic flexion. This is the most common form of cerebral palsy, accounting for approximately 70% of cases.[12]

The basal ganglia are areas of specialized cells buried deep in the brain which are responsible for coordinating muscle movements with the posture of the body. They allow smooth movement to take place by modifying the powerful effects of the motor system. Damage to the basal ganglia results in the condition known as athetoid cerebral palsy where the child or adult will make frequent involuntary movements which interfere with normal body movements, making it very difficult, if not impossible, for the person to be engaged in any activity. Approximately 10% of people with cerebral palsy suffer from athetosis.[12]

Table 14. Distribution, site of injury and form of cerebral palsy

Form of cerebral palsy	Site of injury or damage	%
Spastic	Motor cortex	70
Athetoid	Basal ganglia	10
Ataxia	Cerebellum	10
Mixed	Mixed	10

Damage to the cerebellum causes ataxia. This means the person will have difficulty in walking and balancing. He will appear as if drunk. Approximately 10% of cerebral palsied people will suffer from ataxia. The remaining 10% of cases will have mixed forms of spasticity, athetosis or ataxia (Table 14).[12] Various terms are used to describe paralysis which indicate what part of the body is affected and these can be seen in Table 15.

Table 15. Terminology relating to spastic paralysis

Term	Part of body affected
Hemiplegia	Arm and leg on one side
Monoplegia	One arm or one leg
Paraplegia	Both legs but not the arms
Tetraplegia Quadriplegia	All four limbs
Diplegia	All four limbs but with greater involvement of the legs

CAUSATION

The incidence of cerebral palsy has been estimated as 1 in every 400 hundred births and the causes are multiple. It has been seen from the previous section that cerebral palsy, being a symptom not a disease, occurs as a result of damage or developmental failure of those parts of the brain which initiate, control and modify movement. This may occur as a result of an inherited condition, an abnormality occurring at the time of conception, factors operating during pregnancy or birth, accidents or childhood infections.[19]

It is thought that approximately 5-10% of all cases of cerebral palsy are inherited.[19] Where this is so the baby is more likely to suffer from paraplegia or tetraplegia rather than hemiplegia or athetosis which are more likely to be a result of injury.

Where there are chromosomal defects cerebral palsy is often only one part of the clinical picture; the child frequently suffers from other abnormal conditions.[9]

From conception until birth the developing fetus may be at risk from a number of factors. Maternal infections have been shown to affect the unborn child; of these the most widely known is rubella or German measles. If the rubella virus passes across the placenta and attacks the developing nervous system of the fetus during the first three months of pregnancy it may produce such widespread effects as microcephaly, blindness or deafness as well as cerebral palsy.[9] Other maternal infections have been shown to affect the fetus, causing cerebral palsy; these include cytomegalovirus infection, varicella (chickenpox) and toxoplasmosis.[9]

There is substantial evidence to show that an abnormal or premature birth is associated with the incidence of cerebral palsy. Surveys have shown that in 80% of the children suffering from cerebral palsy there was a history of an abnormal birth or neonatal period.[19] The direct cause of the damage to the brain is usually a lack of oxygen to the baby's brain cells. Occasionally there may be a more obvious cause, such as damage caused by the use of forceps or by precipitate labour. Here the second stage occurs too quickly and leads to rapid compression and decompression of the baby's head; injury may be due to direct trauma or haemorrhage from torn blood vessels. In these cases the damage is usually to one side of the brain and results in a hemiplegia of the opposite side of the body.

Cerebral palsy may also be caused by a condition called Rhesus factor incompatibility.[14] In this condition the mother's blood does not contain the D or Rhesus factor and is classified as Rhesus-negative. However, the blood of the developing fetus may contain the D or Rhesus factor and will therefore be Rhesus-positive. The first child born is unaffected but during birth some of the baby's blood cells carrying the Rhesus factor may leak into the mother's circulation. In response the mother's blood cells produce antibodies to the Rhesus factor which in subsequent pregnancies may pass across the placenta and break down the baby's blood cells, causing jaundice which may be severe enough to cause cerebral palsy. The area usually damaged in this way is the basal ganglia and the type of cerebral palsy a mixture of rigidity and athetosis.

Childhood diseases can cause cerebral palsy, particularly those that affect the brain or its coverings such as encephalitis (inflammation of the brain substance) or meningitis (inflammation of the meninges, the coverings of the brain).[9] Occasionally cerebral palsy results from severe and prolonged coughing in a child suffering from whooping cough. Here multiple capillary haemorrhages bleed into the brain tissue causing damage.

The brain may also be damaged in childhood by direct violence, for example a road traffic accident.[14] This damage may also cause varying degrees of mental handicap.

With so many causative factors of cerebral palsy a definitive diagnosis is often impossible but generally any condition that affects the brain of the developing fetus or child may be responsible for cerebral palsy, and the earlier this happens the more severe the brain damage will be.

ASSOCIATED HANDICAPS

The child or adult with cerebral palsy may also have to cope with other handicaps in addition to the already incapacitating disorders of movement and posture. These may include visual handicap, hearing loss, feeding and speech difficulties, mental handicap and learning difficulties.

Visual handicaps arise because in cerebral palsy the muscles controlling eye movement may also be paralysed. The most common visual handicaps seen are strabismus (squint), myopia (short-sightedness), nystagmus (rapid flickering of the eyeball) and poor focussing ability. In addition there may also be visual agnosia. This occurs when the person can see correctly but is unable to understand or interpret what he sees.[8]

It has been estimated that approximately 30% or people suffering from the athetoid form of cerebral palsy also suffer from some degree of *hearing loss.*[5] This is seen in babies affected by Rhesus incompatibility and who are jaundiced. The high concentration of bile pigments damages the specialized cells in the auditory system. The hearing loss is rarely total and typically the hearing for low-pitched and very high-pitched sound is better than for sounds in the middle range.[5] As with vision, there may be an auditory agnosia, where the person may hear sounds or speech but is unable to interpret them meaningfully.

In order to speak, a large number of *muscular movements* involving larynx, pharynx, jaws, palate, tongue and lips have to be made. The normal child learns to use these muscles as a result of maturation of the central nervous system and through the establishment of the correct feeding patterns.[17] In cerebral palsy the child is often unable to develop the muscles necessary for speech through inability to eat properly or through incorrect feeding patterns. There may be problems with articulation of words (called dysarthria), or with voice production (called dysphonia), or with language itself (termed executive dysphasia).[17]

As previously stated, there is a relationship between cerebral palsy and *mental handicap* and when this occurs it is a further complication for the cerebral palsied child. In most instances where the child is tetraplegic then mental handicap will also be evident. However, in cases of damage to the basal ganglia resulting in athetosis, the physical disability may be total but the child may be of normal or above normal intelligence.[8] Interestingly, however, children and adults suffering from cerebral palsy are often wrongly thought of as being mentally handicapped because of the way they appear to other people, for all the reasons previously discussed.

Behaviour problems are not normally considered associated handicaps of cerebral palsy, but when they are present their effects can be just as limiting as physical problems.[14] They often have the effect of negatively determining the behaviour of those who provide the care, further depriving the child of opportunities to learn how to cope with his disability.

MANAGEMENT OF CEREBRAL PALSY

Assessment

Full, early and repeated assessments are vital for the child and those helping him as they show what he can do and what he cannot. Assessment also indicates what needs to be done in terms of treatment and management. Assessment of a physically and mentally handicapped child is usually difficult, particularly when the child is unable to communicate with the assessor in a meaningful way.[15] One of the best ways of assessing such a child is through observation of his abilities in particular settings compared with established standards of child development and behaviour. This developmental approach shows the level the child has reached and indicates areas where development is delayed or scattered. The physical assessment should aim at diagnosis of the type of cerebral palsy and the degree of motor involvement. It should also assess sight and hearing. Identification of perceptual problems is important as the child's ability to benefit from treatment may be enhanced or even dependent upon this knowledge. Psychological testing of the mentally handicapped cerebral palsied child is made more difficult by the physical problems. The important criterion is not necessarily the score on the test but the psychologist's interpretation of the results in relation to the child being tested.[15] A combination of standardized tests and structured observation evaluated against the normal milestones of development has proved useful. There are a number of developmental scales which can be used. The Ruth Griffiths Mental Development Scale can be used to determine developmental ability in children under two years in the areas of locomotion, personal social relationships, hearing and speech, hand-eye coordination and performance on simple tests.[2] The late Dr Mary Sheridan[16] devised the Stycar sequences, a number of developmentally graded tests allowing the child's performance to be compared against developmental charts ranging from birth to five years using posture and large movements, vision and fine movements, hearing and speech and social behaviour and play. Formal testing of intellectual ability may be of value and tests such as the Stanford-Binet may be used where the child is able to communicate reasonably well as this test has a verbal bias. An estimate of social maturity is often useful particularly where the child is exhibiting asocial behaviour and a test frequently used is the Vineland Social Maturity Scale.[2]

Accepting that assessment should be full and repeated it should also serve a purpose. The information gained from an assessment should lead to a programme of management designed to meet the child's physical and psychological needs, in the short and long term.

Methods of treatment

When considering treatment of cerebral palsy it is important to remember that a cure cannot be expected and that treatment is aimed at improving function in any way possible. There are a number of approaches which are aimed at producing functional gains, including surgery, treatment with drugs and most often specific programmes of physiotherapy, speech therapy and occupational therapy.

Surgical treatment can be divided into orthopaedic or neurological.[12] Orthopaedic surgery is usually used to try to establish or assist walking, and lengthening the Achilles tendon may help achieve this. Sometimes the spasms may result in a dislocated hip and surgical reduction may be carried out. When the child has stopped growing, arthrodesis may be considered to stabilize the joints of the hand or foot.[7] Neurosurgery is now more feasible as increasing knowledge of the causes and sites of damage are discovered.[12] Where the damage is known to be on one side only and cerebral palsy is further complicated by mental handicap and epilepsy, hemispherectomy (the removal of the affected side of the brain) has been carried out.[7] The aim of this treatment is to eliminate or reduce the epilepsy and produce intellectual functional gains. More recently, stereotactic surgery has been used with success in carefully selected cases. It involves the destruction of parts of the basal ganglia by passing an electrode into a precisely identified area and producing a small lesion approximately

5 x 3 mm.[12] This procedure does not increase the IQ or reduce comprehension, but it often helps those with articulation problems and reduces involuntary movement.[12]

Any surgical treatment must be carried out in conjunction with physiotherapy programmes so that the child may further gain from his new-found ability to learn motor skills not previously possible.[7]

Treatment with drugs is aimed at treating symptoms and includes muscle relaxants such as diazepam. However, to reduce involuntary movements or even spasticity large amounts may be required. This will produce drowsiness which is more of a handicap than the restricted or random motor movement of cerebral palsy.[7] Drugs such as benzhexol may be given to reduce excessive salivation. If the person suffers from epilepsy this can be treated with a number of anticonvulsant drugs.

Physiotherapy is concerned with the development of improved motor skills and the prevention of those factors which interfere with the acquisition of these skills. These factors include the development of contractures and deformities which make the acquisition of motor skills difficult or impossible.[13] A further function of the physiotherapist is to teach others how to handle the cerebral palsied child and advise on specific handling problems, particularly for parents and staff involved in the caring process.[4] This aspect of the physiotherapist's role is seen in Finnie's book *Handling the Young Cerebral Palsied Child at Home.*[4]

After developmental assessment the physiotherapist will plan an individual programme for the child designed to equip him with basic motor skills which will provide the basis for the more complex skills he will acquire. These basic skills include establishing some head control, balance and weight-bearing. The correct posture is all-important in acquiring new motor skills and much of the physiotherapist's work is concerned with correcting abnormal postures caused by spastic muscles.[13] Weak muscles need to be strengthened, particularly those muscles which stabilize the head in midline; this helps the child to coordinate his movements and allows further development of motor skills. Involuntary movement as seen in the athetoid form of cerebral palsy is a major problem and the physiotherapist will help to control it by devising programmes which teach balance and coordination.[13] The physiotherapist will use a large number of aids to help her,[13] including floor mats, parallel and wall bars, rockers, rolls, special chairs and wedges. There are many more aids and pieces of equipment which vary from large expensive toys to home made toys. A further activity increasingly being used for the cerebral palsied child is the heated swimming pool or hydrotherapy pool. This allows for relaxation of stiff muscles and greater freedom of movement. The majority of mentally handicapped cerebral palsied children enjoy this form of activity. Pony riding has proved to be of benefit in those children where balance training is needed; after initial misgivings most children participate eagerly. Both swimming and pony riding help in developing the child's self-confidence. The important point is that the aid or equipment should serve a purpose for the child, so that a particular toy or activity encourages a pattern of movement which is developmentally correct.[4]

The work of the physiotherapist is complemented by that of the *occupational therapist*, who will help the child to use his motor skills in activities such as washing, dressing, feeding and playing.[1] In practice in most hospitals for the mentally handicapped the physiotherapist and the occupational therapist work closely. An important aspect of the occupational therapist's contribution is to design special aids for the individual child to assist him, for example special handles on cutlery.[1]

However, whether it be physiotherapist, occupational therapist, parent, nurse or teacher who is helping the child, the aim is to help the child, or adult, towards a more independent life by the acquisition of basic, self help and social skills.

One social skill which we sometimes take for granted is the ability to communicate. The child with cerebral palsy complicated by mental handicap may experience considerable difficulty in communicating with others; indeed, he may not be able to communicate at all. Initially the *speech therapist* will be interested in the feeding pattern of the young child and often this is incorrect, in that the child will force the tongue forward, pushing food out of the mouth, or will bite the spoon.[17] Correct feeding is vital for normal speech as control over the muscles involved in speech is developed from these early experiences. Where speech is impossible the speech therapist may teach the child a non-verbal system of communication such as the Makaton Vocabulary.[18] This system has 350 signs, divided into nine developmental stages, by means of which the child is taught to communicate. It has proved to be very successful with the severely handicapped.[18]

As has been shown, the management of cerebral palsy is a matter of team work, with each member contributing his or her expertise to ensure that the child gains the maximum benefit from the total care and treatment given. This picture of harmonious professionalism may be modified by the effects of the environment which are discussed in the next section.

Environmental aspects

The cerebral palsied mentally handicapped child may find his immediate environment bewildering, hostile and frustrating. He is extremely vulnerable and at the mercy of every unexpected noise or activity and of the whims of those who care for him. He is unable to control his limbs or communicate his needs to others and may suffer visual or auditory impairment resulting in altered perception. It is hardly surprising that faced with these fundamental difficulties the child may react in such a way that his behaviour becomes a problem.[14] This reaction may be a result of either his handicap or the environment. The physical effects of his handicap may cause anger and frustration and be expressed in aggressive interactions with others. Continued frustration may sometimes lead to a general sadness or depression which will result in the child withdrawing from people and activities.[14] The cerebral palsied child will experience problems in learning, because of intellectual impairment, distractibility and inattention or physical inability to carry out tasks or communicate effectively. These problems sometimes influence the opportunities that the child may have to play and learn about the world around him.[14]

The child's difficulties may be exacerbated by life in residential care. This may be brought about by a lack of continuity of care, with different members of staff treating the child differently. This may vary from rejection to overprotection and make the child feel insecure and confused.

The lack of correct stimulation, which is sometimes apparent in a system caring for large numbers of people, can result in a general lowering of ability affecting all aspects of the child's development.

SUMMARY

Cerebral palsy is a disorder of movement and posture brought about by injury or developmental failure of those parts of the brain which initiate, modify or control movement. The areas of the brain which may be affected are the motor cortex, the basal ganglia or the cerebellum. Injury to the cortex results in spastic paralysis; injury to the basal ganglia results in athetosis; and injury to the cerebellum results in ataxia.

The causes are multiple and include inherited factors, maternal and childhood infections and trauma. There are often associated handicaps which include visual and auditory impairment and poor control of muscles associated with speech.

Treatment is aimed at improving functional levels to enable the child to lead as independent a life as possible. Suitable cases may benefit from either neurosurgery or orthopaedic surgery which may vary from stereotactic techniques to tendon lengthening. Drugs to relax muscle stiffness and control excessive salivation may be used. Every child will benefit from physiotherapy which should be commenced as early as possible. Physiotherapy programmes are individual and are designed following a developmental assessment.

Often, as a result either of the handicap or of the immediate environment, the child will express his vulnerability as fears, frustration, insecurity or confusion in behaviour that is described as difficult or as a problem.

It should be remembered that cerebral palsy is a generic description of the symptoms of underlying brain damage or developmental failure and is not itself a disease. Its management requires enthusiasm, understanding and informed aims so that the cerebral palsied child may be helped to develop those skills which he needs if he is to acquire any measure of independence.

GLOSSARY

Achilles tendon   The tendon through which the calf muscles exert pull on the heel.

Agnosia	Ability to hear or see but not to interpret the sensory information.
Ataxia	A form of cerebral palsy characterized by clumsiness and incoordination of movement, caused by damage to the cerebellum.
Athetosis	A form of cerebral palsy characterized by voluntary movement and lack of postural control.
Athrodesis	The immobilization of a joint such as wrist or ankle to stabilize movement.
Basal ganglia	Collections of nerve cells in the cerebrum. Damage to the basal ganglia may result in athetosis.
Caudate nuclei	Part of the basal ganglia.
Cerebellum	The part of the central nervous system concerned with coordinating movement and balance and maintaining normal muscle tone. Injury to the cerebellum may result in ataxia.
Cortex	The outer part of the brain composed of nerve cells; contains both sensory and motor nerve cells.
Cytomegalovirus infection	A maternal infection which may cause mental handicap and cerebral palsy. It can affect the fetus either early or late in pregnancy.
Diplegia	A form of paralysis where all four limbs are affected but the legs more than the arms. A form of spastic paralysis.
Dysarthria	Difficulty in articulation.
Dysphasia	Difficulty in speaking clearly.
Dysphonia	Difficulty with voice production.
Encephalitis	Inflammation of the brain substance.
Hemiplegia	A form of spastic paralysis which affects one side of the body.
Hemispherectomy	Surgical removal of the affected half of the brain in treatment of cerebral palsy.
Lentiform nuclei	Part of the basal ganglia.
Makaton vocabulary	A form of sign language originally developed for the deaf but found to be of use for the mentally handicapped cerebral palsied child.

Meningitis	Inflammation of the meninges, the three coverings of the brain.
Microcephaly	A condition where the brain has not fully developed either for genetic reasons or because of irradiation. The person has a small head with a circumference of 43 cm (17 in) or less.
Monoplegia	A form of spastic paralysis which affects one limb.
Neonatal period	The first 28 days after birth.
Nystagmus	Rapid involuntary flickering of the eyeball.
Paraplegia	A form of spastic paralysis where the legs are affected.
Quadriplegia	A severe form of spastic paralysis where all four limbs are affected.
Rhesus factor incompatibility	A condition caused by haemolysis of a baby's blood cells, causing jaundice which may result in a degree of athetosis and deafness.
Spasticity	Marked rigidity of the muscles.
Stereotactic surgery	The destruction of specific nerve cells by making a lesion with needles or probes. The site of the lesion is precisely calculated by radiography.
Strabismus	Squint.
Stycar sequences	A series of developmentally graded tests devised by Dr Mary Sheridan.
Toxoplasmosis	A condition characterized by enlarged glands and fever caused by the protozoon *Toxoplasma.* If it is active in pregnancy it may cause serious defects.
Varicella	Chickenpox.
Vineland Social Maturity Scale	A scale which measures social skills from birth to 25 years.

BIBLIOGRAPHY

1. Blencowe, S.M. & Gilbert, M. (1969) Occupational therapy. In *Cerebral Palsy and the Young Child*, ed. S.M. Blencowe. London: Livingstone.
2. Bowley, A. (1969) Psychological aspects. In *Cerebral Palsy and the Young Child*, ed. S.M. Blencowe. London: Livingstone.
3. Deacon, J.J. (1974) *Tongue Tied*, London: NSMHC.

4. Finnie, N.R. (1974) *Handling the Young Cerebral Palsied Child at Home*, 2nd ed. London: Heinemann.
5. Fisch, L. (1969) Hearing loss and cerebral palsy. In *Cerebral Palsy and the Young Child*, ed. S.M. Blencowe. London: Livingstone.
6. Foley, J. (1969) What is cerebral palsy? In *Cerebral Palsy and the Young child*, ed. S.M. Blencowe. London: Livingstone.
7. Foley, J. (1969) Physical aspects. In *Cerebral Palsy and the Young Child*, ed. S.M. Blencowe. London: Livingstone.
8. Foley, J. (1969) Associated disorders. In *Cerebral Palsy and the Young Child*, ed. S.M. Blencowe. London: Livingstone.
9. Heaton-Ward, A. (1975) *Mental Subnormality*, 4th ed. Bristol: John Wright.
10. Hegarty, J. *Educating and Training the Mentally Handicapped Patient— Workbook*. Medical Recording Service Foundation.
11. Hollis, K. (1977) *Progress to Standing*. Wolverhampton: Institute of Mental Subnormality.
12. Hitchcock, E.F. (1978) Stereotactic surgery for cerebral palsy. *Nursing Times*, 2064–2065.
13. Levitt, S. (1969) Physiotherapy. In *Cerebral Palsy and the Young Child*, ed. S.M. Blencowe. London: Livingstone.
14. Oswin, M. (1967) *Behaviour Problems amongst Children with Cerebral Palsy*. Bristol: John Wright.
15. Reynell, J. (1973) Children with physical handicaps. In *The Psychological Assessment of Mental and Physical Handicaps*, ed. P. Mittler, London: Tavistock.
16. Sheridan, M.D. (1975) *Children's Developmental Progress*, Windsor: NFER.
17. Steel, J. (1969) Speech theraoy. In *Cerebral Palsy and the Young Child*, ed. S.M. Blencowe. London: Livingstone.
18. Walker, M. (1976) *Language Programmes for Use with the Revised Makaton Vocabulary*. Farnborough: Makaton Vocabulary Development Project.
19. Woods, G.E. (1969) The causes. In *Cerebral Palsy and the Young Child*, ed. S.M. Blencowe. London: Livingstone.

PART III
Mental Handicap and the Family

Introduction

To the nurse working in a hospital for the mentally handicapped, the needs
and problems of the parents and families of the mentally handicapped may seem
remote to the point of having little relevance to their work. Yet an understanding of the pressures and difficulties faced by parents is essential for the professional worker, particularly from the point of view of giving realistic advice
and practical support. This is becoming increasingly important with the move
towards integration and community care.

Chapter 10 examines a number of factors which may be important in the
physical and psychological adjustment made by families following the birth of
a mentally handicapped child. The unique reaction of individual parents to the
reality of a handicapped child is discussed against the background of parental
expectations, the degree of handicap and possible feelings of inadequacy, bereavement, shock, guilt and embarrassment. The way the parents are told the
diagnosis is seen to be crucial and may be complicated by the timing, the circumstances and the person who tells them. The effect of mental handicap on
the family is seen to be variable and is characterized by a long period of continuing adjustment. These effects may be seen in the areas of marriage, socio-economic
status, parental health, other children and the daily life of the family. The
attitudes and approach of professionals is a significant factor in the successful
adjustment made by parents and families and is a continuing theme taken up in
Chapter 11.

Chapter 11 discusses some of the difficulties that parents experience in
receiving realistic help from official agencies and underlines the need for a
partnership between parents and professionals. Examples of such a partnership
are described, including a scheme which uses parents as therapists, a special
group for parents of Downs' babies and a unique American system of support
called Pilot Parents.

The theme of partnership is continued in a discussion of parents' workshops
designed to help parents understand and meet the needs of their children. The
need for help and information is particularly important in the area of teaching

and stimulating the profoundly mentally handicapped child. The Portage Model of Home Teaching exemplifies the partnership between parents and professionals by involving the parents in the precision teaching of their child in their own home with the regular help and guidance of experienced advisers.

Other forms of practical support for parents are discussed and these include the provision of short-term care, a Family Support Unit and a self-help scheme run by parents.

In the debate about the most suitable way of caring for mentally handicapped children and adults, it should be remembered that the majority live at home. This often results in twenty-four hour care carried out by parents who face immense problems, not only of personal adjustment but in managing their child's handicaps in realistic practical terms. They should be supported and helped in every possible way by an informed and sympathetic team of professional workers.

A bibliography is included at the end of each chapter. A glossary is not included as adequate explanation is given in the text.

Mental handicap and the family   10

Every parent expecting a baby hopes that it will be perfect[3] and a baby that is less than perfect poses immense problems in terms of psychological adjustment and physical management. This adjustment to the reality of a handicapped child will be affected by a number of factors including the nature and extent of the handicap; the way and the time the parents are told and their reactions; the family's socio-economic status; the degree of help and support they receive from family, friends and professional agencies; and the effect of the handicapped child on other members of the family.

There would seem to be a qualitative difference in adjustment when the child is mentally handicapped. The problems of management are not so clear-cut and solutions in the form of curative treatment are not readily available. This has led the professionals concerned in helping the mentally handicapped to concentrate on the problems of managing specific aspects of the child's handicap. Kew[6] has termed this the concentric approach, with each professional concentrating on particular aspects such as speech, motor movement or behaviour, to the exclusion of the family and their needs. The concentric approach may result in marital and family problems not being recognized for a long time, with consequent psychological damage. Even after the recognition that the family may have a problem there may be a failure to link this to the handicapped child. Finally, Kew makes the point that when a professional worker focusses attention on the effect the handicapped child is having on the family, there may be a tendency for the family to project all their problems onto the handicapped child, even though they may be unrelated.

The alternative to the concentric approach is the family-centred approach which views the birth of a handicapped child as yet another event in the life of a family.[6] It has been said that a family with a handicapped child is a handicapped family and that as a result all the family will have special needs of adjustment and support. This view suggests that, although the handicapped child's needs are special, they should be seen in the context of the total family and its needs.[6]

This chapter is concerned with the possible effects of the birth of a mentally handicapped child on the family, from initial parental reaction to the unique physical, psychological and social adjustments that may be necessary.

PARENTAL REACTIONS

The reactions of parents to the news that their child is mentally handicapped must be seen against the background of the normal expectations they have of their child. These reactions may vary from a calm acceptance to 'stunned disbelief and impotent rage.'[11] No two parents will react in the same way and this may give rise to problems within a marriage if one parent accepts the reality of the child's handicap and the other is unable to do so. During pregnancy the parents will be mentally and physically preparing for the arrival of their new baby in the expectation that it will be healthy and normal. This expectation is usually maintained despite worries and vague fears and is strongly reinforced by 'hidden persuaders' such as magazine articles, novels, the media and advertisements which emphasize the beauty and normality of the newborn child. Quite apart from the expectations parents have of their unborn child, they also have the need to produce a healthy normal baby as confirmation of their own sexuality, the femininity of the mother and the virility of the father. A mentally handicapped child may diminish the parents' own self-concept of their sexuality.

Parental reaction will be influenced by the degree of handicap and whether it is obvious at birth or becomes noticeable some time later. Mackeith[7] has described how parents might react to the birth of a handicapped child. He suggests there may be two biological reactions: the first a protective reaction and the second a reaction of revulsion. These biological reactions may be accompanied by feelings of inadequacy, bereavement, shock, guilt and embarrassment. The protective reaction may vary from normal care to highly protective care and Mackeith makes the observation that highly protective care is not necessarily over-protection and should be seen in terms of the mother's needs as well as the child's needs. The reaction of revulsion may lead to rejection of the child, shown in a number of ways. Firstly, there may be a cold rejection as if the child did not belong to them. This may be coupled with the rationalization that such children need special care and should be with other children with similar handicaps. Alternatively there may be a 'dutiful caring without warmth',[7] which at the other extreme may take the form of over-compensation and result in 'lavish care'.[7] This is perhaps one of the most difficult problems for the parents to cope with – the balance between rejection and over protection of the child.

Perhaps as a result of trying to achieve a degree of balance between these extremes, parents often feel *inadequate* both because they have produced a handicapped child in the first place and because of difficulties experienced in bringing up the child. It is almost as if the parents feel it is their fault the child does not achieve the normal developmental milestones. This may lead to an inconsistent approach which does not allow the child to make the best use of his environment to develop and learn and which in turn reinforces the parents' feeling of inadequacy.

Some parents may feel a sense of *bereavement* or grief at the birth of a handicapped child which has been compared to the grief experienced at the death of a child and results from the conflict between expectations and reality. This feeling of bereavement may take the form of anger and aggression which may be directed at the child or at those people trying to help the parents. Charles Hannam[4] describes how he planned to kill his mentally handicapped son. Another reaction connected with bereavement is that of self-pity and Nicola Schaefer[11] describes her initial reaction to the confirmation of her daughter's mental and physical handicap as one of 'overwhelming self-pity'.[11] She goes on to discuss her adjustment to the reality of her daughter's handicap. Whilst her adjustment was rapid, that of others may be long-term and be complicated by grief-induced depression. The length of time that parents suffer bereavement is variable but may be long-lasting and require extensive support and counselling.

Allied to the feeling of grief is the feeling of *shock* at a major personal disaster. This has been described as a feeling of numbness characterized by a withdrawal from reality.[6] Another shock reaction is overt emotional distress coupled with a desperate search for information and reassurance. Occasionally the mental defence mechanism of denial is present; the parents do not accept the diagnosis and will not admit that their child is handicapped, even in the face of physical evidence such as Down's syndrome.

A reaction that is controversial is parental *guilt*. Many writers feel that guilt is over-emphasized and certainly should not be attributed to all parents. Roith (1963) goes further and suggests that the 'myth of parental guilt' is perpetuated by textbooks and articles.[10] However, it is impossible to ignore the writings of those parents who have described their guilt feelings about producing a handicapped child. Charles Hannam[4] describes his feelings of guilt as '. . . at first, almost unbearable. I felt an almost Old Testament sense of having somehow done wrong and that this was a punishment.'

The reactions of other people, particularly family and friends, can give rise to feelings of *embarrassment* and shame. Many parents are acutely embarrassed and ashamed of the child's handicap and seek to avoid situations where the child's differences are accentuated or commented upon. Hospitals, doctors' waiting rooms, baby clinics and even every-day shopping trips become an ordeal of embarrassment for the sensitive parent. One result of this may be a withdrawal from normal social contact[7] which carries as a consequence a form of social isolation just at the time when they need the comfort, help and reassurance of other people, in particular their own family and friends.

Not every parent will react or feel the same way and may not experience any or all of the emotions and reactions discussed above. The variety, duration and intensity of an individual's emotional response will be affected by his personality and personal circumstances and by the degree of support he receives. This last point is important because the quality of support is often determined by the emotional response of the person who helps the parents. This process starts when the parents are being told that their child is mentally handicapped and the way that this is done may be crucial. The next section discusses the implications of telling parents the diagnosis of mental handicap.

TELLING PARENTS THE DIAGNOSIS OF MENTAL HANDICAP

Charles Hannam (1975) writes that 'there is no "good" way of telling parents their child is mentally handicapped, but there must be ways of not making a bad situation worse and of not adding to the suffering that already is bound to be considerable'.[4] A large amount of information has been gained through the experiences of parents, doctors and others who have either received or given the news that a child is mentally handicapped. Against the background of such information it has to be appreciated that each individual family is unique in their levels of acceptance and ways of coping with the situation. Equally, each professional who has to give the information will approach the task differently and will be guided by previous training and experience or lack of it.

Certainly progress has been made since the days when a mother would not be allowed to see her mentally handicapped baby and arrangements were made without consultation for the baby to be admitted to a hospital for the mentally handicapped.

The situation may be complicated by the fact that the child's mental handicap may be suspected for some time by the parents, who may be unable to receive medical confirmation. In these cases confirmation often brings profound relief at knowing the diagnosis after months or years of uncertainty.[11]

The initial experience of being told the news of mental handicap is regarded as being of crucial importance and should be seen as the first step in a continuing counselling process.[8] This is important, as many parents are unable to understand the implications of the diagnosis or frame the questions they need to ask, because of the severe shock they experience.

Gath describes a study of a group of families who had Down's syndrome babies.[3] She found that parents regarded the timing of the news as being the most important factor in their adjustment. The survey showed that parents wanted to be told as early as possible and certainly when they asked for information. There are many examples of situations which have added to the parents' problems. Gath quotes the case of two sets of parents who were told the diagnosis of Down's syndrome when the father had arrived to take his wife and baby home. This led, in one case, to the couple leaving the baby at the hospital for a week and, in the other, to the baby being hidden away from friends and relations for six weeks, as a consequence of the poor timing.

One aspect that is regarded as vital by parents is that they are told the truth about the child's handicap and not given bland assurances. Delay and deceit, real or imagined, generate bitterness and resentment which may result in the parents rejecting further help.[2]

The question of who should tell the parents and also where they should be told has been investigated. Gath describes how a family's doctor arranged for a visit by a paediatrician who was able to confirm the diagnosis of Down's syndrome and also give more information to the parents. In other instances the family doctor told the parents. A particularly difficult situation arises when one parent is told the diagnosis and then has to tell the partner. In the study mentioned above the parents who were 'most satisfied' with the way they had been told had been seen by both the family doctor and the paediatrician.[3]

A further aspect is how the parents are told and despite altered attitudes and new knowledge some doctors appear unfeeling and insensitive to the parents' emotional state. The doctor who told a mother 'mongols make nice pets about the house', cannot have had any insight into the effect that this might have.[8]

Sometimes ill-informed advice is given as it is impossible to predict the future level of performance of a mentally handicapped baby. Some doctors feel it is best to give a pessimistic view of the future so that when progress is made the parents are surprised and delighted and reinforced in their efforts to help the child. Others feel that a reasonably optimistic view should be given so that the parents are encouraged from the beginning. Both approaches may be fraught with difficulties and may be exacerbated by the doctor's own inexperience of mental handicap. A survey carried out to identify the training in mental handicap that doctors received revealed that very few had adequate training.[9]

The whole experience of learning about the diagnosis of mental handicap is extremely difficult, often painful and always a severe emotional shock to the parents. It is complicated by the timing, the circumstances, the person who gives the news and how this is done. The initial experience of being told the diagnosis is often unsatisfactory as the parents may not be able to come to terms with their shock and feelings about the diagnosis.[4]

After the initial interview there should be continuing counselling so that parents are able to work positively towards adjusting to the child's handicap.

Finally, Charles Hannam[4] makes a number of recommendations regarding telling parents of the diagnosis of mental handicap which summarize this section. He writes that it is the parents' right to know the diagnosis as soon as possible after birth and where handicap is suspected these suspicions should be discussed. He goes on to say that the person who tells the parents should be competent to do so, not use technical jargon in explanation and not make decisions for the parents without full discussion. He suggests that advice should be repeated and that a social worker should work in conjunction with the family doctor to help the family.

This continuing help is vital as each family will be affected in different ways. Some of the effects that a mentally handicapped child may have on a family are discussed in the next section.

EFFECTS OF MENTAL HANDICAP
ON THE FAMILY

This chapter has so far concentrated on the initial reactions of the parents and how they were told of the child's mental handicap. The effect of these experiences is both traumatic and far-reaching, marking the beginning of a long period of adjustment to the reality of coping with the child's handicap. Adjustment to the arrival of a new baby is not peculiar to the families of mentally handicapped children but there are fairly well defined stages in the life of a 'normal' family which may be different in a family with a handicapped child. These differences become more obvious and noticeable as the handicapped child grows older.

An alternative view is not to see the family as abnormal or handicapped but simply as an ordinary family unit dealing with particular problems in bringing up a handicapped child. Wilkin[13] puts forward the view that these different ways of regarding a family with a handicapped child lead to a different emphasis and approach to the problems encountered. The view that the family is in some way handicapped emphasizes the psychological problems, whilst the 'normal family' approach emphasizes the practical problems of managing the situation.

Whichever view is adhered to individuals within families may experience problems in particular areas, such as their marriage, their socio-economic status, their physical and mental health, the adjustment of their other children and the daily problems of routine management.

Marriage

Before the birth of a handicapped baby the family may be considered to be 'normal' and as such subject to all the pressures which may affect a marriage. The birth of a mentally handicapped baby may affect the relationship of the parents by increasing the stress level they have to cope with. Some parents draw closer to each other in a united effort to care for the baby, whilst others, at the opposite end of the continuum, will separate or divorce. The vast majority adjust to the new situation and solve any relationship problems in the ways that partners without a handicapped child would do.

Farber[4] devised a scale, the Farber Index of Marital Integration, which measured the degree of similarity between the views and attitudes regarding domestic values. The scale was used to study 240 families, 175 with a mentally handicapped child living at home and 65 with a child away from home. It evaluated the effect on the marriage of the child's sex, age and level of dependence. The findings of the study indicated that mentally handicapped boys had a more adverse effect on the parents' marriage than did girls, particularly in social classes IV and V, and increased as the boys became older. The adverse effects were shown to decrease if the boys were placed in hospital. The level of dependence of the handicapped child was not a significant factor in the parents' relationship but it was shown to have a significantly adverse effect on the handicapped child's brothers and sisters.

Other studies have not confirmed these findings and Farber's concept of 'marital integration' has been criticised on the grounds that couples who do not share similar views or values but have complementary views also enjoy happy and successful marriages.[2]

Gath[3] describes a survey of families with Down's syndrome and found that in families where the handicapped child was placed in a hospital before school are, there was a significant increase (20-30%) in 'broken marriages'. In a detailed study of marital relationships in 26 families with Down's syndrome children compared with a control group, Gath[3] found that 'significantly more marriages in the mongol group had broken or were rated as poor'. She adds that 15 of the marriages in the Down's syndrome group were rated as good. The results can be seen in Table 16.

Table 16. Rating of marital relationships among parents of Down's babies[3]

	Marital relationship			
Parents of	Good	Moderate	Poor	Total
Down's babies	15	6	9	30
Control babies	19	11	—	30
Total	34	17	9	60

There can be no doubt that the presence of a handicapped child may cause the breakdown of a marriage, particularly where one parent rejects the child, but this is the exception rather than the rule and the situation may be affected by a number of other factors.

One factor that may be influential is the presence of other children in the family and whether the parents decide to limit or increase their family following the birth of the handicapped child. Research evidence regarding the limitation of families is conflicting, some studies showing a tendency to limit families and others finding no difference from 'normal' families.

Carr[2] suggests that further research should investigate 'the age of the mother, the size of her family at the handicapped child's birth, and whether she had hoped to have more children following that pregnancy.'

Socio-economic status

The socio-economic factors which may affect a family with a handicapped child include social class, earning capacity, housing and any extra expenses necessary for the care of their child.

The relationship between *social class* and mental handicap is discussed more fully in Chapter 12. Severe mental handicap is distributed evenly through all the social classes of the Registrar General's classification but mild mental handicap is significantly more prevalent in social classes IV and V. An American study showed that where a severely mentally handicapped child is born early in a marriage this may have the effect of limiting upward social mobility, affecting the earning power of the father.

Whilst no firm conclusions may be drawn from the class differences of families with a handicapped child, some generalizations can be made. It is likely that the middle-class parent will be more articulate in demands for services and more able to cope with officialdom. It is also arguable that the middle-class mother will not have the same need to go out to work to earn money that the working-class mother may desperately need.

One of the major financial effects of a handicapped child is the way in which the mother's *earning power* is reduced. Increasingly, mothers are working either full-time or part-time to pay for amenities such as holidays, cars, clothes and labour-saving devices. The arrival of the handicapped child will not only stop the mother working in the long-term but also present the family with *additional expenditure* over and above that of the 'normal' family. With the increasing cost of public transport, families are finding that a car is not a luxury but a necessity, particularly when the degree of handicap makes it difficult, if not impossible, to manage the child using public transport. Items such as washing machines become essential in the event of constant double incontinence. Parents of handicapped children do face additional expenses, particularly one parent families. This may have wide reaching effects on life style, parental health, the child's brothers and sisters and the ways in which the parents approach and manage the multifarious problems encountered in the daily routine of caring for a handicapped child.

Housing may need to be modified or enlarged and although grants may be available the family will incur extra expense in furnishing and equipping following alterations.

Parental health

In the past parents have been advised to place their mentally handicapped child in hospital in order to avoid 'the increasing exhaustion of the mother'.[3] A number of writers have shown how physical or mental ill-health in the parents of a handicapped child can have far-reaching effects and may influence decisions about the continuing care of the child.

Wilkins[13] makes the point that the majority of care for mentally handicapped children at home is carried out by the mother, with the father being much less involved. The mothers in his study were asked about their physical and mental health. They reported physical symptoms of frequent colds, lethargy and a general feeling of being run-down and also more chronic conditions including bronchitis, rheumatism and back pain: 40% of the mothers interviewed had experience some ill-health.

In addition 72% of mothers experienced some form of mental ill-health in terms of 'being nervy, on edge or depressed'.[13] This figure of 72% is two and half times the figure for the general female population.

The combined effects of mental and physical ill-health may make the situation of caring for a handicapped child impossible. Wilkin[13] found that fathers suffered less than their wives from physical ill-health and that the level of mental ill-health was similar to that of the general male population.

A recurring problem described by Bayley[1] is constant tiredness caused by a number of factors. One factor was seen to be the hyperactivity of the handicapped child and yet another was interrupted sleep. Hannam[4] tells the story of how in desperation they sought help from a doctor for their son's hyperactivity. The doctor prescribed a tranquillizer with the advice 'it does not matter whether he takes it or you, it's quite harmless'.

A further aspect of the problem of caring for a severely mentally handicapped child who is totally dependent is that there is no relief from the strain of providing constant care. It is very often a life-long commitment. As a result the physical effects may be cumulative, causing a general level of debility which in turn may lead to mental ill-health.

These general remarks cannot, of course, be applied to all parents of handicapped children. Gath reports that in a study of Down's syndrome children and their families the parents were no more likely to suffer from physical ill-health than those with 'normal families', 'except that there was a tendency for fathers to be more tired and irritable if their child was a mongol'.[12] Mental ill-health was not shown to be significant with the exception that the mothers may suffer from a prolonged grief reaction which shows itself as depression.[2]

A low level of parental health will affect all aspects of family life, particularly any other children. Their adjustment to their mentally handicapped brother or sister is discussed in the next section.

Brothers and sisters

The effect of a mentally handicapped child on the other children in the family is variable and is influenced by the degree of adjustment of the parents; whether or not the child is in hospital; the actual problems experienced; and the coping strategies adopted by the parents.

Kew[6] suggests that the most important factor in the adjustment of the other children to a mentally handicapped child is the degree of adjustment achieved by the parents, and an important element in parental adjustment was seen to be the stability of the marriage. Hannam[4] recommends that the burden of caring for a mentally handicapped child should be shared by the whole family. The view that the parental and family reactions are important is reinforced by Owens and Birchenall[9] who suggest that the brothers and sisters of a mentally handicapped child reflect their parents' 'views, compassions and conflict'.

One of the 'conflicts' that parents may experience is their desire to keep the handicapped child in the family and their worry that this may adversely affect their other children. This is often put forward as the reason for requesting admission to hospital or care[3] and may be prompted by 'well-meaning' advice that the other children will behave like the 'abnormal child', if kept at home.[4] Hannam[4] comments that the financial and other resources available to the family in managing the handicapped child should be considered, as they will affect the quality of life for the other children.

A frequent concern is that brothers and sisters will suffer mental ill-health caused by the presence of the handicapped child. Tizard and Grad[12] investigated this effect and found that where the handicapped child was living at home there were significantly fewer mental health problems (12%) than when the handicapped child was living in hospital (26%). They suggested that this meant that 'parents who have more than one difficult child to cope with are more likely to seek institutional care for a mental defective'.

The problems that may be experienced by the brothers and sisters of a mentally handicapped child are often those that may be experienced by children in non-handicapped families. Gath[3] cites a study by Holt (1957) in which he found that 15% of the children in his survey were adversely affected by a mentally handicapped child living at home and quoted problems such as fear of physical attack, resentment of the attention given to the handicapped child and feelings of shame and embarrassment. Other studies show how normal activities such as outings, holidays, shopping and playing were curtailed or altered owing to the presence of the handicapped child.[2]

A problem that is often discussed is the feelings of insecurity that children experience if their handicapped brother or sister is placed in hospital. Kew[6] describes this as identification and quotes the example of a boy who was afraid of injuring himself in case he became 'handicapped' and was sent away like his sister.

A further aspect is described by Nicola Schaefer when her son was unhappy as a result of teasing by a boy at school about his handicapped sister. He remembered his parents saying that if his sister affected the family she would have to go into hospital and was frightened that his unhappiness would cause his sister's admission.[11]

The strategies that parents adopt to cope with a mentally handicapped child can also cause problems for their other children. Hannam[4] discusses the effects of a dual system of justice, with the handicapped child being allowed different standards of behaviour from his brothers and sisters.

One strategy that may cause stress is that of involving other children in the care of the handicapped child to the extent that they become 'semi-professional helpers', so that they may be readily available baby-sitters and child minders.[6] Owens and Birchenall[9] quote a study by Holt which suggests that some working-class girls may become 'socialised into an auxiliary mother role'.[9] Gath[3] investigated the different effect of a Down's syndrome child in the family on girls and boys. She found that boys were not more affected than their peers from normal families but that girls were more likely to have behavioural and emotional problems. She attributed this difference to social class and role differences, the girls tending to come from large families with fathers in unskilled employment, and boys playing a different role in the home.

Many writers feel that the problems experienced by the children in a family with a handicapped child are the same as those experienced by other children. Owens and Birchenall [9] write that there is little evidence for the hypothesis that a mentally handicapped child adversely affects other socialization experiences of other children. Wilkins[13] quotes an American study in which it was shown that a significant number of brothers and sisters interviewed appeared to have positively benefitted from the presence of their handicapped brother or sister.

Hannam[4] says of his Down's syndrome child, David, that in a sense he was an ideal brother for his son Simon, as he was non-competitive and allowed Simon to appear in a good light by comparison.

It would seem that a mentally handicapped child may have a variety of effects on their brothers and sisters, both positive and negative. These effects are usually a reflection of the parents' degree of adjustment to coping with the handicapped child.

Daily life

The previous sections have discussed parental reaction to the diagnosis of mental handicap and the effects of this on marriage, socio-economic status, parental health and the other children in the family. These issues have to be seen against a background of continuing 24-hour care, 'for anything up to half a century or more',[1] carried out by the family, often with little or no official help. Bayley[1] describes a study carried out in Sheffield in which he examined the problems of caring for mentally handicapped people in their own families. He put forward the view that a large amount of care is carried out by the family and that community care should be seen in these terms rather than the number and type of official services provided. Bayley's study included a wide range of handicap from complete disability to a lady who needed some help with dressing. He identified a large number of problems and described how the family and the 'social network of the family's kin, friends and neighbours' managed them.

The problem that seemed to be common to all was the effect of restricting the family's freedom of action, particularly that of the mother, to the 'extent associated with a pre-school child'.[1] Other problems that emerged were incontinence, managing physical handicaps, getting the individual up in the mornings, bathing, occupying him and the need for constant supervision.

Bayley noted that all the families had a routine, which was either flexible or rigid, for dealing with the child's handicap. This structure for caring involved the routines where other people helped the family and also official help in the form of incontinence pads, help with bathing or attendance at a training centre. The concept of a structured routine was extended to include the parents' social life, with outings and social activities arranged on a regular basis.

Although the informal help received by the families was freely given, Bayley makes the point that it was important for the families to be able to reciprocate. It helped them to see themselves as being valued by the 'community', and not just as someone who needed help.

Finally, the official help that is available and the informal help available in the community should be seen as 'complementary and inextricably interwoven', so that official services strengthen the structure of living that had been created by the families.[1]

In a detailed study Wilkin[13] examined the effect of a mentally handicapped child on the domestic routines of the family, particularly the effect on the mother, who provided the bulk of care. Wilkin identified 15 aspects of child care which were common to families with a handicapped child. These aspects of care were categorized into physical care, child-minding and housework tasks.

The physical child care concerned the tasks of dressing, washing, toiletting, changing nappies, feeding, lifting and carrying. The study showed that few of the mothers were able to share the responsibility for the daily care with others, particularly the more intimate aspects. Mothers reported that the most difficult aspects of physical care include incontinence, feeding and managing menstruation.

Child-minding was examined at the specific times of after school, during weekends and holidays and baby-sitting in the evening. Wilkin points out that many of the severely handicapped children in the survey required the same amount of supervision as a normal child under the age of three. The mothers varied considerably in the degree of help they received. The major problems identified were the need for constant supervision, particularly during school holidays, and the difficulty of providing a learning environment which stimulated the child.

The point regarding the need for constant supervision had an effect on the third category, housework, by preventing the mothers from carrying this out. The tasks involved in the study were washing clothes, cooking, cleaning, shopping and washing dishes. Some tasks were definitely seen as the 'maternal role obligation', such as washing clothes and cooking. With other tasks, washing up and shopping, the mothers were more likely to receive help. It was noted that the handicapped child created more work, particularly with cleaning.

Wilkin concludes[13] from the survey that the 'handicapped child dominated the daily routine' of the mothers, who generally received little help with child care and housework.

SUMMARY

This chapter has discussed the family and its adjustment to the reality of a mentally handicapped child. A number of factors will affect the degree of adjustment achieved and one may be the approach adopted by those people who can help the family.

One approach was seen to be concentric in that specific problems in managing

One approach was seen to be concentric in that specific problems in managing the child were the rationale for help. The other approach was family-centred as it looked at the needs of the total family.[6]

Parental reaction to the diagnosis of mental handicap was seen to vary enormously and should be viewed against a background of the normal expectations the parents have of their new baby. The reactions that may be experienced by parents include revulsion, rejection, over-protection, grief, guilt, self-pity, shock, hostility and shame and embarrassment.[7] The point was made that not all parents suffered any or all of these reactions and this should not be assumed.[10]

Telling the parents the diagnosis was discussed and it was found that the timing of the news was felt to be significant, the earlier the better, and certainly when the parents asked for information.[3] A further important factor was that parents should be told the truth and not fobbed off with vague generalizations.[2] Ill-informed advice, either overly optimistic or pessimistic, regarding the long-term prognosis was viewed by the parents as less than helpful.

The effects of mental handicap on the family were considered under the headings of marriage, socio-economic status, parental health, brothers and sisters and daily life.

The effect of mental handicap on marriage varied from the positive effect of strengthening the marriage to being a significant factor in marriage break-up. One study quoted suggested that mentally handicapped boys had a more adverse effect on the parents' marriage than girls.[2] Another study showed that where the handicapped child was placed in a hospital before school age, there was a significant increase in 'broken marriages'.[2] Overall, most parents adjust to any relationship problem in the same way that parents do in non-handicapped families.

The major effect of mental handicap on the financial status of the family was the reduction of the mother's earning capacity. This was seen to be an additional factor in the increased costs incurred in caring for a handicapped child. These extra costs involved use of public transport and modifications to housing to accommodate the child.

The effect of mental handicap on the physical and mental health of the parents was described in one study as largely affecting the mother.[13] Mothers reported symptoms of frequent colds, lethargy and feeling run-down, with some experiencing chronic bronchitis, rheumatism and back pain. More significantly there was an increase in the incidence of mental ill-health to two and a half times that of the general female population. It was pointed out that the long-term effects of caring for a mentally handicapped child often resulted in the cumulative effects of tiredness and debility.

The brothers and sisters of a handicapped child may be affected, but the degree of adjustment was felt to be linked to the adjustment of the parents and the stability of the marriage.[6] The children tended to reflect their parents' views, compassions and conflicts.[9] Problems reported included mental ill-health, physical attack, jealousy, feelings of shame, embarrassment and insecurity, fear of hospitalization, a dual system of family justice and exploitation of children.

A further aspect was the limiting of normal activities due to the presence of the handicapped child. Positive effects were also reported from the presence of a handicapped brother or sister.

The effects of mental handicap on the daily life of a family were discussed from two viewpoints. The first was a study into the care given by the community as opposed to official community services.[1] The problems experienced by the families included a restriction of the mother's freedom while she daily dealt with incontinence, bathing, occupying and stimulating the child and constant supervision. The study went on to show how families developed a structure for caring which involved carrying out routines which were often extended to include social activities. The second view was that the majority of care in the home was carried out by the mother and this study[13] investigated the following aspects of care: physical child care; child minding; and housework. The significant finding was that mothers were generally unable to share with others the responsibility for the constant care.

This chapter has briefly discussed some of the problems that may be encountered by the family in caring for a mentally handicapped child. The next chapter examines a number of strategies for helping parents in this task.

BIBLIOGRAPHY

1. Bayley, M. (1973) *The Community Can Care*. New Society.
2. Carr, J. (1974) The effect of the severely subnormal on their families. In *Mental Deficiency – The Changing Outlook*, ed. A.M. Clarke and A.D. Clarke, 3rd ed. London: Methuen.
3. Gath, A. (1978) *Down's Syndrome and the Family*. London: Academic Press.
4. Hannam, C. (1975) *Parents and Mentally Handicapped Children*. Harmondsworth: Penguin.
5. Hewett, S. (1970) *The Family and the Handicapped Child*. London: George Allen and Unwin.
6. Kew, S. (1975) *Handicap and Family Crisis*. London: Pitman.
7. Mackeith, R. (1973) The feelings and behaviour of parents of handicapped children. In *The Handicapped Person in the Community*, ed. D.M. Boswell and J.M. Wingrove. London: Tavistock.
8. NSMHC (1967) The stress of having a subnormal child. In *The Handicapped Person in the Community*, ed. D.M. Boswell and J.M. Wingrove. London: Tavistock.
9. Owens, G. & Birchenall, P. (1979) *Mental Handicap: The Social Dimensions*. London: Pitman.
10. Roith, A.I. (1963) The myth of parental attitudes. In *The Handicapped Person in the Community*, ed. D.M. Boswell and J.M. Wingrove. London: Tavistock.
11. Schaefer, N. (1978) *Does She Know She's There?* London: Harper and Row.
12. Tizard, J. & Grad, J.C. (1961) *The Mentally Handicapped and Their Families*. London: Oxford University Press.

13. Wilkin, D. (1979) *Caring for the Mentally Handicapped Child.* London: Croom-Helm.
14. Farber, B. (1959) Effects of a severely mentally retarded child on family integration. *Monograph of Social Research in Child Development*, No. 71.

Supporting the family

11

The previous chapter outlined some of the effects that a mentally handicapped child may have on a family and discussed a number of strategies that could be adopted in coping with these effects.

This chapter is concerned with examples of interventive measures and considers parents, professionals and volunteers working in partnership; the teaching of skills to parents; practical support in terms of available services; and how existing services may be extended to help parents and families.

Generally, the support services for the mentally handicapped and their families receive a low priority in most of the state agencies and, where support services are good, they tend to reflect the enthusiasm and commitment of individuals or pressure groups. The priority that social services departments give to mental handicap is highlighted by Owens and Birchenall[16] who carried out interviews with social workers in different counties. They found that the majority of those interviewed 'felt their involvement to be minimal' and saw no prospect of immediate improvement as a result of cutbacks in social service provision.

Wilkin[22] comments on the result of his survey that the presence of a severely mentally handicapped child was 'insufficient to warrant regular contact with a social worker and the provision of specialised support services' and concludes that the low priority given to mental handicap by social work departments 'reflects a service oriented to crisis rather than to continuing long term support'. He also identified a problem that was common to both health and social services: the discrepancy between the 'felt needs' of the mothers of the mentally handicapped and the needs and services identified and provided by the professional agencies. This was seen to be a crucial factor, as decisions regarding the long-term care of the child were significantly affected if the mothers felt needs were not met.

The general feeling of dissatisfaction with the support services for the families of the mentally handicapped is reflected by the parents themselves in books, articles and interviews. Hannam[9] points out that although his family had received help the initiative had always had to come from them. His interviews with parents showed an apparent reluctance on the part of the authorities to make sure that families received the services and money they were entitled to. This often led to a situation where parents felt they had to fight for services, with the consequence that the officials became 'suspicious and defensive'.

Fox,[6] in a series of interviews with parents, shows how inadequate the health and social services can be in giving advice and support to parents. Some of the titles of the interviews serve to underline this inadequacy: 'They get this training but they don't really know how you feel'; 'Oh well, don't worry too much, he probably won't survive beyond seven'; 'You can see them humouring you, it's no good, sympathy without action'; 'You always get the feeling you're not doing enough, there's something more you should be doing'.

Collins and Collins [4] describe their feelings about the problem of fighting officialdom over the issue of a suitable placement for their daughter. They make the point that a 'family with a handicapped child has a hard enough time coping from day to day . . . without having to take on the experts and the officials of the local government as well'.

A number of these issues are reflected in a study into the homes and life styles of handicapped children in Avon by Butler et al.[3] Their survey revealed that over half of the total sample of parents said 'they were unsure of the ways in which social services could help.' They go on to comment that as a result of cutbacks in financial expenditure the major role of the social services is that of providing a crisis intervention service. The Avon study showed that many families with a mentally handicapped child lived in a state of chronic crisis which suggested they should be placed in a 'particular category of need'.

Given that these circumstances are fairly interspersed and affect a large proportion of families with a mentally handicapped child, the following sections discuss examples of how families may be supported in the task of providing long-term care for their handicapped child.

PARTNERSHIP WITH PARENTS

The reluctance of some professionals to involve parents and actively help them in the care of their child may be due to the stereotype of parents who are unsophisticated, too emotionally involved, unable to work with professionals because they are unable to understand the professionals' approach and have unrealistic goals for their child.[11] There are examples of projects where parents and professionals work together sharing experience and knowledge in partnership, which show that this stereotype is largely unfounded.

Mittler[13] has discussed patterns of partnership between parents and professionals and makes important observations and recommendations. The first point is the degree of common ground between parents and professionals. The professionals became involved in a parental role and the parents increasingly take on elements of professional roles, particularly that of teaching. There is a tendency for the professional to teach 'parents to be teachers, psychologists, social workers, counsellors and speech therapists, so that there may not be enough time for parents to be parents'. Mittler[13] emphasizes that a partnership is a two-way process and involves consultation and mutual agreement concerning programmes and strategies. He goes on to say 'the foundations for partnership surely lie in an exploration of the unique needs of each individual family'. This exploration should include the parents' perception of their child's abilities and also their own abilities and the kind of help they need.

A final point concerns the competence of professionals and Mittler[13] suggests that 'collaboration with parents must in future be seen as one of the hallmarks of a well trained professional'. This involves more than just professional competence in a particular setting, such as a school, a residential care unit or a training centre. The professional must not 'compensate' for the parents but work with them, explaining in non-technical language, consulting fully and being sensitive to the needs of the parents to retain their identity and life-style. A recent development in the partnership between parents and professionals is the formation of parent groups with the involvement of professionals in a leadership or resource capacity.

One such group is described by Mellor[12] as 'a scheme using parents of mentally handicapped children as therapists'. The original group of 12 couples was formed to help the professionals involved understand the problems experienced by the families. The initial meetings revealed a surprising amount of aggression directed at the medical and nursing professions. Further meetings were devoted to supplying the parents with information about services. This led to meetings where specific aspects were introduced by specialist speakers and followed by discussion. Two further groups were formed by the parent themselves, with professionals acting as observers and advisers, although the groups were led by the parents. There was a rapid development of similar groups in other parts of the country, based on the original model, demonstrating the need that parents felt for mutual support. The leaders of the groups act as the contact for the group and families are often referred by paediatricians, consultants, health visitors, social workers and general practitioners. Mellor[12] describes how the groups help parents to come to terms with the diagnosis of mental handicap and the mutual benefit gained from talking to other group members. The professionals learned from parents their needs and problems and how they could help in a positive way. The parents received support and learned how to develop the abilities of their children. Specialist groups were formed for the parents of children with specific needs, such as the multiply handicapped, Down's babies and children and older children and teenagers. One specialist group for Down's babies in Leeds has been described by Swaffield.[21] This group was formed by a psychologist as a result of her observations that the 200 families she visited in the course of a research programme felt isolated. The group was started with seven Down's babies aged from two months to three years. The first need was for information, the common need of all parents, which was met through talks and visits which involved the fathers as well. The result was that parents felt more confident both in using services and in asking for them. Referrals to the group are made by the maternity hospital. One of the strengths of the group is the support given to the families through the informal structure of the meetings. Mothers are able to leave their children with the staff or stay and be involved or 'simply relax together in the lounge'.[21] The mothers in the group operate their own support service for new mothers by visiting them and discussing the new baby. The programme within the group includes sessions in a hydrotherapy pool at a local school and a variety of activities based on an assessment of each child's developmental level using Progress Assessment Charts (Gunzberg).[8]

The above group was formed as a result of the feeling of isolation experienced by a large group of parents with Down's syndrome children. One scheme described by Shaw[19] shows how this isolation may be minimized. The scheme operates in East Nebraska, USA, and forms part of the services for the mentally handicapped provided by the East Nebraska Community Office of Retardation (ENCOR); it is called Pilot Parents. The scheme aims to provide support and information to new parents who have a mentally handicapped child. If the new parents feel it would be helpful to talk to another parent who has a handicapped child they are referred to the coordinator of the Pilot Parent programme. They are then matched as far as possible with an experienced family with a child who is similar in 'functional level; cause of handicap; age of parents and child; family structure; geographical area of residence; marital status and family adjustment; employment; education and income'.[19] The pilot parent is selected and usually contacts the new family within 24 hours. Subsequent meetings are determined by the needs of the new family. The pilot parents have all had the experience of a handicapped child and have made a good adjustment. They have also received special training so that they can provide the new parents with information and support and help them to 'view in a positive manner their child's ability to grow, learn and develop to his/her full potential'. Shaw makes the point that a parent with a mentally handicapped child may find a group unsuitable in the early stages and that, for these parents, Pilot Parents is a particularly useful scheme. A more complete description of the work of ENCOR is contained in Chapters 14 and 15.

TEACHING PARENTS

The previous section stressed that the common need of all parents was for information, about services, about the child's condition and, probably more importantly, about how they can teach their child the developmental skills he lacks. A positive effect of a partnership between parents and professionals is that professional workers share their skills with the parents and work with them.

There are a number of examples of formal arrangements for parents, such as courses and workshops, where the skills of observation, developmental and behavioural assessment, task analysis and teaching techniques are taught.

The Hester Adrian Research Centre at Manchester University has developed a number of workshops and programmes for parents which have served as models of parent/professional partnership. The Hester Adrian Research Centre was established in 1969 under the direction of Professor P. Mittler and 'the involvement of parents in the development of their own child has formed one of the main research interests' of the team.[14] A series of pilot workshops for parents in 1971 was aimed at helping parents to recognize developmental milestones and to teach their children appropriate skills. These workshops led to the Parental Involvement Project or Baby Project, which took place between 1973 and 1977 and was concerned with Down's syndrome babies. The babies were filmed in their homes and developmentally tested at six-week intervals. There followed discussions with individual parents about the baby's developmental level and how they were coping. The parents' ideas about teaching were then passed on to other parents with similar problems. The research findings showed that babies who were visited early were more advanced at eight to ten months than those babies who were not visited for the first six months, but by 14 to 16 months they had caught up with the early group. Quite apart from the improved performance of the babies, a major benefit was the feeling of support and involvement experienced by the parents.

In 1975 the Hester Adrian Research Centre started the Anson House project in Manchester. Anson House is a 'rambling Victorian house' that has been modified to include a classroom with observation facilities that allow the activities to be video-taped, rooms for individual work and a large common room for parents to use during the day.[16] A unique feature is that the two groups of 12 children are mixed in ability and range from the profoundly handicapped, to those who are not handicapped at all – and even those who are advanced for their age.[16] The children are aged from one to four years. The overall project is concerned with the ways in which parents can be involved in teaching their children and looks at the parents' natural teaching styles; with ways of working with the profoundly handicapped; and with the contribution that parents can make to the early learning of their child.[14]

The research group were asked by the parents to help them with teaching techniques. A project was set up to investigate the teaching styles already being used by the parents. Their pattern of interaction with their children was video-taped; they were interviewed and asked to complete a questionnaire. It was found that there were marked differences in teaching styles and the intention was to design a parent teaching course that first 'assessed and then built on existing interaction styles.[14]

A small group of parents of profoundly multiply handicapped children were involved in an intensive six-month project to investigate the effects of parent/professional collaboration. Following assessment by the team a teaching programme was designed for each child. The parents were taught behaviour modification techniques and asked to carry out daily programmes at home. Sophisticated learning techniques such as micro-teaching using video-tapes and role play were used to help the parents. The parents were observed teaching their child in their own home and received advice and help with the programme. The results of the project showed that the children made progress and that the parents were able to use the techniques.

A third project investigated the contribution that parents made to the early learning of their handicapped child. This concerned the parents' perception of their roles as parents and teachers and of the pattern of interaction between themselves and their child. The basis of the research was the daily pattern of care in the home and was aimed at helping professionals to help parents through an understanding of the daily problems they faced. The information gained from observing the parents in practical teaching activities would be used to determine the degree of 'structured guidance' each parent required.[14]

The Hester Adrian Research Centre extended their help with parents in 1977 with the Path Project, which is concerned with handicapped teenagers and their families; specifically the project is concerned with leisure activities and how these can be used to help towards 'greater integration in the community and ensure against social isolation'.[14]

The above discussion has briedly discussed some of the work of the Hester Adrian Research Centre and demonstrates how a sophisticated research-based organization can help parents in a direct personal way and also at a distance through their published material.

An example of this 'spin-off' effect is the Priory Workshop for parents described by Attwood[1] which was based on the Hester Adrian model but with important modifications to meet a local need. The parents' initial request for help was for speech therapy. This stimulated the professionals involved to consider the other needs of the parents; a need for information, for a reduction of the isolation and for help with their problems of managing and teaching their children. As a result it was decided to organize a multi-disciplinary workshop which would cover a range of topics. Eighteen children and their mothers formed the first group. The children were aged from one to 14 years and presented a 'wide range of problems and handicaps'. The workshop was arranged with the mothers divided into three tutorial groups of six, so that one group concerned young pre-school children, another group young physically handicapped children and the third group the needs and abilities of older children. The professionals included three psychologists, three speech therapists, a specialist health visitor, a physiotherapist and a senior medical officer. Each tutorial group had a psychologist and a speech therapist; the pre-school children had the specialist health visitor, the physically handicapped children the physiotherapist and the older children the senior medical officer. The workshop was held once a week for 16 weeks with two evening sessions so that fathers and other relatives could attend.

The first term was based around teaching the mothers observation skills related to motor development, feeding, language, play, physiotherapy, teaching techniques, toiletting, learning principles and management of difficult behaviour.

The second term concentrated on behaviour modification techniques such as shaping, reverse chaining and reinforcement and aimed to help the parents deal with problems they had identified in the first term.

Attwood[1], in discussing the benefits of the workshop, makes a number of points. The first is that, because of the multidisciplinary approach, the range of topics was much wider than is usual and the workshop was able to help a wider range of children. The second point is that the Priory Workshop was not a research-based project but a specially designed community service aimed at meeting a local need. The results of the workshop showed that the mothers were more confident, had an increased understanding of their children and were more aware of the services available. A further benefit was that the professionals learned about the parents' problems at first hand and also learned the role and skills of the other professionals involved in the workshop.

Other features of the workshop included a parents liaison committee which acted as the link between the mothers and the tutors. The committee also provided a crêche and a baby-sitting service which enabled the mothers to attend the workshop. The professional group felt it important that each child was assessed in the home before and during the workshop and for contact to be made with others involved such as fathers and special school teachers.

One clear point that emerged was the changing needs of the parents with older children. Finally, the Priory team feel that the workshop, organized on a multi-disciplinary basis, could be 'the prototype for future community services to help the mentally handicapped'.[1]

The Portage model of home teaching

A large number of parents may not have access to a workshop, either because of family commitments or more usually because workshops are few and far between. However, the Portage model of home teaching can provide help for families on an individual basis. The Portage model was first described by Shearer and Shearer[20] and is named after the town of Portage in Wisconsin, USA. It is a model which involves parents in precision teaching of their child in their own home with the help and guidance of experienced advisors. The model uses a developmental and behavioural approach and concentrates on skill development in the areas of language, cognition, motor skills, socialization and self-help. It also provides a means of assessment, a method of recording progress and makes suggestions for teaching the child new skills.

A key concept of the Portage system is that of assessment and consists of four parts:

1. *Formal* assessment: the use of standardized tests to identify general strengths and weaknesses in the form of a profile.
2. *Informal* assessment: information about the child derived from parents and other members of the family based on personal observation of the child.

cognitive

Age Level	Card	Behavior	Entry Behavior	Date Achieved	Comments
	55	Counts to 10 objects in imitation		2/4/76	
	56	Builds a bridge with 3 blocks in imitation	✓		
	57	Matches sequence or pattern of blocks or beads	✓		
	58	Copies series of connected V strokes VVVVVVV	✓		
	59	Adds leg and/or arm to incomplete man	✓		also adds facial features
	60	Completes 6 piece puzzle without trial and error		2/4/76	
	61	Names objects as same and different			can point – not name yet
	62	Draws a square in imitation		3/11/76	
	63	Names three colors on request	✓		name red, blue, yellow
	64	Names three shapes, □, △, ◌			Δ not consistent
4-5	65	Picks up specified number of objects on request (1-5)			no concepts yet
	66	Names five textures			
	67	Copies triangle on request			
	68	Recalls 4 objects seen in a picture	✓		ok
	69	Names time of day associated with activities			
	70	Repeats familiar rhymes			
	71	Tells whether object is heavier or lighter (less than one pound)			
	72	Tells what's missing when one object is removed from a group of three			
	73	Names eight colors			
	74	Names penny, nickel and dime			names penny
	75	Matches symbols (letters and numbers)			
	76	Tells color of named objects			
	77	Retells five main facts from story heard 3 times			
	78	Draws a man (head, trunk, 4 limbs)	✓		see cognitive 59
	79	Sings five lines of song			
	80	Builds pyramid of 10 blocks in imitation			
	81	Names long and short			

1976 Cooperative Educational Service Agency 12

example from the card deck of the Portage Guide to Early Education (revised edition) **cognitive 58**

AGE 3-4

TITLE: Copies series of connected V strokes VVVVVVV

WHAT TO DO:

1. Draw a series of V strokes. Encourage the child to trace over the letter first with his finger and later with a crayon or pencil. Help by guiding his hand.
2. Have him draw with you making one line at a time.
3. Make a row of connected V strokes. Then have the child draw more rows as you give him verbal directions "up, down, up, down."
4. Have child make a row of V strokes on paper. When he finishes make it into a picture of mountains, grass, trees, etc. for him.

Fig. 27. Examples from the card deck of the Portage Guide to Early Education.[20]

PORTAGE PROJECT   CREDIT: _____ yes _____ no

Child's Name _____ Robby _____

Home Teacher's Name _____ Jan _____

Week of _____ March 10 _____

BEHAVIOR: ACTIVITY CHART

Robby will crawl
forward on knees
using left-right
movement with
stomach off the
floor (towel for
support).

NUMBER OF: feet crawled forward/trial

Trial 3
3-
2-
1-
0-

Trial 2
3-
2-
1-
0-

Trial 1
3-
2-
1-
0-

M T W T F S S M
Days

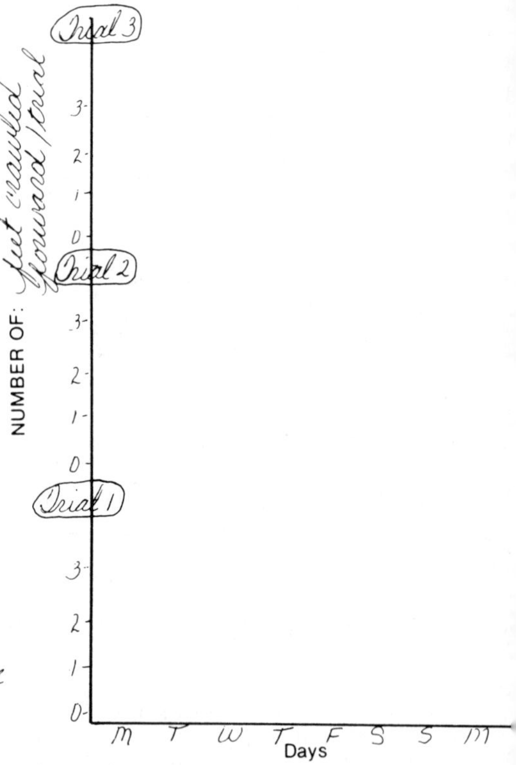

DIRECTIONS:

Place a goodie on the
floor about 1 ft in
front of Robby. Help
position him on his hands and stomach, then
take the beach towel and place it under him
and hold it up until he's on his knees.
Encourage him to move forward to get the goodie
Praise each movement and as he gains in
skill, increase the distance between Robby and
the goodie. Reward with goodie when he reaches
it. Practice 3x/day and record the no. of
feet crawled forward on the first three trials

Fig. 28. Portage Project Activity Charts.[20]

PORTAGE PROJECT

CREDIT: __✓__ yes _____ no

Child's Name _____ *Mary* _____

Home Teacher's Name _____ *Jean* _____

Week of _____ *March 5* _____

BEHAVIOR:

Mary will vocalize
(make sounds) when
being diapered,
bathed, etc.

Sounds made

W oh, oo, ee, ga
T ha, ee, ga, wa
F wa, oh, ma, ga, ee
S ga, oh, oo, ee, wa
S ma, wa, oo, we, aa
M ma, da, oo, ha, de
T da, wa, ge, ma, wa
W wee, goo, ha, oo, ee, da

ACTIVITY CHART

NUMBER OF: *times Mary vocalizes in 10 min*

Days: W T F S S M T W

DIRECTIONS:

When you diaper, feed
and bathe Mary, stimulate
her by cooing and
making baby sounds yourself. Tickle her a bit
just to get her going and when she makes
any sound (other than crying) you make
the same sound back. Be sure to stay in
her line of vision when you are stimulating
her. List a sample of some of the sounds
Mary makes and record the total no. on
the chart. Verbally stimulate Mary at each
diaper change and feeding but just record
twice a day.

3. *Curriculum* assessment: the use of the Portage Guide to Early Education, a checklist to identify specific behavioural skills that the child has acquired and also a set of related cards which give suggestions on how to teach the next skill on the checklist.
4. *On-going* continuous assessment: to monitor the progress each child makes and review programmes and problems.

The checklist contains 580 behavioural items classified into specific developmental areas. The first category is called infant stimulation and relates to the pattern of normal development up to four months and may be suitable for the profoundly handicapped child. The second category concerns socialization and lists in sequence appropriate behaviours that involve living and interacting with others. The third category of language is concerned with both content and developmental sequence. The fourth category itemizes self-help skills such as feeding, dressing, bathing and toiletting. The ability to remember, form concepts and understand the relationship between ideas and things forms the fifth category of cognitive skills. The final category concerns motor development from the view of gross motor skills and fine manipulative skills.[20] Each item on the cheklist has a corresponding numbered card which shows the same behaviour as the checklist, a behavioural description of the item and suggests materials and teaching method that may be helped in the teaching of the skill. Examples of the checklist and corresponding teaching card can be seen in Fig. 27. The process of using the Portage model in helping the parents to teach their children is dependent on a back-up team. The key workers in the scheme are the supervisors, who are usually psychologists with experience of using behavioural techniques and the home teachers or advisers who may have a nursing or social work background. They will have received training in using the Portage model and will be able to complete a checklist, write goals in behavioural terms, carry out task analysis, use basic behaviour modification techniques appropriately and write activity charts.[17] They will also be able to deal with problem behaviours, assist parents to approach other agencies, liaise with and make referrals to other agencies and write progress reports.[17]

The home teacher will visit the home and complete the checklist with the parent and they together choose a task to be taught during the next week. The home teacher will then take a base-line to obtain information to complete an Activity Chart which will be the parents' teaching guide. The activity chart will show a description of the skill in behavioural terms with specific instructions on the steps to teach (Fig. 28). These instructions show the parent the materials to be used, the place of work and how to practice and how to generalize the skill. Following this the home teacher will model the teaching and then supervise the parent in teaching and how to complete the activity chart. The home teacher then leaves the chart with the parent and returns the next week to review progress, observe the child performing the task, record the outcome and set the next week's task.[17] It may be necessary to plan extra steps in the programme if the child is experiencing difficulty.

The supervisors and home teachers meet weekly to review problems and successes, discuss referrals to other agencies and additions or alterations to the cards. The Portage model of home teaching has been successfully implemented in a number of schemes both in the community and in residental care. One scheme in South Glamorgan has been described and evaluated by Revill.[17] Nineteen families were involved, the children's ages ranging from eight months to four years. The evaluation showed that, of the 306 tasks set, 88% were learned, 67% within one week; 4% need to be re-analysed and only 5% had to be abandoned; 21 tasks were continuing at the time of evaluation. The study showed a dramatic increase in the number of skills after introduction of the Portage scheme. The parents were also asked their views about aspects of the scheme and none had difficulty in recording information; they preferred weekly visits from the home adviser; eight preferred to work on one task per week, six preferred two tasks per week and three preferred three tasks per week. They were unanimous in wanting to use the scheme in their own homes and not in a central location.[17]

The three examples of how parents can be helped to teach their children have been discussed at some length because they represent a positive approach which may have far reaching effects on such factors as the decisions parents make about long term care or the viability of the family unit. Although they are different in emphasis and approach, their common purpose is to help the parents of handicapped children through partnership with professionals. The next section discusses other forms of practical support that may be provided.

PRACTICAL SUPPORT

A number of studies have investigated the needs of parents and the ways in which these needs may be met. Parents frequently express a need for information about the child's condition and what they can do about it. They also want information about the services that may be available, particularly short-term care or special units with particular expertise, and the existence of parent groups for mutual support. This need for information and support has led to the concept of the 'key worker' who would relate to each family on an individual basis. The Jay Committee (1979)[5] recommend that a 'specially named worker' should be appointed who would be known to the family and be working with one of the agencies. This person 'would be responsible for helping the family to articulate their needs, personally representing them where necessary, and, in co-operation with other professionals, for marshalling the required service.' This concept of a key worker has been developed in a number of areas with the objective of providing a link between the families and local services. In Wessex, the key worker relates to families within a defined geographical area and the service starts with an initial home visit followed up at regular intervals. One of the functions that a key worker could perform would be to help in the arrangement of short-term care, which is discussed in the next section.

Short-term care

A study of families with mentally handicapped children in Avon described by Butler et al.[3] has shown 'that one of the most important forms of help for such families is the provision of short term care, to enable family members to recuperate from the continual strain of looking after a mentally handicapped child.' The survey also showed that short-term care was the most frequently received form of help from social service departments. Short-term care has been defined as 'the admission of a handicapped person to a residential unit on the understanding that they will return to their previous situation within a relatively short period'.[15] It can be used in a number of ways, from a crisis intervention measure in times of urgent family stress to a planned period in which on-going assessment and teaching take place. The pattern of provision of short-term care is variable across the country, with the majority of places available in hospitals. Approximately 8% or 4000 places are allocated to short-term care in the National Health Service, little distinction being made as to their purpose.

Crisis intervention must remain a priority so that parents can obtain immediate help and relief from intolerable stress or emergency. Less urgently, places should be available so that families can go on holiday, have a rest or participate fully in important family events without the worry of maintaining the constant supervision of the handicapped child.

It should be remembered that this type of help may make the difference between being able to cope with the child at home or admitting him to residential care in the long term. Some hospitals operate a planned system of short-term care and in this way one National Health Service bed can be used for a number of people over the course of a year. Other schemes use the facilities of long-term residents when they are away from the hospital on holiday or with their families.[15]

Where possible short-term care should be a combination of relief for the family and active teaching of the handicapped person involving 'observation, assessment, and the review and design of specific programmes of treatment and training, e.g. in self-care skills, toilet training or in assessing ways of dealing with specific behaviour problems.'[15] Many parents are reluctant to place their child in hospital even for a limited period of time. Recognizing this, the Jay Committee (1979) put forward the radical proposal that short-term care should be sought with 'substitute families' who do not have a mentally handicapped child, rather than using the hospitals. They see this as having a number of advantages in that the disruption of the child is lessened,[19] as the child is able to continue at his own school and is able to 'develop a relationship with the members of his substitute family'.[5] Another alternative to the hospital is short-term care relief for families in a specialized unit serving a local community, such as Honeylands Family Support Unit in Exeter, which is described below.

Honeylands Family Support Unit

Honeylands Family Support Unit is part of the East Devon district general paediatric service serving a population of 350 000. The unit is situated in the centre of Exeter in an eighteenth-century manor house that was previously a tuberculosis sanatorium for children.[2] Following the decision to use Honeylands as a family support unit for handicapped children, surveys were carried out to identify the prevalence and type of handicap and to identify the unmet needs of the parents and children. During the period 1967–71, approximately 7000 children were born in Exeter district and 310 were identified as suffering from a handicapping condition, with 77 severely handicapped. The children that use Honeylands are mixed in degree and type of handicap and include 'chronic illness', physical and mental handicap and social deprivation.[18] The ages of the children range from birth to puberty.

The services Honeylands provides reflect the needs of the parents which were identified in the initial survey. This survey revealed that parents felt the need to deal with one central agency; to be involved with specialists who understand the overall problems; to have on-going consultations with professionals who could explain diagnostic implications; to be able to relate to a 'key therapist' in a multi-disciplinary team; and to have some relief, in the form of short-term care or 'baby-sitting', from the 24-hour burden of care.[7] The services that have been developed at Honeylands to meet these needs have been described by Goddard and Raynor.[7] There is a baby group which cares for babies with major handicaps, feeding problems, failure to thrive or social deprivation/problems. A preschool playgroup, organized on a group basis, is run by nursery nurses and coordinated by a psychologist. The programme includes assessment and play therapy; other professionals give advice to the parents who are involved in their children's programmes. There is a unique home visiting project which uses 'developmental therapists' who visit babies under 18 months with developmental problems on a weekly basis, as soon as possible after birth. These developmental problems include cerebral palsy, Down's syndrome, mental handicap and blindness. The 'developmental therapists' are those who would normally work with the child in their usual capacity as physiotherapist, occupational therapist or nurse. They are able to call on the resources of the Honeylands multi-disciplinary team in helping the mother. Regular six-monthly meetings are held at Honeylands and include the team, the 'developmental therapist', the mother and her child in order to plan programmes for the child.[18] There are various mothers' groups for children suffering from particular handicaps such as the visually handicapped. These groups meet on a regular basis but there are also informal groups which meet daily. There is a class for 'delicate' children staffed by a teacher from the local education authority.

Perhaps the most important service offered to the community is the residential care which has a truly open-door policy with a minimum of formality. Parents can use this facility either on a hotel basis (just ringing and booking a bed) or as an immediate refuge in times of crisis.[18] Honeylands has 30 beds and 15-20 are occupied on any night. In addition to the residential short-term care, Honeylands also provides facilities for baby-sitting, overnight, weekend and holiday stays and day care.[18] There are facilities for five mothers to stay with their children.[2] Parents are also able to use a 24-hour telephone advisory service to obtain immediate help and advice.

Honeylands is staffed by a multi-disciplinary team which includes the consultant paediatricians who hold regular clinics; the nursing staff also provide a 24-hour service all the year and include the sister in charge, state registered nurse, state enrolled nurses, nursery nurses and nursing assistants; the supporting staff include other consultants, psychologists, physiotherapists, an occupational therapist and a medical social worker.[7]

Honeylands also uses voluntary help with considerable success, providing holidays for 250 children each year, involving 1400 volunteers, and running two play groups with the help of 50 volunteers who 'work on a rota basis'.[2] Youth clubs, uniformed movements and students help in the evenings, at the weekends and during holiday periods. This community interest is further reflected in the provision of an all-weather swimming pool, a mini-bus and an adventure playgorund, by voluntary organizations.

Approximately 200 families use the Honeylands facilities in some way. An average of 30-35 children attend on a daily basis with an average of 15-20 children staying overnight. Approximately one-third use the residential care only, one-third use the day care facilities only and one-third use both, with 4000 day care attendances and 6000 overnight stays in an average year.[8] It is important to remember that the services are provided by a staff equivalent to those in a 30-bedded residential unit.[7] The strengths of Honeylands are that it has developed in response to local needs, is child-centred and is flexible in its understanding of the problems of the parents and in providing realistic help through a multi-disciplinary team approach. Not all parents are able to use such imaginative and helpful facilities and often turn to each other for mutual help and support. An example of parental self-help is discussed in the next section.

SELF-HELP BY PARENTS

Maurice and Doreen Collins[4] describe the evolution of a unique pattern of self-help by families of handicapped children in a London borough, that has had far-reaching effects both in supporting families and in influencing professional opinion and practice. The scheme, called Kith and Kids, gradually came about as a result of the Collins' experiences in bringing up their mentally handicapped daughter and the realization that she faced a 'total social desert'.[4] This coincided with the Collins' meeting another family with two boys who were visually handicapped and also meeting an educational consultant who expressed an interest in giving help in the form of practical advice. Quite informally a meeting was arranged to discuss the possible future for their children; 18 'normal' people and five handicapped children were present. The initial meeting was intended to give the children the opportunity to play together and the parents a chance to talk together. This meeting was very successful and gradually the group enlarged and met on a more regular basis. In 1970, a search for better facilities found Coram's Fields, a park which included a large area of grass and play equipment. In addition the group was offered the use of two buildings at Coram's Fields which allowed them to store equipment and to cook. Kith and Kids meets on Sundays and follows a similar pattern, which starts off with everyone helping to prepare a meal and continues with games and activities through the afternoon. Other children playing in the park are encouraged to join in the activities, giving the handicapped children further opportunities to form relationships through play. The games and activities at Kith and Kids reflect the imagination and skill of the parents and are aimed at developing 'familiarity with the games that are the common currency of childhood'.[4]

Gradually, through mutual support, Kith and Kids became more organized in the form of a pressure group dedicated to advancing the cause of handicapped children and their families. One effect of this was the decision to organize a 'summer school' for one week in the summer holidays, in an effort to counteract the regressive effects of long school holidays. The first of these weeks took place in 1972 and was called a 'One to One' as the idea behind the project was that each handicapped child would have his own helper for the week. The helpers were young volunteers recruited from schools, colleges and youth clubs. Eleven children were involved in the first project and their handicaps included visual handicap, deafness, autism, tuberculosis, Down's syndrome and mental handicap.

In 1973 a further scheme was organized but, because of the problems and difficulties of one person interacting with a handicapped child for a six hour day, it was decided to run a 'Two to One' project, again lasting for a week. As a result of the success of these projects it was decided to extend the 'Two to One' to two weeks in 1974 and this has been the pattern ever since.

The 1974 'Two to One' involved 23 children, 18 from Kith and Kids and five from the Borough of Camden, and 46 volunteers. This project was more ambitious than the previous ones in that the children were assessed by their parents who used Progress Assessment Charts[8] to identify the skills that the volunteers could teach. Training sessions were arranged for the volunteers so that aims, programmes and methods could be discussed. During these training sessions the volunteers were introduced to the children. This interaction was observed by two parents from Kith and Kids who matched volunteers and children for the 'Two to One'. The final training session was given over to discussing the daily programmes. During the 'Two to One' the group had the use of a video camera, which proved invaluable in skill teaching, as problems could be identified during play-back. A typical day's programme would be.

9.30 a.m. to 12.30 p.m.	Volunteers working with their child on a predetermined programme
12.30 to 1.30 p.m.	Lunch
1.30 to 2.30 p.m.	Ususally an activity group
2.30 to 3.30 p.m.	Writing notes and planning

The children were collected at 3.00 p.m. and the volunteers would them meet with their supervisors and discuss the day. In evaluating the 'Two to Ones' Maurice and Doreen Collins make a number of points.[4] The first is that any progress should be seen as part of a continuing learning process, although quite dramatic progress has been made during the 'Two to Ones'. The effect on the volunteers was to develop their understanding of handicapped children and to give them an experience they would value for a very long time. The lesson for the official services and hospitals is to use volunteer help in a more positive way in order to strengthen ties and contacts with the local community. A unique service pioneered by Kith and Kids is Network, a legal advice centre for the handicapped. This was 'intended to inform parents and handicapped adults of their rights'.[4] The scheme works on similar lines to other advice centres with clients arranging an appointment and receiving advice from a barrister/solicitor and counsellor. The difference is that at Network the evening concludes with a general discussion on points of law to inform parents and to promote a 'common approach'. Network has tackled problems relating to the attendance allowance, conversions to homes for the disabled and even official responsibility for employing specialist staff.

This brief description of some aspects of the work of Kith and Kids has shown how one group of parents have coped with the problems of their handicapped children, not just coped but made a significant contribution to the body of knowledge relating to the handicapped child.

SUMMARY

This chapter has been concerned with ways in which families may be helped and supported in the task of caring for their mentally handicapped child or relative The need for improved support services was high-lighted in a discussion which identified a discrepancy between the support services provided and the 'felt needs' of the families.[22] This theme was developed through the writings of parents who described the seemingly endless battle they had with the social services and health authorities to obtain services for their children.[9,6] Official studies have tended to corroborate the parents' experiences and revealed a common state of 'chronic crisis'.[3]

There followed a discussion on the need for a partnership between parents and professionals, particularly in view of the common ground, with parents and professionals assuming elements of each others roles.[13] A partnership implies mutual support and two-way communication and should be based on the needs of the family and not merely isolated professional competence. Examples of

/

partnership included parents groups helped by professionals in a leadership or resource capacity. These groups were formed to provide mutual support and were often concerned with meeting the needs of specific groups, such as Down's syndrome children.[12,21] The pattern of support varied from informal help to a highly structured system involving matching a family with a helper, as seen in the Pilot Parent programme of East Nebraska.[19]

Specific help in the form of reaching the parents through the medium of courses and workshops has developed significantly. The work of the Hester Adrian Research Centre at Manchester was described. The various workshops and projects included a Parent Involvement Project, a Baby Project, formal education and projects which studied the effect of parent/professional collaboration on the progress made by profoundly multiply handicapped children, the early learning process in handicapped children and the help needed by mentally handicapped adolescents.[14]

A further example of a Parents Workshop was described which used a multi-disciplinary approach which allowed a wide range of topics specifically to meet local needs.[1] A unique system of teaching called the Portage Model of Home Teaching was shown to be of immense practical help to parents.[20] The scheme uses developmental check-lists to identify the skill level of the child and then uses a card system of suggestions of how the parent can teach the next skill to the child. The developmental check-lists cover a range of skills in language, cognition, motor skills, socialization and self-help. The important factor is the support and help given by home advisers who work with the parents in their home. The success of one Portage scheme in South Glamorgan was discussed and the attitudes and opinions of the parents involved showed not only that they welcomed the personal help and advice but that the children made demonstrable weekly progress.[17]

The question of practical support for families was discussed and particular reference made to the need for readily available short-term care on a regular planned basis or for relief in times of family crisis.[15]

A unique form of short-term care was seen to exist at Honeylands Family Support Unit in Exeter, which combined this service with a multi-disciplinary support team. Honeylands helps parents through a range of services which include residential care, mother's groups, play groups, a home visiting scheme and holidays. The unit serves a local community and is used in some form by 200 families. Help and advice is provided by paediatricians, nurses, psychologists, occupational therapists, a social worker and a large number of volunteers.[2,7,18]

The point was made that not all parents are able to benefit from the services and schemes described in the chapter and may turn to each other for mutual help and support with often dramatic and far-reaching results. One such scheme called Kith and Kids was described by Maurice and Doreen Collins.[4] Kith and Kids gradually evolved through a feeling of frustration at the lack of facilities available for handicapped children and a determination to do something about it. The scheme involves regular Sunday meetings where parents and children meet to provide support, help individual families and children with specific problems and provide an opportunity to play and interact. An extension of Kith and Kids is an annual summer school called a 'Two-to-One', which provides two volunteers to work with one handicapped child for two weeks. As a result of their experiences in dealing with official bodies, Kith and Kids started a legal advice centre called Network, for the handicapped and their families. The lesson would seem to be that social service departments and heatlh authorities should listen to parents when they talk of their problems, needs and anxieties. Following this they should examine carefully their scale of priorities in providing services and opportunities so that these needs are met, remembering that the majority of mentally handicapped people are at home.

BIBLIOGRAPHY

1. Attwood, A. (1977) The Priory Parents Workshop. *Child Care, Health and Development*, vol. 3, No. 2. Kidderminster: Institute of Mental Subnormality.
2. Brimblecombe, F.S.W. (1976) Honeylands, *Action Magazine*, Sept. 1976, 16–21.
3. Butler, N., Gill, R., Pomeroy, D.M. & Fontrell, J. (1977) *Handicapped Children: Their Homes and Life Styles. A Study in Avon.* Bristol University.
4. Collins, M. & Collins, D. (1976) *Kith and Kids.* London: Souvenir Press.
5. DHSS (1979) *Report of the Committee of Enquiry into Mental Handicap Nursing and Care*, Cmmd. 7468, Vol. 1. London: HMSO.
6. Fox, A.M. (1974) *They Get This Training but They Don't Really Know How You Feel.* Horsham: National Fund for Research into Crippling Diseases.
7. Goddard, J. & Rayner, H. (1978) A community resource for handicapped children. Honeylands Family Support Unit. *Apex, 5* (4).
8. Gunzberg, H.C. (1973) *Progress Assessment Chart.* London: National Society for Mentally Handicapped Children.
9. Hannam, C. (1975) *Parents and Mentally Handicapped Children.* Harmondsworth: Penguin.
10. Hogg, J. (1980) The Anson House Project. *Parents' Voice, 30,* 4.
11. Kushlick, A. (1976) Introduction to Two-to-One, a Kith and Kids Community Project, London: Interaction. *Kith and Kids*, ed. M. Collins & D. Collins. London: Souvenir Press.
12. Mellor, M. (1980) Healing the deep hurt. *Parents' Voice, 30,* 10.
13. Mittler, P. (1979) Patterns of partnership between parents and professionals. *Parents Voice, 29,* 10.
14. Mittler, P. (1979) Learning together. *Parents' Voice, 29,* 14.
15. National Development Group (1977) *Residential Short Term Care for Mentally Handicapped People*, Pamphlet No. 4. London: DHSS.
16. Owens, G. & Birchenall, P. (1979) *Mental Handicap: the Social Dimensions.* London: Pitman Medical.

17. Revill, S. & Blunden, R (1980) *The Portage Scheme in South Glamorgan* (Tape/Slide Programme). Colchester: Medical Recording Service.
18. Rubisson, J. (1976) *Honeylands—A Family Help Unit in Exeter.*
19. Shaw, M. (1979) Parent power—learning and sharing. *Parents' Voice*, 29, 12.
20. Weber, J.S., Jesien, G.S., Shearer, D.E., Bluma, S.M., Hilliard, J.M., Shearer, M.S., Schortinghuis, N.E. & Boyd, D.S. (1975) *The Portage Guide to Home Teaching.* Portage, Wis.: Cooperative Educational Service Agency.
21. Swaffield, L. (1978) Charting success. *Community Outlook*, June 1978, pp. 153, 155, 157.
22. Wilkin, D. (1979) *Caring for the Mentally Handicapped Child.* London: Croom Helm.

PART IV
Caring for
the Mentally
Handicapped

Introduction

It has been said that a society can be judged by the way that it cares for those who are handicapped or dependent. Generally speaking the United Kingdom, with its long tradition of humane and sensitive legislation, can be justly proud of its health care provision. However, many people would argue that existing facilities and care practices fall far short of meeting the needs of the mentally handicapped, particularly those living in hospital. Part IV is concerned with those social aspects of caring for the mentally handicapped that lead to the provision of particular patterns of care and some methods of evaluation.

Chapter 12 summarizes the historical development of services for the mentally handicapped from the Poor Law to the present day. It goes on to discuss a number of problems faced by the mentally handicapped in a modern industrial society, by considering the complexities of family structure, social class, role and work, and their possible effects. A major area of difficulty experienced by the mentally handicapped is the acceptable expression of their sexuality and the attitudes of others. The chapter discusses a number of aspects of sexuality and relates these to the rights of the mentally handicapped.

Chapter 13 is concerned with patterns of care for the mentally handicapped in the United Kingdom, and the factors which determine or influence which form of residential provision is made available. These factors are considered within the framework of national, regional and local policy and examples of patterns of care at each level are discussed. The chapter continues with a discussion of the key issues in the debate about hospital and community care. The text describes a number of examples of patterns of care which demonstrate varying degrees of community integration. Finally, the recommendations of the Court Report and the National Development Group and their application to mental handicap are discussed.

Chapter 14 continues the theme of segregation and integration by describing services for the mentally handicapped in Scandinavia and America. The development of a country's services for the mentally handicapped evolves through the stages of diagnosis, specialization, differentiation, and decentralization and integration. The models of care in Sweden and Denmark are compared and contrasted in the light of the guiding philosophy of 'normalization'. The theme of normalization is continued in a discussion of the radical approach to the provision of care for the mentally handicapped in East Nebraska (ENCOR) in America. An interesting correlation between the three models of care is that they are all organized under a single authority, as opposed to the United Kingdom model which is divided between the National Health Service and local authority social services departments.

Chapter 15 is concerned with evaluating or measuring the quality of care that may be provided. Five approaches are considered, each reflecting a different bias and purpose. They include a sociological study of care practices for children; an identification of the variables that contribute to the acquisition of appropriate skills and their relationship to the care provided; and examples of check-lists designed to assess particular aspects of care.

Social aspects of caring for the mentally handicapped

12

The care of the mentally handicapped must be seen against a background of time and social change. Chapter 1 makes the point that mental handicap has been seen as an administrative, medical, eugenic, social and educational problem. In Elizabethan times the Poor Law (1601) was introduced as an administrative solution to the social problems of sickness, poverty, vagrancy, deviance and mental disorder.[11] Part of the provision of the Poor Law, and its successive revisions and amendments, was the establishment and administration of the workhouses and infirmaries for the 'sick and maimed'. Large numbers of mentally handicapped people were 'cared for' in the workhouses and gradually they became segregated and were cared for in the 'asylums' which flourished from the eighteenth century. These asylums were initially provided for the mentally ill, but many of the mentally handicapped were placed there.[6]

The nineteenth century saw an increase not only in the building of more and larger asylums, but also in the volume of knowledge and writing about mental handicap.[2] Particularly influential were Pinel, working in the Bicêtre Hospital in Paris, who advocated the abolition of restraint; Itard, and his work with Vincent 'the Wild Boy of Aveyron'; and his pupil Séguin, who pioneered sensory training of the mentally handicapped.[11]

At the end of the nineteenth and the beginning of the twentieth century the Eugenics Education Society in this country and the American Breeders Association were prophesying that the nation's intelligence would be diluted if the mentally handicapped and other 'degenerates' were allowed to breed.[3,6] One result of this campaign was the popular attitude that the mentally handicapped had to be segregated not only for their own good but for the good of society as a whole. Segregation resulted in the building of large institutions and significantly a changed emphasis from the educational aspect of mental handicap to the medical, as the hospitals and institutions were usually under the control of doctors.[6] The view that segregation was the answer to the problems posed by the mentally handicapped is reflected in the legislation of that time. The Mental

Deficiency Acts 1913 and 1927 allowed the mentally handicapped to be committed and legally detained, very often for reasons that would not warrant admission today.[11]

The National Health Service came into operation in the UK in 1948 and with it a fundamental change in the administrative provisions of care. Hospital and welfare services for the mentally handicapped became the responsibility of the National Health Service with the local authorities responsible for the after-care and day care facilities.[6]

The law relating to mental handicap was changed in the form of the 1959 Mental Health Act which resulted from the work of the Royal Commission on the law relating to Mental Illness and Mental Deficiency (1954–57). The Commission recommended in their report that 'There should be a general re-organisation away from institutional care in its present form and towards community care'.[5] This marked a significant change in official thinking, which until this time had endorsed the view that segregation in hospital was the most appropriate way to manage the mentally handicapped. Unfortunately, the move towards community care, envisaged in the Royal Commission's report, was slow, and in some areas non-existent, owing to a lack of money and staff.[5] As the debate about the suitability of hospital or community care continued into the 1960s, the Report of the Committee of Inquiry into Ely Hospital at Cardiff was published in 1969, following allegations of cruelty. This inquiry stimulated public concern and interest in the mentally handicapped, with a subsequent increase in financial resources and staff, designed to alleviate the problems experienced by the hospitals.[6]

The move towards community care has been facilitated by changes in social attitudes regarding the mentally handicapped.[3] These changes came about, in part, as a result of people questioning whether the hospital met the needs of its patients. Others argued that, as society became more accepting and tolerant, as knowledge of mental handicap was more widely disseminated through the media, the social reasons for segregation were less valid. As interest was reawakened in mental handicap through the 1960s, other professionals such as psychologists, therapists and teachers took an increasingly active part in the care of the mentally handicapped. This professional involvement of other disciplines raised the question of whether the traditional medical model of hospital, doctors and nurses was the most appropriate model of care.

In the early 1970s, there were a number of significant changes in government policy and the law, which affected the mentally handicapped. The Education Act (1970) transferred responsibility for educating mentally handicapped children from the National Health Service to the Department of Education and Science.[6] The act laid down that every child had the right to an education, whereas previous legislation said that children with an IQ of 50 or less (severely subnormal) were 'unsuitable for education in school'. The Social Services Act (1971) set up social service departments staffed by 'generic' teams of social workers, whose responsibility for the mentally handicapped would be to provide a social work service, residential care and Adult Training Centres. The Government White Paper *Better Services for the Mentally Handicapped* (1971) was a major policy statement regarding the future of the provision and services for the mentally handicapped.[5] It recommended that the hospital population should be reduced by 50% and local authority community placements increased by 600% over a 10-20-year period.[6] Finally, the Report of the Committee of Inquiry into Mental Handicap Nursing and Care (Cmmd 7468) published in 1979 recommended a model of care based on the principles that mentally handicapped people have a right to enjoy normal patterns of life within the community; have a right to be treated as individuals; and will require additional help from the communities in which they live and from professional services if they are to develop to their maximum potential as individuals.[6]

This introduction has traced some of the changes in thinking related to mental handicap and has discussed how policy and legislation has developed as a result of these changes.

Some of these points have been discussed elsewhere in the book, particularly in Chapters 1, 3 and 4. They are included in this introduction to provide a background for the next sections which discuss social aspects of the family, social class, role and work and their relationship to mental handicap.

SOCIAL ASPECTS OF MENTAL HANDICAP

In any society there are a number of important factors that influence an individual's development, social interaction and integration. Society is organized and regulated by rules which may be either official or customary, and the more complex the society, the more complex the rules.[13] Social survival depends to some extent on the person's ability to understand and manage his environment. The modern industrial environment poses a number of problems for the mentally handicapped and these include:

1. A complex bureaucracy which demands an ability to read and write and complete a wide range of forms in order to obtain services.
2. A bewildering variety of rules and regulations, often written in legal language, at national, regional and local level.
3. Value systems which are subtle and exclusive.
4. A pace of life which requires speed of thought, action and adaptation.
5. Increasingly technical methods of work in agriculture, commerce and industry.

Gunzburg[8] coined the phrase 'a stranger in his own country' to describe some of the difficulties experienced by the mentally handicapped in modern society. He likened the mentally handicapped person to a tourist who was ignorant of the language and social customs of the country, and went on to make the point that the difference between the tourist and the mentally handicapped is that the tourist's stay is temporary.

The following sections discuss various aspects of society and how they relate to mental handicap.

The family

The family is the basic unit of western society, and has been described as having four phases which can be seen in Table 17. Although this may represent a stereotype of the family it raises issues related to the care of the mentally handicapped. The variable times suggested in phases 3 and 4 may extend in the case of a family with a mentally handicapped child into old age or death of one or both parents.

Table 17. The family cycle

Family phase	Definition	Average time
Phase 1: Home making	From marriage to the birth of the first child	2 years
Phase 2: Procreation	From the birth of the first child to the marriage of the last child	23 years: (1) child-bearing; (2) child-rearing
Phase 3: Dispersion	From the marriage of the first child to the marriage of the last child	Variable
Phase 4: Final	From the marriage of the last child to the death of the original partners	Variable

The family has also been described in terms of its structure and function. In pre-industrial society there was a simple division of labour with work and education largely being provided by the family group. Families tended to be large and integrated and were described as 'extended families'.[13] The mentally handicapped child or adult had few difficulties as a member of an 'extended family' as he could easily be absorbed into family life and work, and there would always be someone to look after him.

The structure of the family subtly changed as there was a move towards an increasingly industrial society, with its complex division of labour.[1] Families tended to become smaller, with the parents and children living together, separate from other generations of relatives such as grandparents. This family structure is known as the 'nuclear family'[13] and represents the average family unit seen in western society and sometimes referred to by sociologists as the 'cereal packet norm'. In this family unit, the mentally handicapped person is often at a disadvantage. This may be because in a small unit the family is unable to manage all the problems of the mentally handicapped person over a sustained period of time, particularly if it is necessary for one or both parents to work. (This point is fully discussed in Part III.) One of the major functions of the family, be it extended or nuclear, is the practice of child-rearing. This is sometimes called socialization and is concerned with the process whereby the child learns how to behave in his particular society.[10] 'Socialization' has been more fully defined as 'the continued process of adaption by the individual to his physical, psychological and social environment, through transactions with other people'.[1] It is within the family and during this period of primary socialization that the child learns about the culture and way of life of his particular society. Some of this learning is, of course, maturational in terms of physical and mental skills and some is sociological in terms of goals, values, role demands and expectations.

The socialization of the mentally handicapped child or adult is modified by the degree of handicap and his ability to learn. It may also be modified by the environment and, because of this, mentally handicapped people who are brought up in hospitals or hostels, or normal families, will have different 'socialization' experiences. This may pose problems in adaptation if their circumstances should be changed. There are thousands of mentally handicapped people who have been socialized to a life in hospital and who find it difficult or impossible to adapt to life in the community when given the chance. This section has discussed aspects of the family and the process of socialization, all of which may be further influenced by social class which is discussed in the next section.

Social class

Social class is one concept used to describe an individual's position in society and involves aspects such as life-style, wealth, prestige, occupation, education, power and social worth. The most usual way of considering social class in this country is the Registrar-General's Social Class Scale which is based on occupation (Table 18).[13] More often, social class is seen as either upper, middle or lower, with specific characteristics being attributed to them. Examples of this labelling may be seen in the assumption that the upper classes are land-owning members of the aristocracy; the middle class form the managerial and teaching professions; and the lower classes make up the 'working class'.

There is an epidemiological relationship between social class and mental handicap and industrial societies. Severe mental handicap occurs in almost equal proportion in all the five social classes of the Registrar-General's classification.[12] However, there is evidence which suggests that mild mental handicap may occur more frequently in social classes IV and V. Birch[19] studied the prevalence of mental handicap in Aberdeen in 1962 and found that mild mental handicap occurred approximately nine times more frequently in the children of unskilled manual workers than in the children of non-manual workers. These findings can be seen in Table 19.

Further aspects of social class that relate to mental handicap concern education and language. Education is particularly relevant to mental handicap as the type of

Table 18. Registrar-General's scale of social classes with examples of occupations (UK)

Group	Occupational class	Examples
I	Professional and administrative	Doctors, lawyers, top civil servants, business executives
II	Intermediate	Managers, teachers, nurses, journalists, pharmacists
III	Skilled	
	(a) Non-manual	Typists, secretaries, police, shop assistants, salespersons
	(b) Manual	Electricians, plumbers, bus drivers, firemen
IV	Semi-skilled manual workers	Agricultural workers, bus conductors, machine operators
V	Unskilled	Labourers, cleaners, road sweepers

Table 19. IQ of children with various degrees of mental handi-handicap relating to social class[19]

	Social class group				
IQ	I–IIIa	IIIb	IIIc	IV	V
60+	—	18.8%	38.5%	68%	76%
50–9	11%	37.5%	23%	16%	15%
<50	89%	43.7%	38.5%	16%	9%

education received generally determines a person's occupation and opportunities. The mentally handicapped are at a distinct disadvantage in the 'normal' state system of education because they are unable to cope with the educational demands made upon them. This may mean that they will be educated in a special school for the educationally subnormal or the adult training centre and will subsequently be labelled as ESN. This labelling has the effect of acting as a self-fulfilling prophecy, in that efforts are not made to help the mentally handicapped – because they are mentally handicapped – with the result that they fail to make the progress they might. This process has been termed the 'cycle of educational deprivation'.[2]

Middle-class families tend to be more articulate and persuasive in their efforts to further their handicapped child's education. The mentally handicapped come into contact with many people who use language that is foreign to them, particularly those from working-class backgrounds.

Bernstein described the use of class-based linguistic codes.[2] The working class tend to use a 'restricted code' or public language that is simple and direct and often used in a controlling way with frequent use of gesture, for example 'shut up'. The middle class tend to use an 'elaborated code' or formal language which is articulate and descriptive, expressing thoughts and abstract concepts, for example 'Please be quiet as I have a headache'.[2] It is possible for the middle class to use either code and one code is not necessarily more effective than another. However, the mentally handicapped person who has learned the restricted or public code may find it impossible to understand a person who uses the elaborated or formal code. This may occur quite often in school or in dealing with officialdom, to the disadvantage of the mentally handicapped.

Social mobility refers to an individual's movement from one class to another and it may be either upward or downward on the social scale.[2] The mentally handicapped person may not have the chance to be 'upwardly mobile', as promotion and higher status jobs usually require education certificates or further training which he may be unable to cope with.

This section has briefly discussed social class; its classification and relationship to the incidence of severe and mild mental handicap; educational opportunity and labelling; and forms of language and social mobility. The next section discusses the related themes of role and work.

Role and work

Role has been defined as the expected behaviour appropriate to a position in a social system, or more simply the part that an individual plays in society. In just the same way as an actor plays a part in a play, so each individual plays a part in life.[9] We each have a script, which is constantly changing, telling us how we should play the part which we commenced to learn in childhood and which we continue to learn through life. The title of the play might be 'Socialization – a life-long process'. Our part in the play consists of learning the rules and values which will enable us to act or behave in a particular way in order to carry out a specific role. In sociological terms, this is known as role-related behaviour and can be seen in everyday life; the nurse taking a patient's pulse; the priest saying mass; and the policeman directing traffic.

The way that people behave tells us a little about their status or the position that they hold. Status is spoken of in two ways. The first is ascribed status and describes the title or label that an individual has, such as doctor or nurse.[13] The second is achieved status which is how other people view the individual's performance in carrying out their role; for example, he is a good doctor and she is a good nurse.[13]

The mentally handicapped may experience difficulty in learning the rules and values leading to appropriate role-related behaviour, owing to faulty or

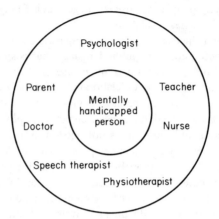

Fig. 29. Role set.

Fig. 30. Multiple roles.

delayed socialization. Other people with whom the mentally handicapped come into contact may ascribe them a low status which is confirmed by their inability to achieve social recognition through conventional means, in terms of life-style or a regular reasonably paid job. This raises the complex matter of involvement with other people and leads to the sociological concept of role set (Merton) and multiple roles.[2] In role set, the individual interacts with a number of different people and past experience and learning will make these interactions different. Multiple roles are seen when the individual has a number of roles to play. The concepts of role set and multiple roles can be seen in Figs 29 and 30.

The problems of interacting with a large number of people and playing different roles often cause the mentally handicapped person to experience difficulty in maintaining relationships. This has been described as 'role strain' and is brought about by stress induced by the demands of the multiple and role set. They may be helped by a few people who are close to them and who become important to them and these people are called 'significant others', as opposed to the rest of society which are termed 'generalized others'.[2]

It may be the 'generalized others' who pose a further problem for the mentally handicapped because of their lack of insight into and understanding of mental handicap. This may lead to labelling the individual as being mentally handicapped and the formation of a stereotype.[2] A stereotype is the exaggeration of particular aspects of a person or role and those commonly applied to the mentally handicapped are that they are violent, unpredictable or lazy. This may lead to people making judgements about whether the mentally handicapped individual is able to fulfil the role required in a particular job or situation. Indeed, other people's expectations of a particular role, termed role expectation, often determine whether a mentally handicapped person is given a choice or a chance in life.

Where there are conflicting expectations of a role, there may be role conflict.[20] An example of this may be seen when an industrial therapy department assigns someone a particular task, such as counting sets of screws for packing. The mentally handicapped person may well see his role as considerably more than just counting and proceed to check the work of other people at his table, with predictable results. A further example of role conflict occurs when two aspects of the individual's multiple roles are incompatible. Often a 'patient' in a hospital does not want to play the role of patient, but would rather be at home playing the role of son and brother with his family.

The above discussion has briefly mentioned some sociological aspects of role theory which may be applied in general to the mentally handicapped and specifically to the working environment. Work roles are learned as part of the process of secondary socialization and this may be either incomplete or inappropriate. The professional staff who are responsible for helping the mentally handicapped should have as their aims accurate assessment of ability leading to realistic and relevant skill training, and sympathetic work placement to allow the mentally handicapped to play a meaningful role in society.[22]

Perhaps the most significant aspect of an individual's role, discussed above, is the importance of adapting to society's demands and expectations and the observation of norms of behaviour. One area of behaviour which gives rise to anxiety and confusion in both parents and professionals concerns the expression of mentally handicapped persons' sexuality. This raises the issues of the right of the mentally handicapped to enjoy relationships of a sexual nature; to receive sex education; and to support and help in expressing their sexuality.

Sexuality and marriage

Recent years have seen an acceleration in the provision of patterns of care which reflect the growing recognition that the mentally handicapped have the same rights as everyone else. This is reflected in the United Nations Organization's Declaration of the Rights of the Disabled (see Chapter 2) and in the provision of accommodation and services in the community as opposed to the virtually automatic hospitalization of the past.

Progress has been made in almost every area of care, particularly that of official and public awareness of the needs of the mentally handicapped, and has been stimulated by concepts such as the Danish view of 'normalization':[11]

'Normalisation means that there should be no special legislation, no special procedures for the retarded. They should have the full right to live, to work, to earn money, to have leisure time, to have a sexual life, to get married, to have children, to pay taxes, to be punished, etc.

'The normalisation principle means especially that all talk about protection, not to say over-protection, should be stopped.'

Unfortunately the principle of normalization is often not applied to normal sexual activity for the mentally handicapped. The reasons for this reluctance on the part of society to accept the rights of the mentally handicapped to enjoy a full sexual life are partly historical, attitudinal and ethical. Historically, segregation of the sexes in hospital was rigidly observed because of fears of unwanted pregnancies and the then prevalent view that indiscriminate breeding by the mentally handicapped would result in a 'dilution' of the nation's intelligence and lead to 'national degeneracy'.[3] This fostered beliefs that the mentally handicapped were promiscuous, indulged in deviant sexual behaviour and had unnaturally large sexual appetites.[15] These attitudes exist today and are held by many people who work in hospitals, as well as the general community. One argument for suppressing the sexuality of mentally handicapped people is that an active sexual life requires a degree of responsibility and maturity that the mentally handicapped do not possess, and that therefore society has the right to reduce the possibility of irresponsible sexual behaviour and its consequences.[15] This argument would be indefensible if applied to the general population and is indefensible when applied to the mentally handicapped.

Studies have shown that, with help and support, severely handicapped people are able to express their sexuality in a way that helps them to more satisfied fulfilled lives.

Sexuality is not limited to sexual practice in the form of sexual intercourse, homosexuality or masturbation. It is defined as the 'quality of being sexual', and is one way in which the individual expresses his or her personality. This can be seen in people's style and fashion of clothing, hairstyles, use of cosmetics, interaction in a social setting and planning of leisure time.[10] 'Sexuality can also be expressed in infatuations and romantic fantasies as well as permanent emotional attachments.'[10] It develops gradually through the processes of physical maturation and socialization experiences, and is so much a part of every-day life that it attracts little comment.

Parents, nurses and care staff all strive to encourage the mentally handicapped child, adolescent and adult to look as attractive as possible. This is achieved by attending to personal hygiene; dressing in attractive fashionable clothing; wearing the hair in a modern style; and teaching social skills. Opportunities are then arranged for the boy or girl to attend mixed-sex work and social occasions, because it is more natural. The problems seem to arise when the natural consequences of sexual attraction occur.[20] This ambivalence is complicated by life in hospital. The policy of segregation of the sexes makes it difficult for the mentally handicapped to acquire mature sexual behaviour. The lack of privacy in hospital means that residents' 'private' sexual behaviour is no longer private and may cause offence to other residents and staff. The staff may adopt dual standards of acceptance in terms of sexual behaviour.[21] They accept as 'reasonable' inappropriate exaggerated expressions of affection such as hugging and kissing visitors to the ward, but feel that it is inappropriate if these forms of affection are extended to another mentally handicapped person of the opposite sex.[20] Curiously, homosexuality is often accepted as normal sexual behaviour in single-sex wards, with staff adopting tolerant attitudes.

Experiments in Sweden have shown that mixed sex accommodation reduces aggression and increases the consideration shown to partners, inappropriate sexual expression, such as open masturbation, ceasing.[21] Sexual relationships, both heterosexual and homosexual, are allowed to the extent of couples living together. Sexual activity was reported to be less than expected and often did not include full sexual expression.[21]

One fact that has emerged from the Swedish experiment is that sex education for the mentally handicapped is vital. Katz[10] points out that most of us acquire information about how to behave in a social situation through the media of books, magazines, radio, television and friends. He goes on to say that for most mentally handicapped people these avenues of information are closed. Their friends often know no more than they do, they are often unable to read and information from the radio or television may be misunderstood. Lee[14] raises the issue of the vulnerability of young mentally handicapped people to exploitation and seduction, and says that if they are to give informed consent to sexual activity, they must have the necessary knowledge and training. Opinions differ as to the best methods to use in sex education, particularly with regard to content and the sequence in which the information is given.

The Swedish approach uses a teacher from outside the institution and is conducted in small mixed groups of not more than six people.[15] The course consists of approximately ten meetings of two hours and the material is arranged in the following sequence: introduction and finding out what the pupils know; a discussion on the differences between people so that individuals can form a self-concept; information on body hygiene and how to make themselves attractive to the opposite sex; descriptions of male and female reproductive systems and sexual maturation, including lessons on conception, pregnancy, birth; masturbation, petting and coitus; marriage and other forms of sexual relationships; and methods of contraception.[15]

Other people would rather use a teacher who is well known to the group and also find it easier to segregate the groups to avoid the problem of embarrassment.[16]

All those involved with sex education for the mentally handicapped should be aware of the curriculum so that they can reinforce appropriate behaviour in the different contexts in which it occurs. Parents, particularly, should be fully involved and consulted about the content and methods used and their views and cooperation sought.[10] One issue which concerns parents is the matter of contraception, with the worry that it may lead to promiscuity. This fear may be balanced by the security from the risk of pregnancy which modern contraception gives. The two methods which seem most appropriate are the intrauterine device (IUD) and oral contraception (the Pill).[10] Intensive teaching and counselling will be necessary to ensure that the person understands the importance of taking the 'pill' every day as instructed; in some cases, supervision will be necessary.[10]

A possible consequence of a loving relationship may be the natural desire to marry and have a family. Many people instinctively reject the idea of two mentally handicapped people marrying, on the grounds that they will inevitably become a 'problem family', making unreasonable demands of the local authority services and at risk of child abuse or neglect. Those who have spent some time in a hospital will certainly need a great deal of help in learning about the daily responsibilities of marriage and factors such as regular employment, housing and level of continuing support will need to be thoroughly discussed. One factor that has emerged is that two handicapped people often complement each other in terms of social competence.[17] Greengross[7] feels that this is due to the greater degree of independence they have in marriage and makes the point that 'the success of such a marriage is based on the same principle as that of any other marriage—the desire to succeed'.

The myth that mentally handicapped people will breed indiscriminately if given the chance is not substantiated in studies of the marriages of the mentally handicapped.[4] Mattinson (1970) found that there was a smaller family size of 1.5 children per marriage compared to the national average of 2.1 children of the same age group.[17] The fear that mentally handicapped parents would neglect their children is not substantiated either, as the degree of handicap was not the only significant factor in the quality of child care.[18] Factors such as the 'degree of marital harmony, mental health of the parents, the number of pregnancies and children produced, together with the adequacy of family income are crucial'.[18] The point regarding family income is borne out in a study in the USA which showed that the problems experienced by mentally handicapped couples were more often due to poverty than to their handicap.[21] Craft and Craft,[4] in a recent study of 25 mentally handicapped couples in Wales, found that there was 'little or no correlation between degree of handicap and success of the partnership, either in subjective or objective terms'. They also found an appreciably lower birth rate than the general population. Birth control was widely practised and was seen to be a positive measure in the relief of additional problems.[4] The amount of support varied from nil to, in the case of one couple, 'support in every major area - housing, employment and health'. They concluded that a major factor in the success of the marriages in the study was that of companionship but that there were also problems of adjustment, which must be true of the majority of marriages.[4]

SUMMARY

This brief chapter has introduced a number of the social dimensions involved in caring for the mentally handicapped. The introduction traced the development of services from the Poor Law of 1601, through the eighteenth and nineteenth centuries and mentioned the work of Pinel in Paris, Itard and the 'Wild Boy of Aveyron', and Séguin and his theories of training the mentally handicapped.[9] It went on to discuss the development of the 'institutions' in the nineteenth and twentieth centuries and the legislation, the Mental Deficiency Acts of 1913 and 1927, that accompanied and even stimulated their initiation. Gradually, as attitudes changed, official thinking in the form of the Royal Commission of 1954-57 recommended a move away from institutional care to the community. This movement was continued through the 1960s when interest in facilities and care of the mentally handicapped was further stimulated by the major enquiry at Ely Hospital.[6]

The 1970s saw the publishing of important government policies and legislation in the form of the 1970 Education Act, giving every child the right to an education whatever their handicap; the Social Service Act 1971 which led to the formation of 'generic' teams to care for the mentally handicapped; the major policy statement in Cmmd. 4683 (*Better Services for the Mentally Handicapped*) which reiterated the need to reduce the hospital population and develop community care facilities.[5] Finally, the 'Jay Committee', in their report of their enquiry into the nursing and care of the mentally handicapped, recommended an acceleration of the move towards a normal life-style as a basic right of all mentally handicapped people. The section on the social aspects of mental handicap discussed some of the problems faced by the mentally handicapped in a complex industrial society and the rules and values it was necessary to learn if successful integration was to be achieved. The mentally handicapped person's position was compared to that of a foreign tourist: 'a stranger in his own country'.[8]

The family was considered from the viewpoint of the family cycle and the social patterns of the extended and nuclear families. The point was made that the modern nuclear family often posed problems for the mentally handicapped in terms of care and supervision, particularly if both parents needed to work. The functions of the family were discussed within the context of the socialization process. Social class and its relationship to the mentally handicapped formed the next section, which discussed the Registrar-General's classification and how it related to the epidemiology of mental handicap. It was noted that there would seem to be a significant number of mildly mentally handicapped people born to parents in the social classes IV and V.[19]

Education, language and class were seen to be linked in terms of educational opportunity and specific language codes, described by Bernstein.[2] The working class tended to use a 'restricted' or public language, as opposed to the middle class who used an 'elaborated' or formal language code. The mentally handicapped, who experience difficulty with language anyway, often find it difficult to understand the 'elaborated' code.

This basic difficulty in understanding was seen to apply to mentally handicapped people's conception of the role they should undertake in society. Various aspects of role theory were discussed and included both ascribed and achieved status, role-related behaviour, role set and multiple roles, role strain and role conflict. This discussion of role theory was widened to include the effect that other people, both 'significant others' and 'generalized others' had on the mentally handicapped, particularly in the processes of labelling and forming stereotypes. The discussion of role theory was applied to the working environment and the point was made that a positive way of helping the mentally handicapped to adjust to work and society was to assess accurately their ability and limitations and then provide realistic and relevant skills training before sympathetic work placement.[22]

Finally, the problems of adjustment to society's demands and expectations in the spheres of sexual behaviour and marriage were discussed. The limited progress in achieving sexual emancipation for the mentally handicapped was contrasted with the considerable progress made in meeting residential needs. The principles of 'normalization' was discussed and the point made that the mentally handicapped have '. . . the full right to . . . have a sexual life, to get married, to have children'.[15] The reasons behind this general reluctance to accept the basic right of the mentally handicapped were discussed in the content of historical, attitudinal and ethical view points. The discussion was widened to include the expression of a person's sexuality, and the need to help the mentally handicapped, particularly in hospital.[20] A successful programme of mixed accommodation and sex education used in Sweden was described to demonstrate how some of the problems of sexuality can be tackled.[15] The issue of contraception was linked to that of marriage, and a number of studies were quoted in a discussion of the problems and benefits of an active sexual life for the mentally handicapped.[10] If we accept the principle of normalization and agree that the mentally handicapped have the same rights as other people, we must accept that they have the same sexual rights and they should not be discouraged but helped to achieve satisfying emotional relationships.[21]

This chapter has been specifically written to introduce the other chapters in this part. It is deliberately brief and written at an introductory level and, because of this, may be said to contain a number of wide generalizations. Those who wish to read further are referred to the bibliography.

GLOSSARY

Elaborated code   A descriptive term used by Bernstein to differentiate the language used by the middle class which is articulate and descriptive and is used for arguing, hypothesizing and expressing personal feelings.

Epidemiology   The study of disease in a given population. Here it is used in relation to surveys which identify mentally handicapped people, the extent of their handicaps and the services they are receiving.

Eugenics   Study of possible improvement of human stock by encouraging the breeding of those presumed to have desirable genes. Eugenic Education Society were concerned that the mentally handicapped were not allowed to breed as they held this would dilute the nation's general intellectual level.

Extended family   A large family with up to three generations living in the same house.

Generalized others   A sociological term used to describe the people in society with whom an individual interacts but who have no special significance for him.

IUD   Intrauterine device. A form of contraception where the device is inserted into the cervix of the uterus.

Itard   Doctor in Paris (1744-1838) who described the 'Wild Boy of Aveyron' and designed training programmes.

Linguistic code   A term used by Bernstein to describe the ways in which different classes used language. The working class use a restricted code and the middle class an elaborated code.

Multiple roles   Where an individual has a number of roles to play.

Normalization   The Scandinavian concept of providing as normal an environment and services for the mentally handicapped as possible. This concept also extends to such issues as the human rights of the individual.

Nuclear family   Modern family of married couple and their children living in one house.

Pinel   Working in Paris in the nineteenth century, advocated the abolition of restraint for mentally disordered people.

Registrar-General's classification   The social class scale which is used in the UK and based on occupation.

Restricted code	The linguistic code which Bernstein attributed to the working class. It has a limited range of possibilities and expresses common viewpoints and group solidarity.
Role conflict	Experienced when there are conflicting expectations of a role or when aspects of a role are incompatible.
Role set	The interactions with other people which may be different depending on the circumstances of the interaction.
Séguin	Itard's pupil and successor (1812–1880) who pioneered sense training programmes for the mentally handicapped.
Self-fulfilling prophecy	A prophecy that is fulfilled simply because it is made.
Significant others	A sociological term used to describe those people who are important to an individual and whose attitudes and values are important.
Socialization	The process by which an individual learns about society.
Social mobility	An individual's upward or downward progression from one social class to another.
Stereotype	The exaggeration of particular aspects of a person or role, an extreme form of classification.

BIBLIOGRAPHY

1. Brown, H. (1976) Socialisation. In *Making Sense of Society*. Milton Keynes: Open University Press.
2. Chapman, C.M. (1977) *Sociology for Nurses*. London: Baillière Tindall.
3. Clarke, A.M. & Clarke, A.D.B. (1974) *Mental Deficiency: The Changing Outlook*, 3rd ed. London: Methuen.
4. Craft, M.J. & Craft, A. (1976) Subnormality in marriage. *Soc. Work Today*, 7, 98.
5. DHSS (1971) *Better Services for the Mentally Handicapped*, Cmmd 4683. London: HMSO.
6. DHSS (1979) *Report of the Committee of Enquiry into Mental Handicap Nursing and Care*, Cmmd 7468, Vol. 1, London: HMSO.
7. Greengross, W. (1976) *Entitled to Love*. London: National Marriage Guidance Council.
8. Gunzburg, H.C. (1973) *Social Competence and Mental Handicap*, 2nd ed. London: Baillière Tindall.
9. Hamilton, P. & Worth, V. (1976) Social interaction. In *Making Sense of Society*. Milton Keynes: Open University Press.
10. Katz, G. (1972) *Sexuality and Subnormality — A Swedish View*. London: NSMHC.
11. Kirman, B.H. (1972) *The Mentally Handicapped Child*. London: Nelson.

12. Kushlick, A. & Blunden, R. (1974) The epidemiology of mental subnormality. In *Mental Deficiency: The Changing Outlook*, ed. A.M. Clarke & A.D.B. Clarke, 3rd ed. London: Methuen.
13. Lawton, D. (1975) *Investigating Society*. London: Hodder and Stoughton.
14. Lee, G.W. (1976) *Sex Education and the Mentally Retarded*. London: NHSMC.
15. Lee, G.W. & Katz, G. (1973) *Sexual Rights of the Retarded*. London: NHSMC.
16. Lowes, L. (1977) *Sex and Social Training—A Programme for Young Adults*. London: NHSMC.
17. Mattinson, J. (1970) *Marriage and Mental Handicap*. London: Duckworth.
18. Mickelson, P. (1947) The feeble minded parent—a study of 90 family cases. *Am. J. ment. Defic.*, *57*, 644.
19. Office of Health Economics (1975) *Mental Handicap: Ways Forward*. London.
20. Owens, G. & Birchenall, P. (1979) *Mental Handicap: The Social Dimensions*. Tunbridge Wells: Pitman Medical.
21. Shearer, A. (1974) Sex and handicap. In *The Handicapped Person in the Community*, ed. D.M. Boswell & J.M. Wingrove. London: Tavistock Publications.
22. Whelan, E. (1974) The 'scientific approach' in the practical workshop situation. In *Experiments in the Rehabilitation of the Mentally Handicapped*, ed. H.C. Gunzburg. London: Butterworths.

Patterns of care, 1   13

Patterns of care for the mentally handicapped have been debated for hundreds of years. The previous chapter outlined some of the changes in the provision of care from the Elizabethan Poor Law to the Report of the Committee of Enquiry into Mental Handicap Nursing and Care (1979).[5] This chapter discusses some effects of national, regional and local policy decisions as they affect patterns of care; debates the issues involved in hospital and community care; and concludes with examples of patterns of care in this country. Chapter 1 gave a general outline of the service available to the mentally handicapped in terms of residential and specialist provision. The residental services include hospitals, hostels, group homes and accommodation provided by voluntary and charitable organizations. The hospitals, some hostels and group homes are administered by the National Health Service, with the local authorities administering most of the remaining hostels and group homes. A number of factors will influence or determine which form of residential provision is made available to individuals.

NATIONAL, REGIONAL AND LOCAL POLICY

Policy decisions at national, regional and local level all influence the type and availability of residential provision. An example of the far-reaching effects of national policy can be seen in the Government's proposals for mental handicap, set out in the White Paper *Better Services for the Mentally Handicapped* (1971).[3] In this document the stated policy was that no new large hospitals for the mentally handicapped would be built and that any new hospital provision would be of 100–200 beds only and would serve a defined district. The government also reiterated that local authorities had a statutory duty to provide residential care for those people who did not require the special care provided by the hospitals.

The recommended shift in the balance from hospitals to the community was of major proportions, with an estimated increase in local authority residential places of more than 600% and a reduction of nearly 50% in hospital places (Cmmd 7468).[5] This programme of change was timed to occur over a period of

Table 20. Number of residential Local Authority places in 1969 and 1974 with the White Paper target for 1991 (UK)[6]

	Provided 1969	Provided 1974	White Paper Target 1991
Residential Care, Local Authority, Voluntary and Private			
Adult	4200	7800	28 900
Child	1700	1800	4800
Hospital			
Adult }	60 000	55 000	26 500
Child }			6300

20 years and Table 20 sets out the progress made by 1974 towards achieving the White Paper targets of 1991. To achieve the target figures set out in the table above would mean that by 1985 there should be something in the order of 22 000 places in local authority homes and a continuing annual increase of 1000 residential places.[6]

National policy is not always interpreted in the same way or at the same speed by individual regional health authorities and local authorities. This may lead to wide variations in the form of residential provision affecting such important aspects as length of stay and the amount of short-term care available in hospital, and opportunity to live in a hostel and attend an adult training centre in the community.

A striking example of regional policy influencing residential provision can be seen in the Wessex Region. Following an epidemiological survey carried out by Dr A. Kushlick and his research team in 1966, the Wessex Regional Hospital Board adopted Dr Kushlick's proposals to provide the estimated 450 new hospital places over a ten-year period, in the form of community-based hospital units.[8] Each locally-based unit of 20–25 places would serve an area of 100 000 population. It was planned that 150 places would be for children and admission would be on a non-selective basis, so that eventually all the children living at that time in traditional hospitals and those on the waiting list for admission to hospital, would be cared for in a community-based unit. The 300 places planned for adults would be in the form of 15 community-based units, each serving a population of 100 000. Admission to the adult units would be selective and the residents would be drawn from the existing hospital population.[8]

˙ One of the major criteria for admission to the new units is the individual's home address. This policy, termed sectorization, is designed so that the residents of the community-based units live in their home area. This has the effect of ensuring that the unit residents will be mixed in gender, degree of ability and handicap. A further effect is that it will be possible for parents and relatives to visit more frequently and less formally and to be more involved in the care of their child or relative. For the same reason, it is possible for the individual's social worker to provide a more personal comprehensive service in terms of links between the family, the unit staff and the resident.

An unusual example of care determined through a local policy decision can be seen in a group home project in Cardiff.[16] The Cardiff University Social Services, a university-based voluntary organization, were involved in voluntary work at Ely Hospital for the Mentally Handicapped. As a result of their involvement, the decision was made to set up a group home for five mentally handicapped young people. Following extensive fund-raising and negotiations with the area health authority, the Welsh Office (DHSS) approved the plan. Cardiff University offered suitable accommodation and the home was opened in 1974.[16]

The difference between the Cardiff group home and others is that the five mentally handicapped young people, two women and three men, share the home with four university student volunteers. The students are in their second year, having got to know the home and the residents in their first year at the university. This means that every year there is a new group of students living in the home.[16] Continuity is maintained through the services of a social worker employed by the voluntary organization, paid by a joint funding with the area health authority and the county council.

The above discussion has shown ways in which policy can affect patterns of care at national, regional and local levels. Multiple factors influence the implementation of policy related to the provision of services for the mentally handicapped, including existing facilities and services; priorities in health and social services; allocation of finance and resources; publications and reports from official agencies; and media representation of national and local issues relating to successful or inadequate patterns of care.

The next section discusses some of these issues and their significance in the perennial debate concerning the appropriateness of hospital or community care.

HOSPITAL AND COMMUNITY CARE

Recently, both professional and public opinion has shown a tendency to polarization on the issue of hospital or community care for the mentally handicapped. This is reflected in the national policy, stated in *Better Services for the Mentally Handicapped*, of shifting the balance of residential provision from the hospitals to the community, and the apprehension of those working in hospitals who are sceptical of the local authority social services' ability to cope with large numbers of mentally handicapped people, from the point of view of both knowledge and understanding of mental handicap as well as of the suitability of residential provision.[13]

The debate about which form of care is most appropriate has been stimulated by the growing recognition and acceptance that mentally handicapped people have the same rights as the general populations. This view is categorically expressed in the United Nations Declaration of the Rights of Disabled Persons, adopted in 1975.[10] 'Disabled persons have the inherent right to respect for their human dignity. Disabled persons, whatever the origin, nature and seriousness of their handicaps and disabilities, have the same fundamental rights as their fellow citizens of the same age, which implies first and foremost the right to enjoy a decent life, as normal and full as possible'.

Specific rights included:

1. The same civil and political rights as other human beings.
2. Help to become as self-reliant as possible.
3. Proper medical care and treatment.
4. Education, training and rehabilitation and guidance.
5. A decent level of living, including the right, according to individual abilities, to secure and retain employment.
6. A normal living environment, within a family where possible, including participation in all social, creative or recreational activities.
7. Protection from exploitation, discrimination, abuse or degrading treatment.

The National Development Group in their report, *Helping Mentally Handicapped People in Hospital*, make the point that 50 000 people live in hospitals for the mentally handicapped; 20 000 of them have been there for more than 20 years.[19] The report goes on to say 'Anyone who looks at mental handicap hospitals today cannot fail to be struck by the discrepancy between the quality of life of the general population and that of many mentally handicapped hospital residents. The physical conditions under which mentally handicapped people are expected to live and work for year after year, have long been regarded as unacceptable for the rest of society'.[11] This statement by a government-appointed professional advisory body has been reinforced by media presentation of the poor conditions that exist in many hospitals for the mentally handicapped. While the National Development Group fully support the government policy of a 'radical shift of emphasis from hospital to the community',[3] they are also committed to improving the quality of life for those who are in hospital and likely to remain there and for those whose handicaps are so severe that they will always require medical and nursing care.[11]

In spite of the generally poor physical conditions of the hospitals there are those who argue that the majority of the mentally handicapped should be segregated from the general population so that their special needs can be met more easily, through the hospital's medical and nursing resources. They point to the dangers of exposing mentally handicapped people to an increasingly technical society: the sometimes dramatic effects of 'behaviour disorders'; the problems of communication and adjustment: the possible associated problems of epilepsy or neurological disorder; and the need to provide special medical, nursing and teaching resources in the form of professional expertise.

Some hospitals resemble small towns in their efforts to meet all the residents' needs. There are health care facilities in the form of daily medical rounds, a hospital dentist, physiotherapist, speech therapist, occupational therapist, chiropodist and a 'hospital' ward. Educational and work needs are met by the hospital school, industrial training department and hospital departments such as the stores or gardens. Leisure facilities may be provided in the form of a cinema, gymnasium, swimming pool, picnic areas and sports field. Leisure activities are often organized by a recreational officer and include outings, games and dances. Many hospitals have their own denominational churches, shops and hairdressing salons. Residential accommodation is often in the form of wards called 'villas' that accommodate a number of other people with similar handicaps, abilities and interests.

The essential difference between the two viewpoints is how mental handicap is regarded. Those who advocate the view that hospitals should provide the bulk of residential care, believe that mental handicap is best managed through the medical model of care. Conversely, those who support the view that hospital care is inappropriate, and argue for community care for all mentally handicapped people, see mental handicap as a social and educational problem rather than a medical problem.[13]

The arguments for community care are based on a number of principles and are not concerned solely with providing an alternative form of care with better staffing and physical conditions than the hospitals, although this is obviously important. The central principle concerns the rights of the mentally handicapped persons as outlined in the United Nations Declaration of the Rights of Disabled Persons, particularly points 5 and 6, which relate to 'a decent level of living . . . in a normal living environment, within a family where possible',[10] Those who argue for community care point to the restrictive nature of life in hospitals for the mentally handicapped. They feel that the hospital with its large-scale bureaucratic organization of activities and services such as catering, laundry and recreation, denies the individual essential experiences of normal every-day life with its opportunities for developing skills which help towards a level of independence. On a more personal level it is argued that residents in hospitals are denied privacy and the opportunity to have personal possessions and are subject to a rigid routine which often precludes learning at their pace.[17] A further point that is often made is that hospital staff attitudes and practices are overprotective, to the extent that the essential elements of risk and discovery in learning are lost.[11]

These characteristics of hospitals for the mentally handicapped have been described by Goffman[7] as being typical of a 'total institution'. Goffman differentiated between organizations which cared for dependent people in a residential setting ('total institutions') and other organizations with a different purpose.[17] He further differentiated between the types of 'total institutions' by placing them in five categories.[7]

1. Those institutions caring for the incapable and harmless, e.g. homes for the blind, old people, orphans and the poor.
2. Those institutions which care for the incapable but who also constitute a threat, however unintentional, to the community, e.g. mental hospitals and hospitals for the mentally handicapped, tuberculosis hospitals and leper colonies.
3. Those institutions designed to protect the community from intentional threat or danger, e.g. prisons, concentration camps, prisoner of war camps.
4. Those institutions designed for a particular task, e.g. army barracks, ships and boarding schools.
5. Those institutions deliberately organized as a retreat from society, e.g. monasteries, abbeys and convents.

Owens and Birchenall point out that, although the hospital for the mentally handicapped is placed in the second category, it could equally well be placed in categories one, four or five, depending on the individual hospital's aims and orientation.[15] Category one includes those institutions caring for the incapable and harmless and the majority of the severely mentally handicapped would meet these criteria. In category four are institutions designed for a particular task and many people see the hospital as having the specific task of training and rehabilitating the residents. Institutions designed and organized as retreats from the world form category five and the hospital certainly meets this criterion.[15] Indeed, some hospital authorities, alarmed by minority public reaction to the mentally handicapped and faced with the unfamiliar problems of staffing and administering community residential care, advocate a return to the old-style 'colony' but with greatly improved facilities.

It is this tendency towards absolute control of every aspect of a person's life, which led Goffman to coin the term 'total institutions'. He describes[7] the characteristics of institutional control in the following way: 'a basic social arrangement in modern society is that the individual tends to sleep, play and work in different places, with different co-participants, under different authorities, and without an overall rational plan. The central feature of total institutions may be described as a breakdown of the barriers ordinarily separating these three spheres of life. First, all aspects of life are conducted in the same place and under the same single authority. Second, each phase of the member's daily activity is carried out in the immediate company of a large batch of others, all of whom are treated alike and required to do the same thing together. Third, all phases of the daily activity are tightly scheduled, with one activity leading at a pre-arranged time into the next, the whole sequence of activities being imposed from above by a system of explicit formal rulings and a body of officials. Finally, the various enforced activities are brought together into a single rational plan designed to fulfil the official aims of the institution.'

It is these characteristics of hospitals for the mentally handicapped, added to the problems of isolation from the general community and an inability to provide normal experiences, that have attracted criticism of institutional care from a number of writers with regard to both general and specific issues.

Paul Williams argues that although a good hospital may be able to meet many of the needs of the mentally handicapped, any hospital falls short in the attempt to meet the need for continuity of care and provision; the need for links with the family and local community; the need to live in a truly homelike environment.[20] He feels that the reasons for the hospitals' inability to meet those needs are the large size of the hospitals, the extent of their catchment areas and the outdated design of the accommodation.[20] Williams goes on to recommend that the needs of the mentally handicapped could be best served by replacing the present hospital system by the provision of small local units in adapted ordinary housing.[20]

Oswin,[14] in a study of the care received by the most seriously physically and mentally handicapped children who live in hospital, criticized the assumption that these children required admission to hospital because they needed continuous medical and nursing care. She found that long-term admission to hospital was caused by lack of support for parents; problems within the family; lack of a parental home; and a lack of residential accommodation in the community.[14] A further point made in relation to admission policy for children was that local authority administrators thought it would be impossible to manage multiply handicapped children in the community. Oswin felt that this thinking was in part due to official policy outlined in *Better Services for the Mentally Handicapped* (1971) which stated 'some (children) will need to go to hospital because of physical handicaps or behaviour problems that require medical, nursing or other skills.'[3] She feels that the white paper emphasis on the need for hospital care for multiply handicapped children encourages administrators and medical staff to see the child in terms of difficulties of management and points to the successful locally based community based units set up in Wessex by Dr A. Kushlick which care for all degrees of physical and mental handicap.[14]

In summary, the issue of hospital and/or community care is unresolved. Most people reject the continuing use of outdated institutions which geographically and socially segregate the mentally handicapped from the rest of the community. The argument is essentially about the degree of integration into the community and the form in which residential care should be provided.

The next section discusses examples of patterns of care which demonstrate the concept of community integration.

EXAMPLES OF RESIDENTIAL CARE

An early example of an experimental approach to community care can be seen in the Brooklands Experiment described by Tizard.[19] The impetus for the experiment came from the influential Curtis Report (1946) which investigated the condition of children in care and recommended that they should be cared for in small family groups, by an experienced housemother. In 1958, Brooklands, previously a home for mentally handicapped adolescent girls, became vacant and the opportunity was taken to provide a home for 16 children organized on the model of a residential nursery. This was part of a research project set up to:

'1. serve as a pilot scheme in which a particular technique of care and education coud be studied
'2. compare the development over a two-year period of children in the small unit with that of a matched control group of children living in the parent hospital
'3. explore the administrative and social implications of a system of residential care for the mentally subnormal children deprived of a normal home life, based as far as possible on the type of care offered to normal children who require it.'[19]

Thirty-two children were selected and matched in terms of ability (IQ), age, sex and diagnosis; 16, aged between four and ten, were to go to Brooklands, whilst the control group of the remaining 16 were to stay in hospital, so that a comparison of the children's progress could be made. All the children were ambulant. Their average age was 7½ years, their mental age was 3½ years and their IQ 25. Although 'psychotic' children were excluded from Brooklands most of them were 'more or less socially and emotionally disturbed'.[19]

At first the care was organized so that the nurses on duty looked after all the children, but in 1959 it was felt that there were sufficient staff to implement a 'family system' of caring. This resulted in the children being looked after in two groups of eight. Gradually the groups developed their own individual ways of doing things, with the staff caring for their 'families'. Mealtimes, bathtimes and bedtimes became more personal. The children, after an initial period of uncertainty, responded well and related to their individual housemothers.

An important feature of Brooklands was its emphasis on play 'as the main educational medium'. This was achieved through a programme of daily activities which included instruction in self-help skills and outdoor play whenever possible or otherwise play modelled on nursery school lines with organized visits. The scheme was fortunate that Brooklands, a large Victorian house in its own grounds, had plenty of space both indoors and out for the children to play in. Initially the children engaged in play which involved gross motor activity and this was reflected in the play equipment, which needed to be strong and 'scaled up' to meet the children's physical demands.[19]

The programme set out to develop the children's personal independence by developing their self-help and verbal skills. Every opportunity was taken to increase language ability through every-day situations and play: the methods used included close relationships with personal communication; learning at 'mother distance';[18] standardization of vocabulary; singing and action songs; and music and movement sessions.

Although Brooklands continued as a home for mentally handicapped children, the experimental analysis of the pattern of care was concluded in 1960. At the start of the experiment the children were 'characterised by lack of speech; an inability to play; extreme emotional lability coupled with apathy; grossly asocial and immature behaviour; and an extreme dependence on adults and on the other hand, hostility towards them'.[19] Indeed, two of the children had to be returned to the hospital because of difficulties experienced in their management and their interactions with other children. The findings on conclusion of the experiment showed considerable change in the children. They were physically well and alert, with good appetites and normal sleep patterns. As they became familiar with the environment and the changes, they learnt to play 'socially and constructively', with less evidence of the previously noted social and emotional disturbances.[19] This was reflected in the increased level of interaction between the children, with each other and with their houseparents. As they developed more self-help skills they became increasingly independent. The major difference noted between the Brookland's children and the control group of children was the rise in the verbal mental age. The Brookland's children averaged a 14-month increase in their verbal mental age as opposed to the increase of six months noted in the control group, over the two years of the study. Somewhat surprisingly, there was no significant difference in the non-verbal mental ages of the two groups.[19] Clarke,[2] in evaluating the approach used at Brooklands, suggested that more progress could have been made if skilled staff had been used. Tizard,[19] however, felt that the marked improvement in the children's behaviour and adjustment more than justified the experiment and he would have counted it a success even if there had not been the measurable improvements in their verbal mental ages.

The Brooklands experiment has been fully discussed as it represents an early research-based experiment in residential care for the mentally handicapped child. It showed the value of caring for severely handicapped children in a normal, stimulating, child-centred home environment and pointed the way to improvements in patterns of care.

An example of a different form of residential provision which attempts to combine hospital and community care is the Gloucester Centre in Peterborough. Opened in 1977 and described as a community hospital, it was designed to provide a comprehensive service for 100 severely mentally handicapped children and adults. The accommodation is arranged in five residential units, subdivided into seven 12-bed houses for adults and two eight-bed units for children. It aims to provide 'residential care, community care, a family relief service and further education'.[12] In addition the centre caters for 30 people who attend on a daily basis.

The underlying concept of the centre was that it should be part of the local community. In view of this, the location chosen was near a residential area, and the 13.5 acre site included a public cycle-track and footpath.[12] The units were designed to blend with nearby housing which had the advantage of avoiding an institutional design. This bias is reflected in the interior design, with sleeping accommodation arranged in rooms for one, two or four people; separate living and play areas; and dining rooms.

The central facility is the activities centre in the main building which also includes administrative offices, occupational and industrial therapy and individual rooms for teaching. An important feature of the care and training is that it is individual, with individual needs determining the programme. The more able attend an adult training centre (ATC), whilst the less able are helped by the staff in the centre.[12] This is in contrast to the pattern of care at Brooklands, where all the children followed the same programme. Community care is facilitated by an established team of local authority teachers and social workers (based at the Gloucester Centre), consultants, community nurses, speech therapists, physiotherapists and occupational therapists. The team work with the families of the mentally handicapped in the community providing support and practical help, from counselling to advice on behaviour problems to help with teaching skills. This practical help is extended in the form of a voluntary 'sitting in' service so that parents can have an evening out.[12] Alternatively, the child or adult can be left at the centre while the parents go shopping. Short-term care is available and parents can arrange this directly with the nursing staff.

Special further education craft classes have been arranged for all those over 16 in the District on a joint basis, with the centre providing facilities and materials and the local authority the trained staff.[12] This is in keeping with the recommendations of the Warnock Committee Report (see Chapter 4).

The Gloucester Centre cares for the severely mentally handicapped and provides a comprehensive service for a defined local population, working closely with the local group of the National Society for Mentally Handicapped Children (NSMHC) and individual families.[12]

This concept of community care, coordinated by the National Health Service and backed by National Health Services resources and expertise, can be seen on a larger scale in the services provided in Gloucestershire and described by Bavin.[1]

The Gloucestershire project was evolved by a planning team from 1974 to 1976 and culminated in a ten-year plan for an alternative form of residential/community care.[1] The plan provides a variety of facilities designed to keep the mentally handicapped living in the community. These facilities include a domiciliary support system for parents and families; group homes for the mildly handicapped; supervised homes for the moderately handicapped; and staffed community homes of approximately 12 beds for the less able, in the form of ordinary housing; with children attending schools and adults attending adult training centres in their neighbourhood.

The National Health Service acts as a resource agency, providing help and advice for families and community agencies. The scheme is organized as a joint undertaking with all the community agencies and the active participation of parents and local societies. A key element of the plan is the local counselling team based on the social service areas. These counselling teams are intended to provide expertise that can be used by the primary health care team and include a paediatrician, a specialist social worker, a health visitor and a community mental handicap nurse.[1] The teams maintain a register of the mentally handicapped in their area and assign a specific person to act as the family's personal counsellor.

As with the Gloucester Centre in Peterborough, each home provides a local service of short-term care and baby-sitting. The principle of using public services and facilities is encouraged, whilst comprehensive on-site developments such as swimming pools and cinemas are discouraged, on the grounds that these further isolate the mentally handicapped from the general community.[1] Parental involvement is encouraged to the extent of arranging workshops for parents to learn the special skills needed to care for their children.

In addition there are a number of task forces which work on particular problems affecting the provision of a comprehensive service. The ultimate aim of the project is 'to provide in ten years, uniformly across a defined population of nearly half a million, an on-demand, consumer orientated, multiple choice service to a high standard'.[1]

The above examples of new initiatives in patterns of care for the mentally handicapped stress the importance of community living and the vital need for comprehensive support of both parents and professionals in sustaining high standards of care. Official recommendations have recently proposed measures designed to provide this level of support. The Report of the Committee on Child Health Services, *Fit for the Future* (1976)[4] recommended the formation of district handicap teams, and in 1977 the National Development Group in *Mentally Handicapped Children: A Plan for Action*, put forward the suggestion of forming community mental handicap teams.[9]

The Report of the Committee on Child Health Services (1976), the Court Report, reviewed the existing health services facilities; made judgements about how these services met the needs of the children and their parents; and made proposals for a new integrated child health service.[4] It is beyond the scope of this chapter to discuss the Court Report in detail as it concerns services for all children. A major part of the Report was concerned with the provision of services and recommended the creation of a number of new posts, which included a general paediatric physician (GPP), child health visitor (CHV) and a consultant community paediatrician (CPP).[4] These specialists in child health would provide expertise in caring for children at home, in clinics, in hospitals and in schools. The child health visitor would be 'attached' to the general paediatric physician and they would provide primary health care for a geographically defined area. The consultant community paediatrician would be based in the district general hospital and would provide support and specialist services for the general paediatric physician.[4]

The district handicap team, based on the district general hospital, would work from a child development centre and provide a special diagnostic, assessment and treatment service for handicapped children; advise and support parents and families; and provide support and assistance for field work staff. 'It would provide a single district supporting service functioning both inside and outside hospital'.[4]

In order to provide this comprehensive service the district handicap team would comprise a consultant community paediatrician, a nursing officer for handicapped children, a specialist social worker, a principal psychologist and a teacher, with supporting administrative staff. The committee called for an increase in the services provided by physiotherapists, speech therapists, occupational therapists and social workers, with an increase in training in all aspects of child care for these specialists.[4]

An important recommendation is that parents of mentally handicapped children should have direct access to the district handicap team and should be treated as 'co-participants and not by-standers in the process of assessment and decision making'.[4] Continuing the theme of integrated team decisions, the Report recommends that children in long-stay hospitals should be reviewed every six months. This review should consider issues such as social and educational factors as well as medical and psychiatric conditions and should be carried out by a multidisciplinary team.

The objectives of the Committee have been set out in their Report as follows: 'we want to see a child and family centred service; in which skilled help is readily available and accessible; which is integrated in as much as it sees the child as a whole, and as a continuously developing person. We want to see a service which ensures that this paediatric skill and knowledge are applied in the care of every child whatever his age or disability, and wherever he lives, and we want a service which is increasingly orientated to prevention'.[4]

The Court Report deals with all handicapped children although it recognizes that severely mentally handicapped children have special needs.

The National Development Group proposes the setting up of community mental handicap teams to 'co-ordinate the special expertise available from both health and local authority staff'.[9] The community mental handicap teams would also provide help and advice for mentally handicapped adults so that continuity of care and service is maintained. The particular functions of the teams would be:

1. To act as the first point of contact for parents and to provide advice and help.
2. To coordinate access to services.
3. To establish close working relationships with relevant local voluntary organizations, particularly the local and regional branches of the National Society for Mentally Handicapped Children.

The National Development Group see these teams as serving a population of 60 000–100 000. In view of this it would be necessary to provide two or three teams for the average health district, possibly based on social service catchment areas[8] (Fig. 31). The National Development Group recommend that the care team should consist of two or three professionals working full-time, who would be able to refer particular problems to other professionals and coordinate the services needed by individuals. Although there are no specific recommendations

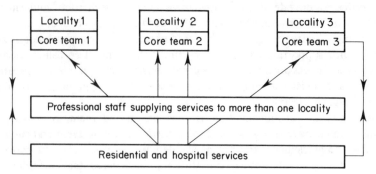

Fig. 31. The organizational structure proposed for community mental handicap teams.[9]

regarding membership of the care teams, the National Development Group believe that the skills and experience needed are most likely to be found in National Health Service mental handicap nursing staff, local authority social work staff, specialist teachers and the staff of adult training centres.[9] Important aspects of the work of the community mental handicap teams would be to be involved in the planning and management of short-term care; periodic assessments and reviews of individuals and ensuring that recommendations are carried out; helping and advising on placement in day-care facilities such as nursery schools and play groups and day foster homes; providing information on how to obtain essential services; and liaising with hospitals over the use of community facilities by mentally handicapped children and adults living in hospital.[9]

SUMMARY

This chapter reviewed some of the factors which influence or determine the form of residential provision and discussed examples of national, regional and local policy and their effects. This included the national policy outlined in *Better Services for the Mentally Handicapped* (1971),[3] The Wessex Regional Health Authority policy resulting in the Wessex experiment[8] and an example of local policy involving a voluntary group and the National Health Service in provision of a group home project in Cardiff.[16]

The continuing debate about hospital and community care was discussed by considering whether the mentally handicapped should be seen as a medical or social and educational problem. The growing awareness among official bodies and the general public that mentally handicapped people have the same rights as everyone else, has stimulated a move from the model of hospital care to that of community care. However, it is generally recognized that there will be a small proportion of profoundly multiply handicapped people who will require full-time nursing care.[5] Those who support hospital care for the majority of the mentally handicapped do so from the viewpoint that only hospitals can meet their special needs. Those who support community care point to the restrictive nature of care in hospital, with the overprotective attitudes and practices of the staff, the negative characteristics of hospitals described by Goffman as typical of 'total institutions'[7] and the problems of isolation and lack of normal experiences. This theme was taken up in the section which outlined three examples of residential care, based on varying degrees of community integration. The Brooklands Experiment described by Tizard[19] investigated the effect of care, organized on the lines of a residential nursery, on a group of 16 severely mentally handicapped children, formerly living in hospital. Apart from a general level of physical well-being it was noticed that the children attained a 14-month increase in their verbal mental age; more than double the 6-month increase achieved in the 16 children forming the control group in hospital.[19] Brooklands showed the value of caring for severely mentally handicapped children in a normal, child centred home environment.

The Gloucester Centre in Peterborough, described as a community hospital, was opened in 1977.[12] It aims to provide comprehensive care for 100 residents in the form of 'residential care, community care, family relief service and further education'.[12] The centre provides a range of activities and facilities designed to meet the individual needs of the residents. This care is extended into the community through a team of local authority social workers and teachers, and backed up by consultants, community nurses and specialist therapists. The traditional role of the hospital has been widened to include a counselling service, a 'baby-sitting' facility and easily arranged short-term care.[12]

Bavin[1] describes a project of community residential care in Gloucestershire. The project involves a number of facilities designed to keep the mentally handicapped in the community and is supported by a domiciliary nursing service and the full range of community facilities. A key feature of the service is the 'local counselling teams' which provide expertise in mental handicap for the primary health care team, the education services and families. Each family has a personal counsellor. The scheme includes short-term care and help for parents in the form of skill workshops, helping them in the management of their children.

The team concept of care is reflected in the recommendation of the Committee on Child Health Services[4] and the National Development Group.[9] The Court Report recommended a number of specialist appointments which included consultant community paediatricians, general paediatric physicians and child health visitors who, with a specialist nursing officer, psychologist and teacher, would form a district handicap team, providing a comprehensive support system for parents and professionals.[4] The National Development Group recommend the setting up of Community Mental Handicap Teams[9] smaller, more locally-based teams which would provide a service for mentally handicapped children and adults to ensure a measure of continuity. The community mental handicap teams would work specifically for the mentally handicapped in contrast to the Court Report recommendations which included all handicapped children.

The official reports and new initiatives reflect a dissatisfaction with the outdated concept of the large isolated hospital for the mentally handicapped, with its narrow restrictive approach to care. Having said this, it should be recognized that at the end of the day, over 50 000 people have been cared for in hospital, often in very difficult conditions: a 'daily miracle'. Those who call for new patterns of care recognize this enormous commitment and effort on the part of the staff in hospital, but believe that the 'vicious spiral' of institutionalization must be broken if real progress is to be made.

In the author's opinion, the current move towards a normal life-style in the community with a parallel development of family support services should be accelerated.

GLOSSARY

Better Services for the Mentally Handicapped
Government White Paper (Cmmd 4683) published in 1971 which reviewed services for the mentally handicapped and recommended extensive changes in services, particularly a move towards community care.

Brooklands
A research project set up by Tizard from 1958 to 1960, designed to evaluate the effects of caring for mentally handicapped children using nursery school methods.

Child Health Visitor
A specialist appointment recommended by the Committee on Child Health Services.

Community Mental Handicap Teams
Teams recommended by the National Development Group who would provide locally-based expertise and advice for families and professionals caring for the mentally handicapped.

Community Paediatric Physician
A specialist appointment recommended by the Committee on Child Health Services.

Care Teams
The teams of two or three people coordinating services in the Community Mental Handicap Teams.

District Handicap Teams
Specialist teams of child health experts recommended by the Committee on Child Health Services to provide a comprehensive service in a District for all handicapped children.

General Paediatric Physician
A specialist appointment recommended by the Committee on Child Health Services.

Goffman, Erving
American sociologist who coined the phrase 'total institutions' to describe the effect of institutional care (1957).

Kushlick, A. Director of the Health Care Evaluation Research Team, Wessex Regional Health Authority. Following a survey in Wessex in 1966, recommended providing future accommodation for the mentally handicapped in the form of small community-based homes.

Sectorization The admission policy advocated by Dr Kushlick which means that children are accommodated in a community in the area of their family home address.

Total institutions A term coined by Goffman (1957) to describe those organizations which cared for dependent people in a residential setting.

BIBLIOGRAPHY

1. Bavin, J. (1979) The Gloucestershire Project. *Nursing Times, 75*, 887.
2. Clarke, A.D.B. (1973) The basic problem. In *The Education of Mentally Handicapped Children*, ed. R. Hermelin. London: NSMHC.
3. DHSS (1971) *Better Services for the Mentally Handicapped*, Cmmd 4683. London: HMSO.
4. DHSS (1976) *Report of the Committee on Child Health Services*, Cmmd 6684, London: HMSO.
5. DHSS (1979) *Report of the Committee of Enquiry into Mental Handicap Nursing and Care*, Cmmd 7468. London: HMSO.
6. DHSS (1976) *Priorities for Health and Personal Social Services in England: A Consultative Document.* London: HMSO.
7. Goffman, E. (1961) *Asylums.* Harmondsworth: Penguin.
8. Kushlick, A. (1967) The Wessex Experiment—Comprehensive care for the mentally subnormal. *Br. Hosp. J. Soc. Serv. Rev.*, 77 (2).
9. National Development Group (1977) *Mentally Handicapped Children; A Plan for Action.* London: DHSS.
10. National Development Group (1977) *Day Services for Mentally Handicapped Adults.* London: DHSS.
11. National Development Group (1977) *Helping Mentally Handicapped People in Hospital.* London: DHSS.
12. North, P.S. (1979) The Gloucester Centre. *Parents' Voice, 29*, 7.
13. Office of Health Economics (1978) *Mental Handicap Ways Forward.* London: HMSO.
14. Oswin, M. (1978) *Children Living in Long Stay Hospitals.* London: Heinemann Medical.
15. Owens, G. & Birchenall, P. (1979) *Mental Handicap: The Social Dimensions.* Tunbridge Wells: Pitman Medical.
16. Pithouse, M. (1978) Living in harmony. *Parents' Voice, 28*, 14.
17. Raynes, N.V., King, R.D. & Tizard, J. (1971) *Patterns of Residential Care.* London: Routledge and Kegan Paul.
18. Sheridan, M.D. (1975) *Children's Developmental Progress.* Windsor: NFER.

19. Tizard, J. (1964) *Community Services for the Mentally Handicapped.* London: Oxford University Press.
20. Williams, P. (1976) What is a hospital? In: *Hospitals and Their Future, Report of an Information Exchange Session*, ed. J. Brown. London: NSMHC.

Patterns
of care, 2

14

The previous chapter discussed policies and examples of care aimed at achieving integration of the mentally handicapped into their local community. The issue of integration or segregation is at the heart of the debate over the form of residential and educational provision. Although it is often seen only in these terms, there are underlying attitudes and misconceptions about the condition of mental handicap which may have an important effect in determining the extent of integration or segregation. Issues such as the value of property, the lowering of educational standards in schools or the apparently unpredictable behaviour of the mentally handicapped are frequently raised.

Segregation is advocated to meet the 'special needs' of the mentally handicapped, but further examination shows that the specialists who would meet these special needs, such as physiotherapists, speech therapists and occupational therapists and even nurses, are in short supply in the hospital.[5] A further aspect of segregation is that the mentally handicapped child or adult is seen in terms of his handicap, rather than as a person who has needs, feelings and desires that are common to the non-handicapped individual.[4] The implication is that the mentally handicapped person will benefit in some way by being isolated from the general community.

Integration, whilst having many benefits, may also pose problems for the mentally handicapped and their families. Successful integration is dependent on factors such as community awareness and degree of acceptance and careful preparation in terms of facilities and staff training. One argument put forward in favour of integration is that if handicapped children are integrated into schools other children will learn how to relate to them in a non-prejudiced way, fostering acceptance.[4] This in turn will help the mentally handicapped child learn the social norms of society as a result of more normal socialization experiences. Integration will help the parents of the mentally handicapped by reducing the social isolation that is a common experience. They would be able to maintain closer contact with their children's school or home and consequently be more involved in their day-to-day care.[4]

Whilst official policies and services for the mentally handicapped in this country are slowly moving towards partial integration, there are examples of integrated patterns of care in other countries, notably in Scandinavia and parts of America.

Dr K. Grunewald, Director of Mental Retardation Care Services for the Swedish Board of Health and Welfare, has described the characteristic stages in the development of a country's services for the mentally handicapped.[2] He outlines four basic stages and suggests that all services should develop this way.

The first stage is that of diagnosis and is concerned with the identification of the problems that the mentally handicapped may have. This stage is also concerned with the formulation of plans and policies designed to meet the identified needs.

The second stage is termed specialization and is characterized by the centralization of services for the mentally handicapped. This inevitably leads to the building and administration of large facilities such as hospitals. These centralized facilities are organized by the various specialists involved and one of the effects of this may be that the needs of the mentally handicapped are not met. An example of this can be seen in the large numbers of institutionalized adults living in hospitals, who are still there because they were admitted to hospital during this phase of specialization.

The third stage is termed differentiation and leads on from specialization. Differentiation of services comes about with the acceptance that a standardized service cannot meet all the needs of the mentally handicapped. Factors such as age and the need for a multi-disciplinary approach in solving the different problems posed by varying degrees of mental handicap, will lead to differentiation of services. The services in this country are either in the stage of differentiation or moving towards it.

The fourth stage is that of decentralization and integration. This stage is characterized by the development of small community based services, serving a defined geographical area. Integration is a gradual process brought about by the increasing use of community facilities by the mentally handicapped.

THE SWEDISH MODEL[3]

Unlike those of the United Kingdom, the services for the mentally handicapped in Sweden are organized under a single authority—the Mental Retardation Care Services—which is part of the Swedish Board of Health and Welfare. Sweden developed their services through the stages of diagnosis, specialization and differeniation. Dr K. Grunewald, Director of the services in Sweden, estimates that the services for the mentally handicapped are now moving into the fourth stage of decentralization.[3]

A further difference between the services in Sweden and the UK is that the facilities in Sweden are smaller, more numerous and administered on a social model rather than on a medical model.[3] This is reflected in Table 21.

Table 21.   Comparison of facilities for the mentally
handicapped in England and Wales with those in Sweden

	England and Wales	Sweden
No. of facilities	111	185
With less than 100 beds	21%	82%
With more than 500 beds	40%	1.6%
Hospital beds administered on a medical model	89%	15%

The social model of care has been developed from the principle of 'normalization', which aims to provide living conditions that are as normal as possible.
However, because there is a wide variation in the degree of dependence in
mental handicap, there is a need for a corresponding variation in the facilities
available. The Swedish view is that, whilst accepting the need to provide accommodation which will vary from the highly specialized to the normal house or
flat, this should be integrated into the general community.[3]

Sweden has a population of eight million and provides a range of services for
approximately 30 000 mentally handicapped children and adults (Table 22).
These services are designed to cater for a wide variation in dependency and
reflect the philosophy of progression towards independence. 'Progression from
hospital to a residential home, to a group home and finally to an individual
home; from living in a large group to a small group to individual living; from a
specialised facility to normal accommodation in the community'.[3]

In 1974, there were six special hospitals catering for approximately 1700
(5.8%) mentally handicapped people. They had the specific function of providing care for the antisocial and delinquent, people from the courts and the
profoundly and multiply handicapped; increasingly, they provide short-term
care. Their future is seen as specializing in the diagnosis of mental handicap
and the residential commitment decreases each year.[3]

The majority of the mentally handicapped (37%) are cared for in the residential homes which have been described as 'socially orientated community-based
institutions' organized and run on a social model. Sweden is administered on
the basis of 25 counties and each county has one central residential home of
approximately 100–200 beds, caring for the moderately and profoundly handicapped. In addition there are smaller local residential homes which equate in
size with hostels in this country. They cater for smaller numbers of people, with
an average of 40.[3]

Both types of residential homes have their own facilities for training, including occupational and industrial therapy. The homes for children, which are increasingly placed on separate sites, have their own training schools.

Table 22. Forms of living of all the mentally handicapped receiving provision and services in Sweden (1977)[3]

Form of living	Children and youths	Adults	Total
Parental homes	6687 (51.3%)	4886 (28.6%)	11 573 (38.4%)
On their own	11 (0.1%)	784 (4.6%)	795 (2.6%)
Other private homes (foster homes)	361 (2.8%)	647 (3.8%)	1008 (3.4%)
Boarding schools and group homes (children)	2569 (19.7%)	—	2569 (8.5%)
Group homes (adults)	83 (0.6%)	624 (3.6%)	707 (2.4%)
Residential homes	2633 (20.2%)	8435 (49.4%)	11 068 (36.8%)
Special boarding schools	164 (1.3%)	—	164 (0.5%)
Special residential homes	86 (0.7%)	166 (1.0%)	252 (0.8%)
Special hospitals	390 (3.0%)	1354 (7.9%)	1744 (5.8%)
Other forms of living	38 (0.3%)	194 (1.1%)	232 (0.8%)
Totals	13 022	17 090	30 112

During the 1960s there was a proliferation of boarding schools for children. These schools operated a five-day week, the children going home at weekends. The introduction of group homes and class integration in normal schools has meant that no new boarding schools have been built since 1970 and children are being moved from the existing boarding schools, to avoid the problems of isolation and segregation.

A natural progression in the chain of care is the group home. 'Group homes for children usually take the form of a small house or flat for 4-6 children. They are cared for by foster parents with the father carrying on his usual occupation.'[13]

Group homes for adults take the form of flats for one or two people combined with a larger home for four or five people, the 'mother flat'.[3] A pre-requisite for living in a group home is the ability to use public transport to attend a training centre or to go to work. There is very little supervision in group homes for adults, although the 'clients' have easy access to the staff in the 'mother flats'.[3]

The Swedish view is that the group home principle is the best approach in integrating the mentally handicapped with the community.[3] Their experience has shown that reducing the numbers of residents, careful selection of houses and flats scattered in a local community, coupled with a practical training in social skills has helped in forming positive attitudes towards the mentally handicapped.

THE DANISH MODEL[1,6,7]

The services for the mentally handicapped in Denmark bear some resemblance to those of Sweden in their philosophy, history and administration.[1] In 1959 the National Service for the Mentally Retarded was formed to administer, under a single authority, the country's services for the mentally handicapped.[7] The Service is administered by a board with representatives from the Parents Association, officials from the Ministries of Housing and Health, with a chairman appointed by the King. The board is responsible to the Minister for Social Affairs. All services for the mentally handicapped are fully financed by the state as a statutory responsibility.[1]

The philosophy underlying Denmark's services is that of normalization and integration, the aim being to provide as normal a life as possible for the mentally handicapped through normal living conditions and use of community facilities.[1] The aim of normalization is modified to take account of the small number of the mentally handicapped who will always require special support care or treatment.

Denmark has a population of 5 million with approximately 22 200 mentally handicapped people receiving some form of care[6] (Tables 23 and 24). The country is divided into 12 regions based on the concentration of the population. Each region has a central institution under the management of a multi-professional

Table 23. Mental retardation services in Denmark (population 4.9 million)[6]

Type of service	No. of clients	Per 1000 population
Institutional care		
Residential		
State institutions	9000	1.84
Semi-private homes	450	0.09
Total	9450	1.93
Non-residential: kindergartens, schools and workshops	6350	1.29
Total institutional services	15 800	3.22
Clients in both residential and non-residential care	500	0.10
Total number receiving institutional care	15 300	3.12
Services in the clients' own homes	6900	1.41
Total number of persons served	22 200	4.53

Table 24. Specification for institutional care in Denmark

Type of institution	No.	No. of clients
Residential institutions		
Central	12	6405
Local	27	1903
Relief and holiday homes	7	73
Care homes	1	22
Special treatment homes	2	14
Homes for children	3	14
Treatment homes	1	8
Boarding schools	2	19
School homes	14	242
Weekend care facilities	2	14
Youth boarding schools	7	95
Hostels	18	216
Private care homes	23	446
Total	119	9471
Non-residential institutions		
Schools	67	3579
Kindergartens	34	739
Workshops	40	1887
Youth schools	3	125
Total	144	6330
Overall total	263	15 801

team composed of an administrator, a chief psychiatrist or paediatrician and directors of education and social work.[1] This multi-professional team is also responsible for all the activities that occur in their area. These activities include smaller institutions such as kindergartens, schools, work-shops, nursing homes, children's homes, old people's homes and hostels.

It is in the administration of their services that Denmark differs from Sweden. In Denmark there is a tradition of doctors and psychiatrists in charge of institutions, whilst in Sweden the tradition is for educationalists and teachers to be in charge.[1]

One of the functions of the regional centres is to collect information from doctors, police and teachers who have a statutory duty to report the information, for inclusion in a central register. Regional centres also provide diagnostic services and help with job placement in conjunction with the National Employment Service.[1]

Education receives a high priority, all the mentally handicapped being registered for compulsory education from the normal school starting age of seven to the age of 21. There is also provision for earlier education through the system of kindergartens.[1]

The Danish services for the mentally handicapped inherited a traditional pattern of institutional care in 1959. As a result of pursuing an active policy of normalization and a programme of public education, significant progress has been made. The Danish service is at the stage of decentralization, more autonomy being given to the regions.

This concludes the brief discussion of the services for the mentally handicapped in Sweden and Denmark. The next section discusses one American solution to the problems of institutionalization and integrated care for the mentally handicapped.

ENCOR (EAST NEBRASKA COMMUNITY OFFICE OF RETARDATION)[8]

The four stages through which a country's services develop were described earlier in this chapter.[2] The services in East Nebraska have developed over a period of approximately ten years. As a result of this, the third developmental stage of differentiation has been omitted, the services moving directly into the fourth stages of decentralization and integration into the community.[3]

The reasons for this rapid acceleration in the provision of services for the mentally handicapped can be traced back to the conditions existing prior to 1968. At that time provisions for the mentally handicapped centred on the Beatrice State Institution which cared for 2300 people in conditions described as 'archaic, immoral and wasteful'.[8] These conditions stimulated the parents to form a state pressure group with local offshoots. One of these, the Greater Omaha Association for Retarded Children (GOARC), was to play a major part in the formation of alternative services. The second factor was the commitment and interest of a group of professionals who had the necessary expertise to formulate plans based on realistic goals and aims. Finally, there came the recognition that in order to achieve any significant changes, parents and professionals had to work together to achieve a common goal.

A direct result of this mutual cooperation was the formation of the Citizens Study Committee on Mental Retardation (1968), to reappraise all the services for the mentally handicapped in Nebraska.

Nebraska itself is predominantly rural, with a population of 1.5 million. It is administered through a system of counties, one of which, Douglas County, contains Omaha, the largest city in Nebraska, with a population of 400 000.

The Citizens Study Committee on Mental Retardation produced plans for new services for the mentally handicapped of 'all ages and degrees of disability in their own home community'.[8] These plans were based firmly on the principles that the mentally handicapped were citizens and therefore had the same rights as any other citizen. This meant that there should be continuity of contact between the mentally handicapped person, his family and the community at large. In order to achieve this service, agencies should provide 'an environment conducive to their clients' physical, intellectual, social and emotional wellbeing and growth, with special emphasis on the development, welfare and happiness of children'.[8]

At the same time a report was being prepared by the Greater Omaha Association for Retarded Children specifically for Douglas County, which complemented the report of the Citizens Study Committee. The combined effect of these reports resulted in state legislation aimed at improving conditions in the Beatrice State Institution and helping the development of alternative patterns of care in the community. The Douglas County Authority accepted the GOARC proposals and as a measure of their commitment provided funds to establish pilot projects. In 1970, four adjoining counties were persuaded to come into the scheme and form the East Nebraska Community Office of Retardation (ENCOR). ENCOR serves five counties, four rural areas and Douglas County with the city of Omaha, with a total population of 569 000.

ENCOR and normalization

ENCOR's aim to provide services and facilities for all mentally handicapped people, regardless of age or degree of handicap in their own community, was based on the principle of normalization pioneered in the Scandinavian countries. Wolf Wolfensberger, research psychologist at Nebraska's Psychiatric Institute, who was closely associated with the development of ENCOR, has defined normalization as 'the utilisation of means which are as culturally normative as possible in order to establish and/or maintain personal behaviours and characteristics which are as culturally normative as possible'.[9] This principle means that informed consideration of the type of environment that will assist and maintain the acquisition of behavioural skills is vital. In this sense it is preventive as well as educational, in that a mentally handicapped person exposed only to normal circumstances and settings will not learn maladaptive behaviours characterized by institutionalization. Normalization is further reflected in the way that other people, both professionals and the public, behave towards the mentally handicapped. In applying the principle of normalization ENCOR's aim is to minimize the 'differences' in both the appearance and behaviour of the mentally handicapped and the environments in which they live and learn.

Structure and services

ENCOR is formally structured into the four main divisions: educational services, vocational services, residential services and family guidance. In addition there are support divisions which service the four main divisions: a planning department, a public education department, a staff development team responsible for staff training and a multi-disciplinary team of professionals.[8]

Educational services

One of the benefits achieved by the early state legislation of 1968 was the official recognition that the mentally handicapped had the same rights as other citizens. However, it was not until 1973 that the State of Nebraska passed the

'Right to Education' Bill which enabled the most severely handicapped children to receive education within the normal State system. In 1970 ENCOR was running one 'developmental centre' (special school) and by 1973 this had increased to six developmental centres, catering for 225 children aged between two and 12 years.[8] Since 1973 ENCOR has pursued the Swedish policy of integrating mentally handicapped children into special classes in normal schools.

At the pre-school age integration can be seen at two levels. The first level is termed a 'cooperative' playgroup or nursery where handicapped children, supervised by trained ENCOR staff, spend part of their day with non-handicapped children.[8] The second level is complete integration with other children.

The policy of integration is continued during primary and secondary education and by 1976 ENCOR had closed down their six 'developmental centres'. All the children, with the exception of five, had moved into the normal state education system, supported by ENCOR-trained teachers.

In 1973 two Special Education Units for adolescents were set up to cater for both ESN(S) and (M) adolescents between 12 and 18 years, and by 1974 were responsible for 50 people. However, as a result of the success of the programme of integration these units were closed in 1977. This example serves to show how flexible the ENCOR pattern of care is; a facility is not used just because it is there, but only if it meets the needs of a group of mentally handicapped people.

Vocational services

The principle of normalization was applied to work for the mentally handicapped. It was argued that many mentally handicapped people were potential taxpayers and through their work could help to pay for some of the services they received.[8]

In 1977 there were four industrial training centres, similar to the adult training centres in the United Kingdom. At first the programme concentrated on social skill development with some work experience. Later the emphasis was changed to work programmes using work subcontracted from industry. After an initial training period of up to 18 months the trainees move on to more advanced programmes.

In order to meet the increasing demand for more normal work experience, ENCOR set up work-stations. These involved placing a number of mentally handicapped workers, with their own instructor, in a normal work setting.[8] Examples of work schemes used include ten men working in a firm manufacturing shop fittings; a team of women working as domestic staff in a hotel; and a team of men and women who operated a dishwasher at the local general hospital. These work stations were regarded as training for normal employment and were part of the total vocational programme, which included job placement and counselling, a social training scheme and evening education.

Residential services

The range of ENCOR's residential services reflects their overall aims of providing accommodation for the mentally handicapped of 'all ages and degree of disability in their own home community'.[8] The residential provision developed through the opening of small staffed hostels scattered through East Nebraska. ENCOR started with two hostels acquired from GOARC in 1970 and by 1973 they had opened 12 hostels catering for about 70 people. These hostels were ordinary houses in the community, which were at first purchased and later rented in order to allow maximum flexibility in meeting their clients' needs.[8] As the service evolved the hostels became known as 'training residences' and in 1977 there were seven caring for 31 children and seven caring for 31 adults. At first sight this would appear to represent little or no progress but ENCOR had diversified and developed a range of special services to meet particular needs.

One need that was recognized as having a high priority was that of emergency short-term care. In 1971, the 'crisis assistance' unit, a rented house in Omaha, was opened for six children or adults. It was designed to cope with sudden crises such as bereavement, the admission to hospital of one of the parents or guardians or loss of residential placement. Other circumstances such as moving house or allowing a family to have a holiday were catered for on a priority basis. However, it was also recognized that the 'crisis assistance' unit based in Omaha did not always meet the needs of the rural population. In an effort to reduce the problems of travel and interruption of programmes ENCOR started a scheme of short-term foster homes which they called 'crisis homes'. These homes operated on exactly the same scale of priorities as the 'crisis assistance' units, with an individual family member receiving training and being employed by ENCOR.[8]

One of the problems facing ENCOR in their development of services was the rapid movement of mentally handicapped people from Beatrice State Institution into the community. In 1974 a 'behaviour shaping unit' was set up to 'develop self-help and social skills in severely handicapped and disturbed children and to reduce mal-adaptive behaviour'.[8] By 1977 it was accepted that the 'behaviour shaping unit' was unsuccessful, in that the children had learned inappropriate maladaptive behaviours from each other. Those handicapped children who had been integrated with normal children showed more appropriate adaptive behaviour.[8]

Mentally handicapped offenders were traditionally admitted to the state institution or prison, but ENCOR, using a special grant, introduced 'structured correctional units' to avoid this.[8] These units comprised a staffed group home and two staffed apartments catering for 11 people.

The only institutional accommodation provided by ENCOR is the 'developmental maximation unit' situated in a formerly disused wing of the Douglas County Hospital.[8] Started in 1972, it was designed to provide residential care for 16 multiply handicapped children. The children often had complicating medical conditions. In 1975, owing to staff cutbacks, the number of children cared for was reduced to six. With this reduction in staff came a change in policy, in that the unit was used to evaluate multiply handicapped children through comprehensive assessment and intensive care, with the children spending a maximum of one year in the unit.[8]

In keeping with ENCOR's philosophy of providing accommodation that met their clients' needs they began to question whether a system of long-term residential care was the best, particularly in view of sharply rising costs. In 1974 they pioneered the concept of 'alternative living units'.[8] These took the form of foster homes for children and a range of options for adults from semi-dependence to independence. It was argued that the mentally handicapped were more capable of living in the community, providing they received skilled back-up in the form of domiciliary support. The services were based on the existing group home with the staff finding and developing 'alternative living units' in the immediate community: the core and cluster principle. The 'core' home was able to give support and guidance to the 'alternative living units' attached to it. This system has the advantage that it is extremely flexible and in one instance an adolescent boy with severe behaviour problems lived with two members of ENCOR's staff in an apartment, undergoing an intensive training programme. The principle of 'alternative living units' enabled ENCOR to increase its residential provision from 90 places in 1973 to 230 in 1977.[8]

ENCOR's next development was to consider the problems of settling the profoundly handicapped into the community, using ordinary housing and providing 24-hour care. The elderly mentally handicapped were accommodated in existing old people's homes in the community. In 1970 there were 550 people from East Nebraska living in the Beatrice State Institution with a waiting list of 40. By 1977 ENCOR had accommodated 260 people from Beatrice State Institution and reduced the waiting list to nil.[8] The situation in 1977 can be seen in Table 25.

Family guidance services

The success of the residential services was due in no small measure to the work of the family guidance services in supporting and coordinating services. Gradually the role of this division was developed to include administrative, counselling and support functions.

The administrative function involves acting as the initial enquiry service for ENCOR. A small team deals with approximately 30 enquiries per month, giving information on ENCOR's services. It is also responsible for keeping comprehensive records on all clients and vacancies.[8]

The counselling service is provided by 'neighbourhood advisors', the United Kingdom equivalent of a social worker. This person visits each new contact and decides on the most appropriate course of action for the individual. Further aspects of the 'neighbourhood advisors' role are to coordinate individual programmes and to carry out a regular assessment of the programmes every three months.[8]

The support services include arranging transport, organizing a toy library, coordinating voluntary services and maintaining a central record system.

Table 25.   Eastern Nebraska Community Office of Retardation (ENCOR) in 1977[8]

Population of five-county region served by ENCOR	569 000
ENCOR clients	
1976/7	891
active, July 1977	773
ENCOR staff, July 1977	
total	414
part-time	43
full-time	371
People who have returned to ENCOR region from Beatrice State institution since 1970	259
People from ENCOR region still in Beatrice State institution	290
People waiting for admission to Beatrice State institution	
1965	42
1977	0
Educational and vocational services	
ENCOR pre-school programmes, June 1977	9
Children served in these	60
Home training (0–3)	11
School age programme, June 1977	1
Children in this	5
Children moved into ordinary schools, 1976/7	57
Children in integrated pre-schools, 1976/7	96
ENCOR industrial training centres, June 1977	4
Clients served in these	217
ENCOR advanced training centre, June 1977	1
Clients served in this	42
ENCOR work stations in industry, June 1977	5
Clients working in these	73
Clients who moved into competitive employment, 1976	76
from ITCs	31
from community	45
Residential accommodation for children	
Training residences, July 1977	7
Children living in these	31
Developmental Maximation Unit, July 1977	1
Children living in these	6
Alternative Living Units, July 1977	32
Children Living in these	53
Residential accommodation for adults	
Training residences, July 1977	7
Clients living in these	31
Alternative living units, July 1977	64
Clients living in these	110

Table 25. Eastern Nebraska Community Office of Retardation (ENCOR) in 1977[8] *(continued)*

New clients given accommodation 1976/7	
Children and adults	42
Crisis assistance	
Children and adults given this help for a total of 1179 days	
(duplicated figure)	125

The four major divisions of education, vocation, residential and family guidance are supported by:

1. The staff development team responsible for the specialized training given to ENCOR staff.
2. The public education department that develops tape-slide and video tape recordings for use with the public.
3. The multi-disciplinary team of professional advisers which includes psychologists, nurses, occupational therapists, speech therapists and physiotherapists.
4. The planning department responsible for the long-term planning of ENCOR's services.
5. The administration department providing a general administrative service which includes clerical duties, accounting and purchasing, property management and a personnel function.

SUMMARY

This chapter has discussed the patterns of care for the mentally handicapped in Sweden, Denmark and East Nebraska in America. These examples were chosen as they show how a national or state system of care can move from a centralized pattern of segregated services to a decentralized pattern of integrated care in the community.[2] This progression towards a smaller-scale, more normal pattern of care was shown to develop through the four distinct stages of diagnosis, specialization, differentiation and decentralization and integration.[2] The rate of progress in achieving any level of integration depends on the guiding philosophy of those planning and organizing the services. In all of the examples of care discussed in this chapter the guiding principle has been that of normalization: the provision of as normal a life as possible for the mentally handicapped through normal living conditions and use of existing community facilities.[9] Normalization was also shown to be related to the ways in which other people interacted with the mentally handicapped.

Sweden's services for approximately 30 000 mentally handicapped children and adults are administered under a single authority and are based on a social model rather than a medical model.[3] The Swedish model of care provides a wide range of accommodation and services, hospitals, regional homes, local homes, group homes and fostering, designed to assist the mentally handicapped towards independence and integration.

The Danish model of care provides accommodation for approximately 22 000 mentally handicapped people and like Sweden is administered under a single authority.[6]

The Scandinavian system of care has been criticized in this country as being too lavish in terms of accommodation and therefore somehow inappropriate to the needs of the mentally handicapped. It is said that because the physical standards are so high they do not represent 'normal' conditions and that as a consequence it is more difficult for a mentally handicapped person to be integrated into the 'real' community. This view is not borne out by experience and the important lesson to be learned is how an imaginative system of care, catering for a wide range of handicap and based on the principle of normalization, can reduce the 'differences' between the general public and the mentally handicapped and help them to lead normal lives.[9]

ENCOR's pattern of care in East Nebraska represents a radical approach to the problem of institutionalization and segregation.[8] They provided a number of options for children and adults specifically tailored to meet individual needs. In doing this they missed out the third developmental stage of differentiation and moved directly to the stage of decentralization and integration. A major determinant in ENCOR's success was the existence of a single specialist agency, under the direction of a strong leadership with a workforce committed to the principle of normalization for the mentally handicapped. This gave rise to a degree of flexibility that enabled the rapid development or closure of a facility when a particular need arose.

ENCOR's programme suffered financial cutbacks and a number of services and personnel were lost. However, the services in East Nebraska continue to develop and change to meet the identified needs of their clients.

ENCOR's model of 'core and cluster' homes has been developed in the UK by the Dr Barnado's organization in Skelmersdale, Lancashire. The core home caters for six children who attend local ESN schools. Smaller 'cluster' houses or 'alternative living units', which relate to the core home, have been set up in the local community. The 'core' unit also offers a day-care service to local families with mentally handicapped children.

Each of the three systems of care has been subject to continuous monitoring to determine whether it continues to meet individual needs and reflect the philosophy of normalization. An analogy might be that each individual teaching programme needs to be based on accurate base-line measurement and firm objectives, in order that the programme is designed to suit the individual and progress can be evaluated. Precisely the same principle should be applied to the provision of services to assist the planning and implementation of a community based pattern of care.

The next chapter discusses the question of evaluation of services and measurement of the quality of care.

GLOSSARY

Alternative living unit	A special term devised by ENCOR to encourage their staff to 'think flexibly' about the development of new alternatives in accommodation and make more creative use of existing facilities.
Behaviour shaping unit	A unit set up by ENCOR to teach self-help and social skills to profoundly handicapped young people.
'Cooperative' playgroup	A type of integration at pre-school level. Similar to the British equivalent of an opportunity group.
Core and cluster home	A 'core' home which may be a staffed hostel which gives support and guidance to 'alternative living units' clustered around the core residence in the community.
Crisis assistance unit	A house providing emergency short-term care in times of crisis.
Crisis home	Emergency short-term fostering.
Decentralization	The fourth stage in the development of services described by Dr K. Grunewald and characterized by small locally-based autonomous units.
Developmental centre	The term used by ENCOR to describe the British equivalent of a special (ESN) school.
Developmental maximation unit	A special unit set up by ENCOR initially to provide 24-hour residential care for profoundly handicapped children. Later used as a diagnostic and assessment centre.
Diagnosis	The first stage in the development of services concerned with the formulation of plans and policies for the mentally handicapped.
Differentiation	The third stage in the development of services concerned with the development of a range of facilities designed to meet the different needs posed by varying degrees of mental handicap.
ENCOR	East Nebraska Community Office of Retardation.
GOARC	Greater Omaha Association for Retarded Children.
Medical model	The model of care which assumes that behaviour has a physiological cause and is therefore treatable by medical means.
Neighbourhood adviser	A term used by ENCOR to describe a social worker.

Normalization The principle which states that services, living conditions and life-style should be as normal as possible for the mentally handicapped.

Specialization The second stage in the development of services characterized by centralization of services, institutions and the medical model.

Structured correctional unit A special unit set up by ENCOR to care for mentally handicapped offenders.

Training residence The ENCOR term for small hostels.

Work stations Small units for the placement of mentally handicapped workers under the supervision of their own instructor in a normal work setting.

BIBLIOGRAPHY

1. Bank-Mikkelsen, N.E. (1970) Paper One. *The Quality of Care—Report of a Study Tour in Denmark.* London:NSMHC.
2. Grunewald, K. (1972) The guiding environment: the dynamic of residential living. In *The Handicapped Person in the Community*, ed. D.M. Boswell & J.N. Wingrove. London: Tavistock.
3. Grunewald, K. (1974) The practical experiences of settling the mentally handicapped in the community—the Swedish model. In *Experiments in the Rehabilitation of the Mentally Handicapped*, ed. H.C. Gunzburg. London: Butterworths.
4. Kendall, A. & Moss, P. (1972) *Integration or Segregation?—the Future of Educational and Residental Services for Mentally Handicapped Children.* London: Campaign for the Mentally Handicapped.
5. National Development Group (1978) *Helping Mentally Handicapped People in Hospital.* London: DHSS.
6. NHMHC (1970) Appendix 1: Statistical survey of the retardation services in Denmark. *The Quality of Care—Report of a Study Tour in Denmark.* London: NSMHC.
7. Shearer, A. (1970) Paper Three. *The Quality of Care—Report of a Study Tour in Denmark.* London: NHMHC.
8. Thomas, D. Firth, H. & Kendall, A. (1978) *ENCOR—A Way Ahead.* London: Campaign for the Mentally Handicapped.
9. Wolfensberger, W. (1972) *Normalisation*, Toronto: National Institute of Mental Retardation.

Measuring the quality of care

15

One of the major difficulties concerning the measurement of the quality of care is the apparent incompatibility of using objective measurement techniques to evaluate a subjective area such as the excellence or quality of care. For this reason, many research programmes and surveys, in the past, have shown a tendency to concentrate on such criteria as the number or amount of services available and the quality of the physical accommodation compared with a given standard. Vital factors such as staff attitudes and skills, care practices and the progress made by individuals receiving the care have not received so much attention.

However, in the last decade a number of studies have measured different aspects of the quality of care received by the mentally handicapped. This chapter briefly examines five approaches to measuring the quality of care, each reflecting a different bias and purpose.

The first of these reflects a sociological bias and is the study by King et al.[3] into child management practices in different institutions. The second research project reflects a behavioural bias and was carried out by the health care evaluation team in Wessex.[1,8] The aim of this study was to identify the variables that contributed to the acquisition of appropriate skills and relate these to the care practices used. A number of instruments or check lists have been designed to help organizations, groups or individuals assess particular aspects of care and the remaining three studies are examples of these. The third study is a unique contribution from the health care evaluation team (Wessex) and contains detailed rules for the setting up and maintenance of locally-based hospital units.[2] The rules, if implemented, represent standards of high quality care and enable an organization to monitor the quality of its services. The fourth piece of work was developed by ENCOR in America to evaluate its own services and is called programme analysis of service systems (PASS).[6] It is framed in the form of a number of questions related to normalization. Finally, as a result of the wide variation in services experienced in this country the National Society for Mentally Handicapped Children (NSHMC) has produced a checklist to help parents evaluate the quality of local care provision.[5]

Any system of care should provide opportunities for development of those skills leading to a measure of independence. This view is reflected in the definition of the quality of care which will be used in this chapter. This states that the quality of care is the extent to which a person is enabled to function in a particular setting as a result of the care received.

THE SOCIOLOGICAL APPROACH[3]

Chapter 4 gives a brief description of the study by King et al.[3] and shows how care practices may affect the learning of children. The background to the study was the belief that the way the institution or home was organized determined the care practices of the unit and that these practices significantly affected the behaviour of the children.

In the course of their research, which lasted five years, from 1963 to 1968, King, Raynes and Tizard studied over a hundred residential units in 26 institutions and homes. So that objective comparisons could be made between the care practices found in different types of institutions, a 30-item child management rating scale was devised. This measured aspects of care such as rigidity of routine, block treatment, depersonalization and social distance. The scores achieved on this scale showed whether the unit was institutionally oriented or child-oriented in its care practices. Not surprisingly, the hospital units were shown to be institutionally oriented and the hostels and voluntary homes were more child oriented.

The Revised Child Management Scale[3]

The Revised Child Management scale consisted of 30 items which are reproduced here. Scoring categories are given for each item. A score of 0 indicates child-orientation; a score of 2 indicates institution-orientation; a score of 1 indicates a mixed pattern. This section is reproduced from the work of King et al.[3]

Rigidity of routine

Management practices are institutionally-oriented when they are inflexible from one day to the next and from one inmate to another; individuals in different situations are treated as though they were in the same situation and changes in circumstances are not taken into account. Management practices are child-oriented when they are flexible, being adapted to take into account differences among the children or different circumstances.

1. Do the children aged 5 years and over get up at the same time at weekends as they do during the week?

    0 Different times for all on 2 days
    1 Different for some, or on 1 day only
    2 Same time

2. Do the children aged 5 years and over go to bed at the same time at weekends as they do during the week?

   0 Different times for all on 2 days
   1 Different for some, or on 1 day only
   2 Same time

3. Do they use the yard or garden at set times?

   0 No, whenever they like
   1 Under various conditions
   2 Yes, set times only

4. Do they use their bedrooms at set times?

   0 No, whenever they like
   1 Under various conditions
   2 Yes, set times only

5. Are there set times when visitors can come to the unit?

   0 Any time (except during specified times)
   1 Any day, but set times
   2 Certain days only

6. Which children are routinely toileted at night?

   0 None/some only once
   1 Some more than once
   2 All once or more

'Block treatment'

Child management practices are institutionally oriented if the children are regimented, that is, all dealt with as a group, before, during or after any specific activity. These practices involve queuing and waiting around, with large groups of other children and with no mode of occupation during the waiting period. Management practices may be described as child-orientated where the organization of activity is such that residents are allowed to participate or not as they please, and where they are allowed to do things at their own pace.

7. After getting dressed, do the children wait around doing nothing?

   0 No, they are occupied
   1 Some wait doing nothing
   2 Everybody waits doing nothing

8. Do they wait in line before coming in for breakfast?

   0 None wait
   1 Some wait
   2 All wait

9. Do they wait together as a group before bathing?

   0 None wait, all occupied elsewhere
   1 Some wait, or mixed pattern
   2 All wait

10. Do they wait together after bathing?

   0 None wait, return individually
   1 Some wait, or mixed pattern
   2 All wait

11. How do they return from the toilet?

   0 Individually
   1 In groups, or mixed pattern
   2 All together

12. Do they sit waiting at tables before the meal is served (tea or evening ¦ meal)?

   0 Less than 5 minutes (mean day 1 and day 2)
   1 6–10 minutes
   2 More than 10 minutes

13. Do they sit waiting at tables after the meal is finished and before the next activity (tea or evening meal)?

   0 Less than 7 minutes (mean day 1 and day 2)
   1 8–14 minutes
   2 15 or more minutes

14. How are the children organized when they go on walks?

   0 Taken a few at a time
   1 All at once, but in separate groups
   2 In 'crocodiles' or similar

De-personalization

Child management practices may be seen as institutionally-oriented when there are no opportunities for residents to have personal possessions or personal privacy. De-personalization is also shown where there is an absence of opportunities for self-expression, or of situations in which initiative on the part of the child may be shown. Where there are opportunities for residents to show initiative, to have personal possessions, to be alone if they so desire, the child management practices may be described as child-oriented.

15. What is done with the children's private clothing?

    0 Kept and used by children
    1 Used only on visits, special occasions
    2 Not used or not allowed

16. What is done with the children's private toys?

    0 Kept and used by children
    1 Kept for a time, but become communal
    2 Not used or not allowed

17. How many of the children possess *all* of the following articles of cloth-ing; shirt or blouse, trousers or skirt, jacket, jumper, topcoat, shoes, dressing gown, slippers?

    0 67-100%
    1 34-66%
    2 0-33%

18. Whereabouts do they keep their daily clothes?

    0 In private provision
    1 In shared provision, supplied weekly
    2 In communal provision, supplied daily

19. How many children have toys or books of their own?

    0 67-100%
    1 34-66%
    2 0%-33%

20. Do they have pictures, pin-ups, photos in rooms?

    0 Yes, in all rooms
    1 In some rooms
    2 No

21. How much time do they have for playing?

    0 At least half an hour each day of observation
    1 At least quarter of an hour each day of observation
    2 Less than this

22. How are the children's birthdays celebrated?

    0 Individual presents or parties
    1 Mixed pattern
    2 Joint parties or no recognition

23. How are tables laid for meals? (tea or evening meal)

    0 Tables laid for all children
    1 Tables laid for some children
    2 Not laid, food and spoon handed out by staff

Social distance

Management practices are institutionally-oriented when there is a sharp separation between the staff and inmate worlds. This may be because separate areas of accommodation are kept for the exclusive use of staff or because interaction between staff and children is limited to formal, and functionally specific, activities. Child-orientation involves the reduction of social distance by the sharing of living space and allows staff and children to interact in functionally diffuse and informal situations.

24. Do the children have any access to the kitchen?

    0 67-100%
    1 34-66%
    2 0-33%

25. Do the children have access to other areas?

    0 Yes, no restrictions
    1 To some areas
    2 No, doors are kept locked

26. How do staff assist children at toilet times?

    0 One staff member for each child
    1 Mixed pattern
    2 'Conveyor-belt' system
       (Conveyor-belt system means that one child passes through the hands of two or more members of staff during this routine.)

27. How do staff assist children at bath times?

    0 One staff member for each child
    1 Mixed pattern
    2 'Conveyor-belt' system

28. Do staff on duty eat with the children (tea or evening meal)?

    0 All staff (at least sometimes)
    1 Some staff, or sit but don't eat
    2 Stand, serve and supervise only

29. Do staff on duty sit and watch TV with the children?

   0 Someone usually does
   1 Someone sometimes does
   2 Sporadic supervision only

30. How many children have been on outings with the staff in the last 3 months?

   0 67-100%
   1 34-66%
   2 0-33%

Initially, the research was carried out in four large institutions, two children's homes and two hospitals, one of which was a mental handicap hospital and the other a paediatric hospital. As a result of this initial work a further survey was carried out in order to 'quantify some aspects of organizational structure, to explore their inter-relations and especially to examine their relationship to patterns of care'.[3]

As a starting point, King et al. formulated thirteen hypotheses which they felt would explain the differences in patterns of care noted between the hospitals and hostels. The findings of the survey are briefly summarized below:

1. The first hypothesis was that there would be significant differences in the care practices in the different types of institution. This was proved with the hospital wards having high (institutionally oriented) scores and the hostels having low (child-oriented) scores on the child management rating scale.

2. The second hypothesis stated that there was no relationship between the degree of handicap and the care practices. On a level this was substantiated although there were difficulties in interpretation. For example, the children in hospital were usually more handicapped than those in hostels, but even so differences in care practices were observed in groups of children of a similar degree of handicap in different institutions.

3, 4. The third and fourth hypotheses stated that the differences in care practices were not related to the size of the institution (3) or the living unit (4). These hypotheses were proved.

5. The fifth hypothesis stated that there was no relationship between the number of staff allocated to a unit and the care practices of the unit. This was substantiated and the example given of a hospital ward with a staff ratio of 1:3 with a significantly higher score than another hospital ward with a staff ratio 1:8.

6. The sixth hypothesis held that in a child-oriented unit, the staff would be used more effectively taking account of peak periods of activity. This hypothesis was substantiated with institutionally oriented units showing the same staff ratios during slack periods as during peak periods.

7. The seventh hypothesis was that, in child-oriented units, there would be greater staff stability than in institutionally oriented units. This again was proved and was thought to be due to a higher turnover rate of staff and the fact that learner nurses were allocated to a unit for a limited period. Indeed, it was estimated that in some hospitals in the survey a child may have to adjust to a hundred or more adults in a year.

8. The eighth hypothesis concerned the role of senior staff and stated that the head of a child-oriented unit would spend more time involved in activities related to the care of the children, whilst the head of an institutionally oriented unit would spend more time involved in administration. This was borne out in the survey and is related to the following hypotheses.

9. The ninth hypothesis concerned not just the amount of time heads of units spent with the children, but stated that in child-oriented units the interaction would be more frequent and warmer than in institutionally oriented units. This was substantiated with the findings that in a child-oriented unit the heads 'spoke to the children one and a half times as often, were twice as likely to accept, and three times less likely to reject the children than the heads of institutionally oriented units'.[3]

10. The tenth hypothesis predicted that in child-oriented units the junior staff would be involved in much the same activities as the head of the unit. In contrast it was predicted that in institutionally oriented units there would be more 'specialised division of labour'.[3] This was found to be true.

11. The eleventh hypothesis was related to the ninth and concerned the warmth and frequency of interaction by the junior staff of the unit with the children in their care. The findings were similar to those in the ninth hypothesis in that the junior staff in child-oriented units spoke to the children more frequently and rejected the children less than the junior staff in institutionally oriented units.

12. The twelfth hypothesis stated that there was a relationship between the degree of involvement with the children and the amount of responsibility given to the unit heads. This was 'provisionally confirmed' in that it was found that the heads of units such as hostels had more autonomy than their counterparts in hospitals, which is linked to the findings in the eighth, ninth and tenth hypotheses.

13. The thirteenth hypothesis concerned the relationship between the level of interaction with the children and the type of training received by the staff. It was predicted that high rates of staff/child interaction were a consequence of child care training and low rates of interaction were associated with traditional nurse training. The findings supported this hypothesis in every case.

The research by King, Raynes and Tizard has shown that the quality of care is determined and maintained by a number of inter-related factors which are often different from those traditionally held to be important to high quality care.[7] Factors such as the size of institutions and living units and the level of staffing were not found to be significant in providing child-oriented care, whilst factors such as the structural and functional organization of the unit and the type of training received by the staff were highly significant.[7]

THE BEHAVIOURAL APPROACH

The sociological bias of the research precluded concentration, to any degree, on the effects of the different care practices on individual children.[3] Research carried out in Wessex by the health care evaluation team describes a method of measuring the quality of care directly related to the individual child's or adult's progress.[1,8]

The Health Care Evaluation Team in Wessex decided that 'high'-quality care should mean that mentally handicapped children will develop and maintain appropriate behavioural skills and lose inappropriate behaviour.[8] In other words, they would make progress as a consequence of living in a particular environment. Mentally handicapped people experiencing high-quality care will have more opportunities to acquire and develop new skills and be more likely to receive social reinforcement from the staff for appropriate behaviour.[4] This behavioural approach led to the formulation of the general hypothesis that most of the behaviour of the mentally handicapped in residential care is determined and maintained by staff attention. The hypothesis led to the classification of both child and staff behaviours. The classification of child behaviours was necessary to differentiate between those behaviours judged to be appropriate and those thought to be inappropriate.[8]

1. Appropriate behaviour: any active adaptive behaviour in which it is likely that new skills will be acquired.

2. Neutral behaviour: any totally passive behaviour (sitting on chair etc.) or behaviour which has very little impact on the physical environment (bizarre hand movements etc.), or behaviours which are already highly developed and embedded in the client's repertoire (e.g. walking for a completely mobile child).[1]

3. Inappropriate behaviour: any behaviour which is socially unacceptable but is not very destructive of the physical environment (screaming, chewing toys etc.).[1]

4. Disruptive behaviour: any behaviour which is likely to, or does, cause physical damage to the client or others (biting, hitting self or others etc.) or which does cause physical damage to furniture or fittings (pulling down curtains etc.).[1]

In addition child behaviour was further classified into degrees of mobility as this affected the child's ability to interact with members of staff.[8]

Staff behaviour was classified into the two categories of either paying attention to the child or not paying attention. Staff attention includes verbal and physical contact which may also take the form of prompts and cues used in teaching appropriate behaviour.[1]

The application of these classifications to the research in measuring the quality of care gave rise to a more specific hypothesis. 'The quality of residential care is "high" if, among a group of clients, a high proportion of their appropriate, and a low proportion of their neutral, inappropriate and disruptive behaviour is followed by staff contact. The converse follows in units providing "low" quality of care'.[8]

A pilot study was carried out to test the validity of the hypothesis.[1] The method used to quantify both child and staff behaviour was time sampling. This involved a trained observer 'sampling' a five-minute period, recording the child's behaviour under the headings of disruptive, inappropriate, neutral and appropriate (DINA) and the staff behaviour under the headings of physical and verbal contact and the type of cue or prompt used. The pilot study showed that the scores obtained were reliable.[1]

A further requirement of the measures to test the quality of care was that they should be capable of discriminating between the quality of care in different units. To achieve this, a number of indices were formulated so that accurate comparisons could be made, and these are outlined below.[1]

1. The behaviour index measures the proportion of time children spend behaving appropriately.
2. The contact index measures the proportion of time during which staff contacts are given to all classes of child behaviour.
3. The reinforcement index measures the proportion of appropriate child behaviour followed by staff contact.
4. The efficiency index measures the proportion of staff contact following appropriate child behaviour.
5. The cue index measures the proportion of time during which staff give cues to appropriate child behaviour.
6. The discrimination index measures the proportion of appropriate child behaviour followed by staff contact less the proportion of neutral and inappropriate and disruptive behaviour followed by staff contact.

In the pilot study mentioned above two children's units were compared using the indices as a measure. The children's day was divided into defined activity periods: getting up, breakfast, recreation (1), lunch, recreation (2), tea and going to bed (3). On completion of the pilot study the indices were shown to discriminate clearly between the quality of care found in the two units.[1] The research described above is an extremely sophisticated method of evaluating and measuring the quality of care in a residential setting. It involves the classification of child and staff behaviour, the coding of these behaviours by specially trained observers and the interpretation of the collected data in terms of discriminative indices. It represents a breakthrough in enabling a scientific measure of the abstract concept of quality and care.

THE SELF-ASSESSMENT APPROACH

The self-assessment approach is usually seen at two levels. The first level is organizational and enables large organizations and groups to evaluate the quality of existing services and care practices and to plan new services in keeping with high-quality care. Applied at organizational level this approach has the advantage of helping to ensure a consistent standard of high-quality care across a large area with a wide range of residential care options.

The second level is individual and personal and enables parents and professionals to evaluate local provision in terms of the quality of care, both existing and required, so that they may discuss individual instances with those responsible for providing the care.

The remainder of this chapter discusses three examples of the self-assessment approach to the evaluation of the quality of care in residential settings.

Health Care Evaluation Team[2]

The Health Care Evaluation Team have developed a comprehensive set of criteria or rules which may be either used as a check-list for individual components of a unit or as a 'specific list of rules for the Wessex locally based hospital units'.[2] There are 99 rules evaluating 12 dimensions of residential care. An example selected from each dimension or aspect of care is given below.[2]

'Location   The size of the catchment area is based on epidemiological estimates of the prevalence of eligible clients which will yield a 'demand' for residential care places equal to the provision.

'Design   (a) Sufficient number of toilets and wash basins near both day and bedroom spaces, upstairs and downstairs and accessible without intervening locked doors.
                   (b) No special treatment or assessment rooms, e.g. physiotherapy or clinical rooms.

'Transfer   In the event of a parental request for a client to go out for the day or sleep nights at home, the person in charge of the unit may authorise this.

'Establishment   The managers of the unit will recognise alternative qualifi-
and recruitment   cations to nursing for the positions of Persons in Charge and Deputy Person in Charge. They may appoint a person who holds one or more of the following:
                   1. S.R.N., R.N.M.S., R.M.N., etc.
                   2. Teaching certificate
                   3. Certificate in child care
                   4. Certificate of the Nursery Nurse Examination Board

5. National Association for Mental Health diploma
6. Experience in residential social work

'Maintenance of
recruitment

The managers of the unit will organise a three months induction course for all staff prior to the opening of each unit and thereafter an in-service course of training for all subsequent newly appointed staff.

'Staff terms
of service

Managers may promote non-nurse house-parents to the positions of person in charge and deputy person in charge on the basis of good experience and good performance.

'Staff allocation

PIC will nominate individual care staff to look after small groups of clients throughout the day.

'Performance of
managers

Managers will secure the agreement of designated local specialists, responsible for providing services to the resident population of the catchment area, to provide services to the residents of the unit, e.g. these will include psychologist, social worker, paediatrician.

'Performance
of external
professionals

External specialists will inform family of results of investigations and plan with parents a long-term programme (life-long for SSN clients).

'Performance
of person in
charge

Plan the daily routine so that:
1. Times of getting up and going to bed, types of food and clothing relate to the client preferences and programme objectives.
2. Activities are arranged and transition periods scheduled (e.g. recreation to lunch) to promote the active participation of all clients, including the most severely handicapped and disruptive.
3. Activities are scheduled to promote the active participation of all clients all the time, even on wet days and weekends.
4. Children or adults are allowed to spend time alone in their bedrooms or in a reading room.

'Performances of
direct care staff

The DC staff will teach skills to the clients. They will encourage and help clients to do as much as possible for themselves at all time, and will only do a task for a client when it is not possible to set the occasion for the client to do it himself. The areas in which skills must be taught include washing and bathing, toiletting, brushing and combing hair, cleaning teeth, cutting nails, dressing, serving meals and eating, bedmaking and going to bed.

'Contact with   Parents and relatives will be able to participate in activities
the community   with their children and relatives both in the unit and out-
                  side. They may take clients home to stay at night, or out
                  for the day, or on holiday.'

The full value of the report is that it sets out in detail the benefits of implementing the rules and the consequences if there is failure to implement them, or
if they do not exist. The rules provide detailed guidelines for setting up and
maintaining high-quality residential facilities for the mentally handicapped. Use
of the rules as a check-list will help relatives, staff, planners and researchers to
define, discuss and implement proposals for providing facilities for residential
care.[2] Finally, the rules provide a systematic method of evaluating existing and
proposed facilites by comparing them with the Wessex locally-based hospital
units in performance terms.

Programme Analysis of Service Systems (PASS)[6]

The previous chapter described the services for the mentally handicapped in
East Nebraska through the state agency of the East Nebraska Community
Office of Retardation (ENCOR). A feature of ENCOR's philosophy was the
flexibility of approach brought about as a result of a self-critical approach—'a
system of helping services is no stronger than the systems to monitor its quality'.[6]

The emphasis in PASS is on whether ENCOR's residential facilities and
services are in accord with the principle of normalization. PASS is designed in
the form of a series of questions which focus on attitudes and practices related
to 'integration; age appropriate structures; culturally appropriate structures; the
degree of specialisation in residential facilities and programmes; developmental
growth and the quality of the setting or atmosphere'. A summary of PASS
follows.[6]

'A system of helping services is simply no stronger than the systems to
monitor its quality. But what to look for—that's the question.

'Training as a PASS rater involves a lengthy process. It's well worth it because
one's approach to human services will never be quite the same after PASS. The
purpose here, though, is to focus on the attitudes and observations imbedded
in this evaluation tool. While complex, PASS leads the advocate to ask questions
which often boil down to the simple maxim of whether a person would want to
be treated in the same way.

'ASK YOURSELF THESE QUESTIONS ABOUT OUR HOSTELS, HOUSES
AND SERVICES*
'INTEGRATION — to take part in the mainstream. To be accepted by peers.
Size or Dispersal
   1. Are there so many handicapped persons being served that the surrounding
      community is not able to accept them?

2. Is the number of people servied in a residence so large that the people don't go outside for their personal relationships?

Program and Facility Labels
1. Does the sign outside tell that the people inside are "different"?
2. Would the labels produce a negative or hopeless feeling among most people?

Social Opportunities
1. Does the handicapped person interact with non-handicapped persons; where he lives? Where he works or goes to school? In his free time? When he shops, attends church, and the like?

'AGE APPROPRIATE STRUCTURES – to be valued by others as a true peer.
Facilities, Design and Decorations
1. Is the facility, the design of the facility and wall decorations appropriate for the age of the persons being served? Are adults living or working in child-like settings?

Possessions
1. Are the possessions owned by the handicapped person appropriate to his age? Does what an adult owns make him appear child-like?
2. Are attempts being made by staff to encourage their clients to own age appropriate possessions?
3. Is there appropriate space where a person lives for the possessions he owns?

Labels and Forms of Address
1. Are handicapped adults addressed as though they were children? Is a a child-like nickname used, such as Tommy or Bobby?
2. Are labels such as kid, child, youngster used when referring to a handicapped child?
3. Does the staff use a tone of voice with handicapped adults that would be used with children?

Activities and Routines
1. Are handicapped persons engaged in activities that are appropriate for their age? Do adults work during the day? Is a child's school sessions limited to two hours?
2. Are the daily routines of handicapped persons typical and age appropriate? Is an adult given a coffee break – or is it a recess? Is a nap scheduled during a child's school day?

Autonomy (self direction) and Rights
1. Are handicapped persons given a chance to make input into decisions regarding their lives? Who makes the decisions in a person's life?
2. Are handicapped persons assisted in becoming independent rather than dependent? Will he need just as much support six months from now?

3. Do handicapped persons exercise more rights as they grow older?
4. Are handicapped persons encouraged to exercise their rights, such as voting or privacy?
5. Are rights removed only where there has been a determination of reduced competency in the area to be limited? Is the restricting of a person's rights used only as a last resort? Are there other alternatives?

Sex Behaviour
1. Do handicapped interact with the opposite sex? Are they given time alone?
2. Are handicapped persons given support to understand their sexual identity? As a life long process, does it begin at an early age?
3. Is counselling available to handicapped adults who may need assistance about dating, marriage, and birth control?

Personal Appearance
1. How typical of his age is a handicapped person's hair style and clothing? Are there subtle mannerisms that make him look different than his peers?

'CULTURE APPROPRIATE STRUCTURES – to know and respond to local customs
Labels and Forms of Address
1. Are labels or forms of address used for handicapped persons which are demeaning, devaluing and implying inferiority? Does the form of address show the person to be valued as an equal?
2. Are handicapped persons labelled by their diagnosis, such as "he is an epileptic" or "his is a retardate"?
3. Are courtesy and respect towards handicapped persons lacking when staff talk to them?
4. In his presence, is a handicapped person talked about as a third party? Does the conversation go on as if he were not there?

Personal Appearance
1. Are staff committed to correct physical defects which make a person look different?
2. What is being done to help handicapped persons and bizarre mannerisms such as self-mutilation, extreme destructiveness, and repetitive behaviours? Do these measures work? Is there a persistent and creative effort to try again?

'SPECIALIZATION – to meet the needs of each person at his particular stage of growth.
1. Is the program designed to meet the specific needs of every handicapped person?
2. As needs change, how does the program change?
3. Is a person regressing because he does not fit into the group by reason of his age, ability or behaviour?

4. Is the activity being done in an appropriate setting under the right need?
5. Does the staff have what it takes in skills and attitudes to meet the specific needs?

'DEVELOPMENTAL GROWTH – to enable a person to learn at his own pace.
Physical Overprotection
1. Are physical features built into the facility to prevent handicapped persons' movement?
2. How are situations involving risk used to prompt growth?

Social Overprotection
1. Is control so emphasized or challenging opportunities so lacking that an individual's growth is restricted?
2. Are there some rules in the program that non-handicapped people would not tolerate?
3. Are handicapped persons denied new experience because "they are unable to handle them"?

Intensity of Programming
1. Is there a conviction among the staff that handicapped people are growing? Do their records prove growth is taking place?
2. Is the teaching effort reorganized? Does it push people to their potential?
3. When growth is stalled, where is the responsibility placed – on the person's handicap or the staff's lack of creativity?

'QUALITY OF SETTING – to create an atmosphere where a person feels comfortable and accepted.
Physical Comfort
1. Is the furniture and physical environment comfortable?
2. Is the temperature controlled? Is it quiet? Do the people like the food?
3. If a home, does it have a "lived-in" quality?
4. "Would *I* feel comfortable if I worked or lived in this place"?

Environmental Beauty
1. Has attention been paid to the appearance of the surroundings? Do the efforts show good taste? What about details?
2. "Is this place pleasing enough to have my family live there?"

Individualization
1. What evidence is there that people are encouraged to express themselves in their own way?
2. Is there a place where a person can be alone?
3. Do people usually do things as a group?
4. Do the individualized program plans reflect the differences in people?
5. Is it evident that staff appreciate individuals as having their own rich personality?

Interactions

1. What interaction is going on between clients, staff and the public? Is it warm, or cold and distant?
2. Are there individual friends among staff and clients? Are people listened to?
3. Who seems left out?
4. 'Would I be happy here?'

National Society for Mentally Handicapped Children (NSMHC)[5]

As a result of the wide variation in the services provided by the statutory authorities, the NSMHC has produced Stamina Paper No. 3, which is in the form of a check-list, designed to help parents evaluate local residential provision for the mentally handicapped.[5] It starts from the assumption that the parents of the mentally handicapped have a right to choose residential provision for their children and outlines some of the choices available.[5] It summarizes the responsibility of the local authority social services and the health services.

There are separate check-lists for children under sixteen and for adults. The check-list for children covers services for those living at home, in foster homes and in residential care in hostels and homes. The adult check-list identifies those services which should be available for those living at home or in residential care in hostels/homes/group homes.[5] However, the paper is most than just a checklist of desirable qualities in homes and is concerned with aspects of care such as the quality of life, opportunities for development and learning and the help needed to make full use of community facilities. The Stamina Paper follows.

'Services for the mentally handicapped provided by Statutory Authorities vary considerably from one part of the country to another and many parents are un-acquainted with the quality and standard of services which the authorities should provide.

'For this reason the National Society has produced a series of "check-lists" to enable parents to evaluate the provision made locally.

'The best services for the mentally handicapped are likely to be achieved through a clear evaluation of what is provided now, and an agreement between parents and authorities on what is required. Where parents are conscious of serious deficiencies in existing services, these should be a matter of urgent and constructive discussion with the appropriate authorities.

'INTRODUCTION

'1. This paper assumes that parents of the mentally handicapped (and the mentally handicapped themselves as they grow older) have a right to a choice of residential provision.

'2. The choice should include:

Living at home	Group Homes (with support)
Living with foster parents (for the under 16's)	Group Homes (unstaffed)
	Subnormality Hospitals

Residental Nurseries   Independent living
Hostels   Village Communities

'3. Statutory responsibility for providing residential care for the mentally handicapped is divided thus:

Local Authority Social Service Departments are responsible for the welfare of all the mentally handicapped who are able to live in the community (e.g. in their own home, in hostels, group homes, etc.). See Section 5 below.

The Area Health Authority is responsible for those who require medical and nursing care.

Finance has been provided by central Government for the joint planning of certain facilities to be undertaken by Local Authorities and Health Authorities and Voluntary Organisations acting together to meet local needs (DHSS Circular HC.77/17).

'Regulations governing the establishment of Joint Care Planning Teams provide for the representation of voluntary organisations. Local Societies should (in consultation with the Regional Officer) ensure that they are represented on such Teams locally.

'4. Provision of residential care is therefore, in the first instance, the responsibility of the Director of Social Services who will have a specialist officer responsible for residential services.

'5. The main duties of the Social Services Department of a Local Authority are outlined in the following legislation:

National Assistance Act 1948, Mental Health Act 1959 and the Chronically Sick and Disabled Persons Act 1970.

'National Assistance Act 1948
'It should be the duty of every Local Authority to provide.

'1. Residential accommodation for persons who by reason of age, infirmity or any other circumstances are in need of care and attention which is not otherwise available to them.

'2. Temporary accommodation for persons who are in urgent need thereof, being need arising in circumstances which could not reasonably have been foreseen or in such other circumstances as the authority may in any particular case determine (Section 21).

'Mental Health Act 1959

    Part 1   Persons with whom the Act deals.
    Part 2   Local Authority service.
    Part 3   Registration of Mental Nursing Homes and Residential Homes.
    Part 4   Compulsory Admission to Hospital and Guardianship.
    Part 5   Admission of Patients concerned in Criminal Proceedings, etc.
    Part 6   Removal and Return of Patients within the United Kingdom, etc.
    Part 7   Special Hospitals.
    Part 8   Management of Property and Affairs of Patients.

'*Chronically Sick and Disabled Persons Act 1970*
Section I   Information as to need for an existence of Welfare Services, e.g., family support services.
Section II   Provision of Welfare Services, e.g., practical assistance; aids; holidays; telephone, etc.

'MENTALLY HANDICAPPED CHILDREN UNDER 16
'*Living At Home*
'For the mentally handicapped who live at home the following services are essential. Check:

'1. That there is regular full support from relevant specialist services, e.g., paediatrician, speech therapist, psychologist, psychiatrist, physio-therapist.

'2. That there is regular support from specialist social worker and/or health visitor. This should include visits at home at intervals of not more than two months.

'3. That visits are covered by regular reports to the appropriate authority and available to parents.

'4. That there is continuing counselling and advice, short-term relief, clinics, opportunity classes, etc.

'5. That full information regarding statutory benefits and services of all kinds is readily available and is conveyed to parents by specialist social workers.

'6. That priority placement on local authority housing lists is available to families with a severely mentally handicapped child.

'7. That parent "workshops", to assist parents with the care of their child, are organised, and aware that support services for families should be provided by the Local Authority.

'8. That a full laundry service is available.

'9. That special equipment, draw sheets, nappies, suitable wheelchairs, washing machines is available.

'10. That adaptions to the home in the form of ramps to door-ways, hoists, etc., are available if required.

'11. That home help and other kinds of support for families are available.

'12. That local short-term care is available regularly, overnight, for weekends, Mondays to Fridays, or in emergencies.

'13. That options for short-term care include foster homes and children's homes.

'14. That there is a "day care" programme available throughout all school holidays.

'15. That any child, irrespective of how difficult, if managed by the parents, has access to short-term facilities.

'16. That local authority social and leisure activities are developed or that financial support is given to voluntary agencies.

'Foster Homes

'All the supporting services listed for the child living at home should also apply to foster homes. Check in addition:

'17. That foster parents receive financial remuneration on an agreed scale together with appropriate supplementary finance for clothing, holidays, etc.

'18. That the local authority provides regular supervision and support for foster parents.

'19. That foster homes are the subject of a regular visit by a specialist social worker.

'20. That links between foster parents and natural parents are maintained where possible.

'21. That foster parents are encouraged to join, and made welcome in the relevant Local Society for Mentally Handicapped Children.

'Residential Care in Hostels and Homes

'22. That all parents have full details of local authority options for residential care, inside or outside their area.

'23. That the selection of options and policy on placement is jointly decided. That parents and/or nearest relatives together with the supervisory staff who will have responsibility for the resident, are always included in such joint decisions.

'24. That in each local authority area there is a sufficient number of places in residential homes to meet the needs of all the mentally handicapped children requiring residential care, including those at present in subnormality hospitals.

'25. That all sources of placement have been properly investigated. (Social Service Departments may use provisions outside their own area until they are themselves able to offer the full range.)

'26. That full assessment of educational and social potential and of physical and emotional needs of each entrant for residential placement is made, or is available prior to or immediately after placement.

'27. That children with severe behaviour difficulties are provided with suitable hostel accommodation and appropriate therapy.

'28. That provision is in ordinary houses, local to the child's home where possible.

'29. That, whatever the size of the house accommodation is so arranged that residents live in groups of not more than five.

'30. That hostel accommodation offers a variety of rooms—to be alone or to share.

'31. That hostels should contain no more than fifteen children.

'32. That hostels are mixed-sex.

'33. That there is space for recreational and leisure activities.

'34. That there is a warm, domestic atmosphere.

'35. That furniture is of a varied and not "institutional" nature.

'36. That the kitchen and laundry is household in character.

'37. That a resident's privacy is respected.

'38. That toilets and bathrooms have adequate privacy.

'39. That the approach of "learning through doing" is accepted as the philosophy of the staff.

'40. That leisure activities involve relationships outside the hostel.

'41. That there is on-going contact with the family of every resident in a home or hostel.

'42. That parents, other relatives and friends, are encouraged to visit.

'43. That senior staff in homes or hostels have relevant experience and training.

'44. That there is support for the staff from professional specialist workers.

'45. That specialist services are available as required (speech therapist, psychologist, etc.).

'46. That there is regular monitoring, and evaluation at least annually, by the local authority of the standard provided in local authority homes.

'47. That parents and relatives are involved in regular discussions on their son's or daughter's development.

'48. That the Local Society for Mentally Handicapped Children keeps in close touch with the staff and residents and that staff are encouraged in this by the Local Authority.

'49. That homes funded by private individuals or voluntary organisations are given the same degree of support and supervision by Local Authorities or Health Authorities, as is provided for official services.

'50. That there is regular contact between the residential home and the special school, especially to exchange information regarding assessments.

'51. That these assessments are in writing—(adequate records are essential for new staff and to facilitate transfer to new residences when desirable)—and that all involved in joint consultation and decision-making, including parents, receive copies.

'52. That while no residential placement should become a "dead-end", the child's need for security and continuity of residence is considered.

'RESIDENTIAL CARE OF MENTALLY HANDICAPPED ADULTS

"The mentally retarded person has the same rights as other citizens of the same country and the same age."

General and Special Rights of the Mentally Retarded. Approved by the United Nations.

'This paper deals with current services and provisions (1978) which should enable mentally handicapped adults to enjoy more fully, their life in the community.

'Since how a person lives is more important than where a person lives, the Paper takes as self-evident, the unalienable right of each of these men and women to be provided with opportunities, and the help that is needed to make realistic use of them, whether living at home, in groups, or alone.

'Living At Home
'For the mentally handicapped who lives at home, the following services are essential. Check:

'1. That there is regular full support from specialist services, e.g., speech therapists, psychiatrist, psychologist, physiotherapist.

'2. That there is regular support from a specialist social worker. This should include visits at home at intervals of not more than two months.

'3. That visits are covered by regular reports to the appropriate authority and available to parents.

'4. That there is regular counselling and advice, with social work support and short-term relief.

'5. That full information regarding statutory benefits of all kinds is readily available and is conveyed to the mentally handicapped person and to parents by specialist social workers.

'6. That priority placement on local authority housing lists is available to families with a severely mentally handicapped adult son or daughter.

'7. That parent "workshops" are organised to assist parents to adjust to the changing needs of their adult son or daughter.

'8. That parents are aware of opportunities for their son or daughter to live independently of the family and that the individually mentally handicapped adult is entitled to specialist services provided by the Local Authority. Check in addition:

'9. That full laundry service is available.

'10. That special equipment (draw sheets, incontinent pads/aids, suitable wheelchairs, washing machines) is available on demands.

'11. That adaptions to the home in the form of ramps to doorways, hoists etc., are available if required.

'12. That home help and other kinds of support for families are available.

'13. That short-term local care is available regularly, overnight, for weekends, Mondays to Fridays, or in emergencies.

'14. That "fostering" in private families is a possible short-term option.

'15. That any adult son or daughter, irrespective of how difficult, if managed by the parents, has access to short-term facilities.

'16. That Local Authority social and leisure activities are developed or that financial support is given to voluntary agencies.

'Residential Care in Hostels/Homes/Group Homes
'17. That full assessment of educational and social potential and of physical and emotional needs of each entrant for residential placement, is made or is available prior to or immediately after placement.

'18. That parents and mentally handicapped adults are provided with full details of local authority options for residential care inside or outside their area.

'19. That the selection of options and policy on placement is jointly decided.

That the individual adult, parents or nearest relatives together with the supervisory staff, who will have responsibility for the resident, are always included in such joint decisions.

'20. That in each local authority area there is a sufficient number of places in residential homes to meet the needs of all the mentally handicapped requiring residential care including those at present in subnormality hospitals who could live in the community.

'21. That mentally handicapped adults with severe behaviour difficulties are not excluded from residential care in the community.

'22. That homes are in ordinary houses, local to the adult mentally handicapped person's home area where possible.

'23. That hostel accommodation offers a variety of rooms—to be alone or to share.

'24. That hostels should contain no more than fifteen residents.

'25. That hostels are mixed-sex.

'26. That there is space for recreational and leisure activities.

'27. That there is a warm domestic atmosphere.

'28. That furniture is of a varied and not "institutional" nature.

'29. That the kitchen and laundry is "household" in character and can be used by the residents.

'30. That a resident's privacy is respected.

'31. That toilets and bathrooms have adequate privacy.

'32. That residents take part in decision making.

'33. That "learning through doing" results in residents being involved in the running of their own home.

'34. That some leisure activities involve relationships outside the hostel.

'35. That there is provision made for holidays (the Chronically Sick and Disabled Persons Act 1970, provides for this).

'36. That there is on-going contact with the family, if any, of every resident in a home or hostel.

'37. That parents, other relatives and friends are encouraged to visit.

'38. That senior staff in homes or hostels have relevant experience and training.

'39. That there is support for the staff from professional specialist workers.

'40. That specialist services are available as required (speech therapist, psychologist, etc.).

'41. That there is regular evaluation at least annually, by local authorities of the standards provided in local authority homes.

'42. That the resident, parents or relatives are included in discussions on progress.

'43. That the Local Society for Mentally Handicapped Children keeps in close touch with the staff and residents and that staff are encouraged in this by the local authority.

'44. That homes run by private individuals or voluntary organisations are given the same degree of support and evaluation by local authorities or health authorities as is provided for statutory services.

'45. That there is regular contact between the residential home and the Adult Training centre to ensure co-ordination of assessments.

'46. That each individual in residential care (of whatever category, from special care to minimal support) participates in a regular review of his circumstances.

'47. That all assessments are in writing—(adequate records are essential for new staff)—and that all involved in joint consultation and decision-making receive copies.

'48. That while no residential placement should become a 'dead-end', there should be regular reviews of the suitability of each placement in consultation with the resident. Regard must be given to the need for security and continuity of residence, in accordance with the wishes of the individual.

'49. That consideration is given to the possibility of the individual living independently, and that provision is made on local authority housing lists for this purpose.

'50. That social work support is available for those living independently.'

SUMMARY

This chapter has examined five approaches to evaluating and measuring the quality of care in residential settings for the mentally handicapped. They each reflect a different bias and purpose and have been developed to meet particular needs. The study by King, Raynes and Tizard (1971)[3] and the development of the Child Management Rating Scale highlights the role of the social organisation of the unit in the quality of care.

The research study carried out in Wessex[1,8] represents a psychological approach. In a sophisticated research design, child and staff behaviours were categorized, quantified and interpreted in the framework of a number of indices of high quality care. Their hypothesis, substantiated in a pilot study, was that high-quality care occurred when staff reinforced appropriate child behaviour and did not reinforce children's neutral, inappropriate or disruptive behaviour.[1]

The self-assessment approach was seen to operate at two levels with the Health Care Evaluation Team research report[2] representing the organizational level. These detailed rules for the setting up and maintenance of residential units represent a blueprint for high-quality care, capable of implementation anywhere in the country.

A further example, PASS,[6] used by ENCOR in evaluating its own services in East Nebraska, is one organization's approach to evaluating such aspects of care as normalization.

Finally, the NSMHC have developed their check-list to help parents identify the components of good-quality services and care for their children.[5]

Mentally handicapped people have a right to high-quality care and society has a duty to provide it. It is because many people are confused or ignorant about the variables in high-quality care that accurate measurement is vital. Where research has been carried out as described above the lessons should be applied to both existing and planned residential facilities.

GLOSSARY

Behaviour index	One of the indices used by Durward and Whatmore to measure the proportion of time children spent behaving appropriately.
Block treatment	A term coined by King, Raynes and Tizard to describe a pattern of care characterized by treating a group of people as one individual.
Contact index	One of the indices used by Durward and Whatmore to measure the proportion of time during which staff contacts are given to all classes of child behaviour.
Cue index	One of the indices used by Durward and Whatmore to measure the proportion of time during which staff give cues to appropriate child behaviour.
Depersonalization	A term coined by King, Raynes and Tizard to describe a pattern of care in which the individual is denied expression of his personality.
DINA	The classifications of child behaviour used by Durward and Whatmore: D = disruptive, I = inappropriate, N = neutral, A = appropriate.
Discrimination index	One of the indices used by Durward and Whatmore to measure the proportion of appropriate child behaviour followed by staff contact less the proportion of neutral, inappropriate and disruptive behaviour followed by staff contact.
Efficiency index	One of the indices used by Durward and Whatmore to measure the proportion of staff contact following appropriate child behaviour.
ENCOR	East Nebraska Community Office of Retardation.
HCERT	Health Care Evaluation Research Team, Wessex.
Hypothesis	A supposition made as a basis for reasoning. A starting point for an investigation.

Normalization	The principle which states that services, living conditions and life style should be as normal as possible for the mentally handicapped.
NSMHC	National Society for Mentally Handicapped Children.
PASS	Programme Analysis of Service Systems. An evaluative checklist in the form of questions used by ENCOR to monitor the quality of its services.
Reinforcement index	One of the indices used by Durward and Whatmore to measure the proportion of appropriate child behaviour followed by staff contact.
Rigidity of routine	A term coined by King, Raynes and Tizard to describe a pattern of care characterized by an inflexible routine which does not allow consideration of individual children's needs.
Social distance	A term coined by King, Raynes and Tizard to describe a pattern of care characterized by a low level of interaction and warmth between staff and children.

BIBLIOGRAPHY

1. Durward, L. & Whatmore, R. (1975) *Testing Measures of the Quality of Residential Care: A Pilot Study*, Research Report No. 11. Winchester: Health Care Evaluation Research Team.
2. Felce, D., Kushlick, A., Lunt, B. & Powell, E. (1977) *Evaluation of Locally Based Hospital Units for the Mentally Handicapped in Wessex*, Research Report No. 124. Winchester: Health Care Evaluation Research Team.
3. King, R.D., Raynes, N.V. & Tizard, J. (1971) *Patterns of Residential Care*. London: Routledge and Kegan Paul.
4. Kushlick, A. (1975) The rehabilitation or habilitation of severely or profoundly retarded people. *Bull. N. Y. Acad. Med., USA, 51*, 143.
5. NSMHC (1978) Residential care of the mentally handicapped. *Community Care Stamina Paper No. 3*. London.
6. Thomas, D., Firth, H. & Kendall, A. (1978) *Encor—A Way Ahead*. London: Campaign for the Mentally Handicapped.
7. Tizard, J. (1974) Services and the evaluation of services. In *Mental Deficiency: The Changing Outlook*, ed. A.M. Clarke & A.D.B. Clarke, 3rd ed. London: Methuen.
8. Whatmore, R., Durward, L. & Kushlick, A. (1974) *Measuring the Quality of Care*, Research Report No. 19. Winchester: Health Care Evaluation Research Team.

PART V
Teaching the Mentally Handicapped

Introduction

The environment affects all aspects of an individual's behaviour. Part V is concerned with those aspects of the residential care environment that may determine the behaviour of both residents and care staff. It examines ways in which the environment can be structured to develop or increase appropriate behaviours and reduce or weaken inappropriate behaviours.

Chapter 16 starts from the premise that a successful residential environment is one that meets the physical and psychological needs of the mentally handicapped resident, and discusses the material and human factors which constitute the 'total environment'. These factors include the physical setting, the available resources, the nature and degree of the residents' physical and mental handicap and the care staffs' knowledge, attitudes and skills. The inter-relationship of these factors is considered in a discussion of the 'group process' and its application to the management of the care environment. Finally, the concept of a prosthetic environment is introduced and the point made that the effect of a prosthesis is to increase greatly the mentally handicapped person's ability to benefit from a wider experience.

Chapter 17 extends the theme of the effect of the environment on human behaviour by discussing ways in which the environment can be structured to provide learning opportunities for the mentally handicapped. One way of achieving this can be seen in the four-stage model of observation and assessment, selection and analysis of task, presentation of task and evaluation. The various aspects of the model are discussed with an emphasis placed on the importance of a developmental approach to play and learning. This theme is considered in more detail in the context of activities which can be used to develop sensory skills, hand/eye coordination, fine finger manipulation, gross motor movement, language and social interaction.

Chapters 18 and 19 are concerned with the principles and practice of behavioural change. Chapter 18 discusses the differences between the medical and behavioural models and analyses the principles underlying the teaching techniques of behaviour modification. Behaviour is defined and the techniques of measuring behaviour such as frequency, rate and duration recording are discussed in relation to the important concepts of determining baselines and selecting target behaviours. The principle of systematic reinforcement is shown to be crucial in behaviour management.

Chapter 19 continues this theme and sets the scene with a discussion of discriminative stimuli and the achievement of stimulus control. Techniques to develop and strengthen behaviours such as shaping, prompting, fading and modelling are described with examples of self-help skills programmes. Techniques to reduce or weaken behaviours include extinction, time out, response cost, restitution, over-correction, shaping incompatible behaviour and differential reinforcement of other behaviours. The effect and application of these techniques to inappropriate behaviour is discussed.

Finally, the point is made that although behavioural techniques appear 'mechanical' and 'inhuman', helping a mentally handicapped person towards a measure of independence, within the framework of a warm and loving relationship, is a very positive way of caring.

The environment and its effect on behaviour 16

The term environment describes an individual's surroundings and its use is often limited to a description of the physical external condition in which a person lives. It is also used to describe human factors and their influence on the physical environment.[3] This concept of a 'total environment' is particularly appropriate in a discussion relating to the mentally handicapped, as their behaviour may be determined or influenced by a number of environmental factors. These factors include the physical setting, the interactions which occur within the physical setting and the psychological and sociological factors which determine individual and group interactions.

The environment can be a measure of the quality of care that is provided in two important ways. The first measure is the extent to which the environment meets the individual's needs and the second is to what extent the person is enabled to function in specific circumstances.[6]

A useful framework for considering an individual's needs is that provided by A. Maslow's theory of hierarchical needs.[17] Human needs are divided into physical (unlearned) needs and psychological (learned) needs. A successful environment would be able to meet both the physical and the psychological needs of the individual, which are set out in Fig. 32. The circumstances will alter the importance of each need. An example would be that of the starving refugee who would regard food and shelter as the most urgent requirement and not fulfilling his potential.

An individual's physical needs are usually well met in residential care, with the possible exception of sexual needs. The psychological needs are more difficult to satisfy, particularly self-fulfilment, and it is this aspect of the environment that is so important to the progress of the mentally handicapped. If the environment is psychologically supportive then the caring process will enable the mentally handicapped to acquire the basic, self-help and social skills which will move them towards a greater degree of independence.

Studies with normal and handicapped children have shown that a poor environment is a direct cause of under-functioning and that when this is changed to a more normal environment there has been an improvement in performance.[2,9]

Although we shall discuss the effect of individual aspects of the environment it should be remembered that all the factors operate at the same time to modify and control behaviour. These factors are shown in Fig. 33.

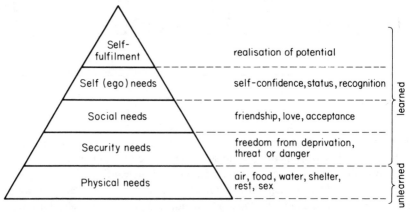

Fig. 32. Maslow's theory of the hierarchy of needs.[7]

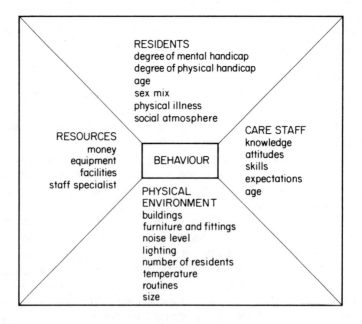

Fig. 33. How the picture of behaviour can be influenced by the controlling framework of the physical and human environment.

THE PHYSICAL SETTING

The major factors which influence the physical setting are those of location and size. Hospitals for the mentally handicapped are typically large, old and isolated from the community. They are a legacy from an era that believed large institutions were the best way to care for the mentally handicapped. As progress was made towards a more individual system of care an extensive programme of 'upgrading' was undertaken.[8] The aim of this work was to make the accommodation smaller and more normal. It is now generally accepted that living units should be small and as 'home-like' as possible, with careful consideration being given to the provision of facilities which allow for:

1. Normal furniture and fittings.
2. Management of the individual, including physical handicap.
3. Personal privacy.
4. Ease of access to important areas.
5. Learning of basic, self-help and social skills.[1]

The Department of Health and Social Security recognize the need for small living units as they recommend that the ideal size for an adult unit is 12 and for a children's unit eight.[8] Many people would argue that even this number should be reduced if the negative care practices of block treatment, rigidity of routine, depersonalization and social distance are to be avoided.[5] The location of the unit or hospital can be a limiting factor if it creates a barrier of distance between the mentally handicapped and the normal experiences found in the community.

Normal furniture and fittings are essential for the creation of a home-like environment. They have the effect of providing repeated learning experiences in every-day skills such as opening doors, switching lights on and off and running water into a sink or bath.[2] Even the profoundly handicapped have shown progress in an improved physical setting.[1]

Careful consideration should be given to the selection of the furniture and fittings. Mass-produced furniture of a standard design can give an overall effect of uniformity and institutionalization.[8] The furniture should be as individual and as varied as is compatible with safety.

In recent years many ideas have been put forward in an attempt to produce a more imaginative and helpful physical environment.[1] Bedrooms should preferably be individual but in any event should not accommodate more than four people. They should where possible reflect the taste and interests of the occupants. This can be achieved by residents exercising choice in wallpaper, design and furniture.[1] There should be a comfortable chair and facilities for displaying personal possessions, pictures, posters and photographs. The furniture need not be of standard design and should be selected to meet the needs of the individual resident. A mirror has proved to be essential in teaching body image and dressing skills and no bedroom should be without one, preferably full-length.

Bathrooms should cater for a small group of people as they do in normal family life. The equipment should include bath, shower and wash-basin with facilities for personal toothbrush and paste, flannel and towel.[8] Washing facilities should be provided in the bathroom, and not the bedroom as in some forms of residential care, to encourage more normal practice.

Toilets should be provided at strategic places in the ward or home and not in a large area, to avoid the problem of block treatment.[5] A major consideration is that they should be private and large enough to accommodate residents' wheelchairs or walking aids. Although they need to be private a mentally or physically handicapped person often needs help in using the toilet and it is essential that this help can be given in private.[8]

As a result of their handicap residents are often excluded from the ward, hostel or home kitchen. Most often they are excluded on justifiable grounds of safety. This consideration is particularly important when the kitchen contains sophisticated mechanical equipment such as deep-fat fryers or potato peeling machines, used in catering for large numbers of people.[1] However, it should be designed and equipped in such a way that small groups of residents can learn basic skills in preparing and cooking food. This will mean that normal equipment such as saucepans, frying pans, whisks, knives and boards will need to be provided in a special area in the kitchen.

The living rooms, or 'day rooms' as they are often called, should be designed to allow for a number of activities to take place at the same time. It may be possible to provide a room for television viewing which is separate from the main area, which has obvious advantages. Indeed, the residential population should be small enough to allow for small groups of people to pursue the activity they are interested in. This concept would allow for the inclusion of special areas such as games rooms and hobbies rooms, properly equipped. Where this is not possible large areas should be partitioned to encourage a variety of activities. There should always be an area that is comfortably furnished and carpeted which may be used in a variety of ways to encourage and develop valuable social skills.

These large 'day rooms' are often used in residential care as a dining room at meal times. In many ways this practice encourages rigidity of routine with the ritual laying up of tables.[5] The dining area should be separate from the living area to allow for greater flexibility in the planning and timing of meals. The tables should accommodate four people and should be laid using as normal equipment as possible. This should include place mats, individual settings, water jugs and glasses and the usual condiments.

The immediate area around the ward or hostel should be seen as an integral part of the residents' facilities and should be planned to meet their varying needs.[2] A flat piece of grass surrounded by chain-link fencing is unlikely to stimulate a resident in any way, except possibly to escape. The garden should be seen as an extension of the residential accommodation so that a variety of complementary activities may be carried out.

The second consideration should be that the environment allows for the management of the individual, including physical handicap. Accommodation is often designed for a specific group of residents with particular needs such as the elderly, children or those with severe physical handicap. In these circumstances the management of the individual resident is made easier. Accommodation that has not been specially designed should be adapted to take account of differences in behaviour and age. Children need space in which to play and engage in activities such as sand and water play and painting. An adventure playground can help the child gain motor skills and self-confidence. Adults will need games rooms and hobby rooms and a place to be quiet, to watch television, listen to music or talk to others. The elderly will require an environment that is suited to their pace of life and should take account of handicaps such as failing sight and hearing and reduced mobility.

There should be access to important areas such as the bathroom, lavatory, bedrooms, kitchen and garden. It is through this normal interaction with different parts of their environment that the mentally handicapped learn to manage their own environment and make choices.[8] These choices are important. Particularly important is being able to choose to be alone and the environment should afford the opportunity of personal privacy.

The physical environment should also play a part in the acquisition of basic, self-help and social skills. Self-help skills such as washing and bathing are easier to teach and learn in an individual environment that is familiar and convenient.[1] Dressing skills are easier to acquire when clothing is kept in a personal wardrobe rather than in a central clothing store. The opportunity to acquire the social skills of daily living will be increased in a small homely environment, devoid of the stresses of large group living.[1]

The environment should encourage the making of choices by the people living in it, and inevitably the process of choosing a course of action involves some element of risk. Risk and choice are essential if learning is to take place.[8] The completely 'safe' environment is a sterile one, where little or no activity takes place. The single most important factor in the care of the mentally handicapped is the opportunity to learn and the environment should be rich in such opportunities. Whether the physical environment is fully exploited to the benefit of the mentally handicapped rests largely with the people responsible for their care.

ASPECTS OF THE 'HUMAN' ENVIRONMENT

The most complicated aspect of the mentally handicapped person's environment is the effect that other people's behaviour may have. This may be to stimulate, motivate, direct, control or teach. It may also anger, confuse or inhibit learning and interaction. One aspect of human behaviour which the mentally handicapped find difficult is the unpredictable nature of other people's behaviour. This applies to the behaviour of other residents, the staff and those people with whom the mentally handicapped may have limited contact, such as doctors, physiotherapists or speech therapists.

The number of residents accommodated in one building can have far-reaching effects. Large numbers and limited space can combine to reduce interactions and learning. This effect has been well documented by Raynes, King and Tizard who showed how rigidity of routine, block treatment, depersonalization and social distance were a feature of large institutional settings.[5] Privacy is almost impossible in these circumstances and this may result in either withdrawal or aggressive over-reaction.

A wide age range can have both beneficial and detrimental effects. The benefits are chiefly in the move towards a 'family' structure, the older residents becoming involved in the care and training of the younger residents.[8] However, too wide an age range may mean that the environment is not capable of meeting all the residents' needs.

Recently mixed units have opened and have proved to be successful, particularly in the area of more normal social relationships.

The degree of mental and physical handicap has been seen to affect the residents' behaviour in a variety of ways. The more able residents often resent living in the company of profoundly handicapped people. They may fear the implication that they are as handicapped as the other residents. On the other hand they may feel protective towards the more handicapped and try to help them as much as possible.[8] The less able may feel it is impossible to attain the skills that the more able have achieved and consequently not try as hard as they might.

The problems generated by numbers, age, mix and degree of handicap can to some extent be alleviated by a careful analysis of the physical environment and how it could best be used. This analysis, combined with an assessment of the residents' abilities, limitations and learning needs, will help to match the mentally handicapped child or adult with a compatible environment. An important finding from a number of research studies is that the number of residents should be small, the ideal number being four to eight in any one living unit; careful consideration should be given to the possibility of mixing the groups in age, gender and degree of mental and physical handicap.[8] The formula that is decided on will be influenced by the staff and the care practices they adopt.

Central to any discussion of staff and the care practices they may implement are the attitudes they hold, how these were formed and the function they serve for the individual. An attitude can be defined as a disposition to respond in a particular way to people, events, actions, objects, or ideas. They have been described as having three components which are:[10]

1. Affective: the liking or disliking of people, events, actions, objects or ideas, the emotional expression of which may be positive or negative.
2. Cognitive: the belief, or disbelief or ideas formed about people, events, actions or ideas or objects.
3. Conative: the tendency to behave in a particular way towards people, events, actions, objects or ideas which is influenced or determined by the affective and cognitive components.

Attitudes represent the ways in which we order and give meaning to our experience. They are an indication of how we predict and perceive events and how we will react. They are formed as part of the continuing process of socialization and are learnt from other people, reinforced by social experience; they reflect the individual's values and allow him to express himself as he would wish others to see him.[10]

Each member of staff will bring to the task of caring for the mentally handicapped a variety of knowledge, attitudes and skills. Their approach and attitudes will have been moulded by their training and life experience and may have led them to form expectations of the mentally handicapped. These expectations may be based on criteria such as an intelligence quotient which may have been determined some time in the past. This can give rise to the phenomenon known as the self-fulfilling prophecy, which occurs when a given IQ determines a low expectation of performance in the mentally handicapped resident. Consequently the staff do not stimulate or attempt to teach skills, with the result that learning does not take place. This then confirms the original prophecy that the person was too severely handicapped to learn in the first place.

Disturbed, aggressive or withdrawn behaviour can determine expectations and cause staff to approach the resident in a way that serves to reinforce the inappropriate behaviour. If the withdrawn resident is approached only in a directive controlling way at particular periods in the day, such as meal times or bedtime, and left to his own devices for the remainder of the day, his withdrawn behaviour will be reinforced. This pattern of interaction is more likely to occur in conditions of staff shortage. The numbers of staff available in a residential setting can be critical in the setting and maintaining of standards of care and may determine the level of interaction and care practice.

Group management

Group management is a method of caring for groups of mentally handicapped children or adults so that their physical and psychological needs are met. This is achieved by one or two staff, caring for a specific number of residents in a group setting. The aims of group management are to:

1. Facilitate individual programmes designed to enable the child or adult to acquire basic, self-help and social skills.
2. Give staff the opportunity to be responsible for a group of children or adults.
3. Reduce administrative problems and allow senior staff more time to practice their caring and teaching skills.

There are severel methods of grouping residents and the choice of method may be determined by a number of factors, which can be categorized under the following headings:

1. Grouping by ability: physical
                      intellectual
2. Grouping by age or sex: children's ward
                           geriatric ward
3. Family grouping: mixed grouping which models a 'family' structure.
4. Mixed grouping: combination of factors such as age, sex, ability, occupation/earnings.

In a group system of management it is important that there is a degree of flexibility which allows individuals to be cared for in the group most suited to their changing abilities and needs. This can be represented diagrammatically as in Fig. 34. The level of engagement or interaction between the mentally handi-

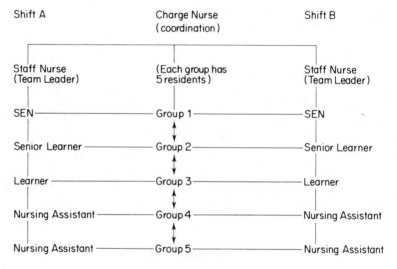

Fig. 34. The structure of a group management system for 25 children or adults.

capped and those who care for them is influenced and modified by the 'group process'. This means that key factors such as group identity, available resources, working method and relationships will have an effect on both the residents and the staff. These 'group factors' are represented diagrammatically in Fig. 35. Probably the major factor is the perception of the group identity that is held by the care staff. If they have a clear agreed policy that sets out the purpose, goals and tasks they will be more likely to meet the needs of the mentally handicapped. The elements of the group process are shown in Fig. 35.

It can be seen from Fig. 35 that each individual brings his own unique experiences to the group and influences the group process. The twin elements of carrying out the task of caring for the mentally handicapped and the interactions between residents and staff constitute the group experiences. The group experiences will in turn be influenced by the goals that are set for the care team and

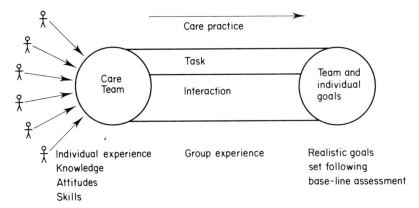

Fig. 35. The elements of the group process.

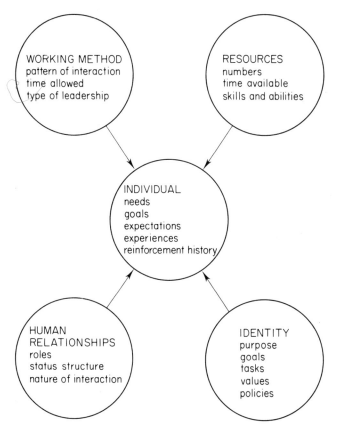

Fig. 36. 'Group factors' which may influence the individual.[4]

the individual resident. These goals should be determined in the light of an assessment of the skills and abilities of both the staff and the residents. The care team's programme and goals should always aim to improve the residents' functional ability against the background of a stable home-like environment.

PROSTHETIC ENVIRONMENT[6]

The concept of a prosthetic environment is an important one for the mentally handicapped and those who care for them. A prosthesis makes up for a deficiency, usually in a physical sense, such as spectacles or a hearing aid. The wider application to the environment takes in not only the physical but also the cosmetic, social and environmental prosthesis.[6] The effect of these aids is to greatly increase the mentally handicapped person's ability to benefit from a wider experience.

Possibly the most striking example of a physical prosthesis is the possum apparatus used by some grossly physically handicapped people. By blowing into a tube the person can open doors, change channels on a television, switch on lights and use a typewriter. The machine can be programmed for a variety of uses to suit the needs and abilities of the handicapped person. The physical prostheses which may be provided for the mentally handicapped include aids such as spectacles, hearing aids and wheelchairs.[6] Being able to hear and see properly will increase the mentally handicapped person's ability to manage the auditory and visual stimuli he is receiving. Using a wheelchair will increase the opportunities the person has of experiencing different environments and learning from them.

Cosmetic prostheses make a person more acceptable or attractive to other people. They include false teeth, make-up, wigs, fashionable haircuts and clothes. The effect that a cosmetic prosthesis can have is to make social interaction easier for the mentally handicapped by reducing other people's embarrassment as a result of improving physical appearance.[6]

Environmental prostheses that are slowly becoming a part of the life of the handicapped are ramps up and down kerbs and into buildings, automatic doors and specially fitted toilets in public places. Any residential care setting that helps the mentally handicapped in terms of furniture, fittings or facilities can be described as prosthetic.

The most important prostheses for the mentally handicapped are the people who care for them. They perform the necessary basic tasks such as washing, dressing, toiletting and feeding.[6] However, it is important for the care staff to understand that doing everything for the individual may make it unnecessary for the person to do anything for himself.[6] Over-protection can lead to total dependence.

SUMMARY

The environment may be seen as a combination of physical and human factors moulding and influencing the behaviour of the mentally handicapped. It can also be a measure of the quality of care in that it should meet the physical and psychological needs of the individual. The physical facilities should allow for normal furniture and fittings; management of the individual; personal privacy; access to important areas; and learning of basic self-help and social skills.

The human factors should lead to consideration of the numbers, age, sex and mix of residents and the effects these factors may have on behaviour. Staff attitudes, knowledge, skills and expectations should be understood in an attempt to devise care practices which meet the needs of the mentally handicapped. One such method of care which has developed successfully is that of group management which aims to provide care for small groups of mentally handicapped people which facilitates individual programmes, gives staff operational responsibility and frees the qualified nurses and more experienced staff to interact with the residents. An integral feature of group work is the planning and setting of goals aimed at improving the residents' functional ability within a homely setting. Progress towards this aim may be helped by the provision of physical, cosmetic, environmental and social prostheses.

GLOSSARY

Affective
Concerned with the liking or disliking of people, events, actions, objects or ideas. This type of attitude allows emotional expression of how the individual feels.

Block treatment
A pattern of care characterized by treating a group of people as one.

Body image
The individual's perception of the parts of his body and their relation to each other.

Cognitive
Concerned with belief or disbelief relating to people, events, actions, objects or ideas. The 'thinking' component of an attitude.

Conative
Tending to behave in a particular way towards people, events, actions, objects or ideas as determined by the affective and cognitive components of an attitude.

Depersonalization
A pattern of care in which the individual is denied expression of his individuality.

Ego
The Freudian concept of 'self', the rational calculating objective part of the personality.

Engagement   A term used to describe the interaction between a mentally handicapped person and anyone caring for or teaching him.

Group   The process of caring for a number of mentally handicapped
management   people by dividing them into small groups with the responsibility for care undertaken by a specific staff member.

Institutionaliza-   A condition brought about by living in an institution
tion   characterized by loss of drive, apathy and stereotyped behaviour.

Prosthesis   An artificial device that makes up for a deficiency and may be physical, cosmetic, environmental or social.

Rigidity of   A pattern of care characterized by an inflexible routine
routine   which does not allow consideration of the individual's needs.

Self-fulfilling   A prophecy that will be fulfilled simply because it was
prophecy   made.

Social distance   A pattern of care characterized by a low level of interaction and warmth between staff and residents.

BIBLIOGRAPHY

1. Elliott, J. & Bayes, K. (1972) *Room for Improvement*. London: King Edward's Hospital Fund.
2. Gunzburg, H.C. & Gunzburg, A.L. (1973) *Mental Handicap and Physical Environment*. London: Baillière Tindall.
3. Gunzburg, H.C. (1974) *Experiments in the Rehabilitation of the Mentally Handicapped*. London: Butterworth.
4. Industrial Training Service (unpublished) *Levels of Learning and Levels of Group Communication*. London.
5. King, R.D., Raynes, N.V. & Tizard, J. (1971) *Patterns of Residential Care*. London: Routledge and Kegan Paul.
6. Kushlick, A. (1974) The rehabilitation or habilitation of severely or profoundly retarded people. Paper presented at 1974 Annual Health Conference of the New York Academy of Medicine.
7. Maslow, A.H. (1943) A theory of human motivation. *Psychol. Rev., 50*, 370.
8. National Development Group (1978) *Helping Mentally Handicapped People in Hospital*. London: DHSS.
9. Oswin, M. (1978) *Children Living in Long Stay Hospitals*. London: Heineman Medical.
10. Stevens, R. (1975) Attitudes, Unit 21–22 D101. Milton Keynes: Open University Press.

The learning environment

17

The previous chapter discussed the physical and human factors which constitute an individual's environment and how these factors may affect the behaviour of the mentally handicapped. This chapter extends this theme to discuss how the environment may be used to encourage the learning of skills.

Learning has been described as 'a change in behaviour, more or less persistent in nature, which is brought about by activity observation or experience'.[7] It may be seen from this definition that learning may occur on a random basis and may therefore be either positive or negative. Positive learning is where the individual learns to behave in a way that enables him to be more independent physically, socially and emotionally. Negative learning occurs when the individual learns to behave in an inappropriate way that inhibits or prevents progress towards independence. To avoid inappropriate learning it is necessary to organize the learning environment so that it is intellectually stimulating, socially valuable, emotionally satisfying and related to the needs of the individual.

ORGANIZATION OF THE LEARNING ENVIRONMENT

One approach to organizing the learning environment has been developed by the Hester Adrian Research Centre in Manchester, as part of their work with parents of mentally handicapped children. Their model for creating a learning environment can be seen in Fig. 37.

Observation and assessment are vital if realistic learning is to take place. The object is to build up a behavioural profile of the child's strengths and weaknesses so that a programme can be devised that will meet his learning needs. A base-line of ability can be determined using a number of measures. One such measure that has proved very useful with residential care staff, teachers and parents is the range of progress assessment charts (PAC) devised by Dr H.C. Gunzburg.[3] An important feature is that they can be completed by someone who knows the individual well and do not require sophisticated training. There

```
┌─────────────────────────────────────────────────────────────────────┐
│ OBSERVATION AND ASSESSMENT                                           │
├─────────────────────────────────────────────────────────────────────┤
│ 1. Assessment using tests to produce a profile of strengths and     │
│    weaknesses                                                       │
│ 2. Observations (a) during specific activities - recording          │
│                  (b) of child in all situations                     │
│ ( Need a base for assessment and observation, normal child          │
│   development chart )                                               │
└─────────────────────────────────────────────────────────────────────┘
                                  ↓
┌─────────────────────────────────────────────────────────────────────┐
│ SELECTION AND ANALYSIS OF TASK                                      │
├─────────────────────────────────────────────────────────────────────┤
│ 1. Selection (a) task relevant for child                            │
│               (b) at correct level of ability                       │
│ 2. Analysis : identify and arrange tasks in series of smallest      │
│    possible steps                                                   │
│ State what it is the child will be able to do after the training    │
│ that he could not do before                                         │
└─────────────────────────────────────────────────────────────────────┘
                                  ↓
┌─────────────────────────────────────────────────────────────────────┐
│ PRESENTATION OF TASK                                                 │
├─────────────────────────────────────────────────────────────────────┤
│ 1. Produce favourable conditions for training ( learning is         │
│    pleasant and enjoyable )                                         │
│ 2. In relation to child and task, decide how, when and where to     │
│    train                                                            │
│ 3. Progress by small steps with complete mastery at each stage      │
│ 4. Reward appropriately, consistently, immediately                  │
└─────────────────────────────────────────────────────────────────────┘
                                  ↓
┌─────────────────────────────────────────────────────────────────────┐
│ EVALUATION                                                           │
├─────────────────────────────────────────────────────────────────────┤
│ Evalute (a) by using tests which measure if the child can do what   │
│          you said he would be able to do                            │
│          (b) constant observation during training and at other      │
│              available times                                        │
└─────────────────────────────────────────────────────────────────────┘
```

Fig. 37. The model for creating the learning situation.[4]

are a number of progress assessment charts available which test different areas of skill; the person carrying out the assessment selects the most suitable chart for the individual being assessed.[3] The progress assessment charts have been designed to provide an on-going, visual record of the social behaviour of the mentally handicapped. The skills that are listed are developmentally graded under the four major headings of self-help, communication, socialization and occupation.[3] An example of the primary PAC can be seen in Fig. 38. There is a manual which defines each item of the various check lists in detail and it is important that those using the charts should also use the manual. Failure to do this will mean that individuals will develop their own standards and most of the value of the PAC will be lost. New charts and manuals are being devised as

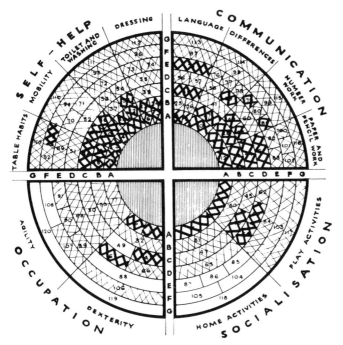

Fig. 38. A primary progress assessment chart. This youth must be considered as generally rather backward and this may be due to over-protection at home, for he fails to score in self-help skills in which assistance can be given by mother; he also scores very poorly in home activities. The boy has not been encouraged to assist actively at home because mother feels she has to do everything *for* him and not *with* him. There is no gross physical handicap to account for the total failure in the agility section and lack of training must be held responsible.

progress is made with item testing. At the time of writing the S PAC2 is the latest to become available, and is specifically for the severely and profoundly handicapped adult.[3] It provides a more detailed and comprehensive check list of skills that is suitable for people who are very difficult to assess.

It is important that the PAC is used constructively. Too often it is used once only and then incorrectly. It should be used to identify the skills that need to be taught and, as on-going assessments are made, as a record of progress achieved by the mentally handicapped person. Often the next skill to be learnt constitutes too great a step and will need to be broken down into smaller increments of learning.

Observation and assessment form the first link in the chain of skill development and learning and should lead to the selection and analysis of further skills to be learned.[4] Two important considerations in selecting skills to teach are the

Stage 1

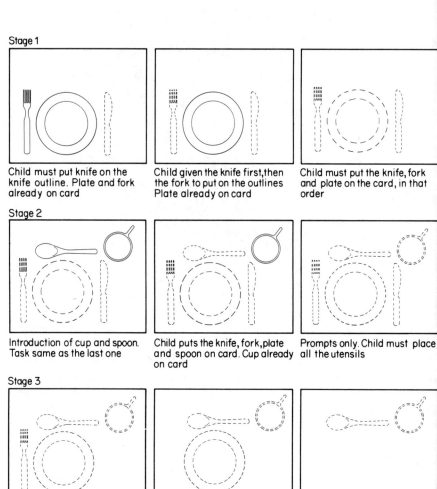

Child must put knife on the knife outline. Plate and fork already on card

Child given the knife first, then the fork to put on the outlines Plate already on card

Child must put the knife, fork and plate on the card, in that order

Stage 2

Introduction of cup and spoon. Task same as the last one

Child puts the knife, fork, plate and spoon on card. Cup already on card

Prompts only. Child must place all the utensils

Stage 3

Removal of first prompt. Child must place all the utensils

Removal of second prompt

Three prompts removed

Stage 4

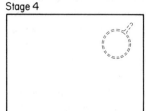

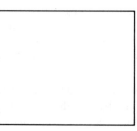

Place setting to be done on the table with no card. N.B. the child is always given the utensils in the same order, and the prompt are removed

relevance of the skill and the ability of the individual to learn the skill.[4] Sometimes it is decided to teach a skill merely because it is the next skill itemized on a particular checklist, regardless of its relevance to the individual's life. Where a particular skill is not required it will not be practised, or there may be no opportunities to practice it, with the result that the skill is lost. An example of this is where a child is taught to tie shoelaces and is then given slip-on shoes to wear or has his shoelaces tied for him. A common cause of failure in teaching is that the skill chosen is too difficult for the child to learn. The learning must be at the correct level for the child's ability, which means that each skill will have to be analysed and its elements identified.[4] An example of task analysis can be seen in Fig. 39. The task of laying a table setting of a knife, fork and spoon, plate and cup has been broken down into four main stages, each of which has been further subdivided into smaller stages. Laying a table setting is a complicated social skill, but the same technique of task analysis with the identification of smaller steps can be applied to any skill or learning programme. A careful analysis should lead to a statement in objective terms of what it is the individual will be able to do after the training that he could not do before. Related to the laying of the table setting a typical statement could be — 'on completion of stage 1 the child will be able to place the knife, fork and place, in that order, on to the card when asked to do so'.

The third stage in the model for creating the learning environment is presentation of the task or the teaching of the skill.[4] This aspect is fully discussed in Chapter 18 and practical examples in Chapter 19. Variables such as the ability of child and teacher, the time available, the physical setting, other people and their commitment and understanding and the teaching programme itself will all have to be carefully considered. The aim should be that the learning is pleasant and enjoyable and this can be achieved by consistent appropriate rewards.

It is important that the next step in the programme is not started until the previous step has been mastered and the child can do what you said he would be able to do. This can be done during the training sessions so that the acquisition of skills progresses smoothly as he works through the programme.

The model of observation and assessment, selection and analysis of task, presentation of task and evaluation provides a comprehensive structure for creating a learning environment. Most residents in care or living at home attend

---

Fig. 39 *(facing page)*. Task: To be able to lay a table place of knife, fork, spoon, plate and cup. Task analysis reveals four main stages:
1 Laying a knife and fork on correct sides of the plate, with prompts
2 Laying a knife, fork, plate, spoon and cup, with prompts
3 Laying a knife and a fork on the correct sides of the plate, no prompts; laying spoon and cup with prompts
4 Laying the complete place without prompts
Utensils are the normal-sized ones used at meal-times, *not* toy ones

some form of occupation or training away from the ward or hostel or home during the day, either at a special school or at an adult training centre. However, some mentally handicapped people are not able to do this and are left at home or in the living unit. They are usually severely handicapped, may be non-ambulant, doubly incontinent with severe behaviour disorders. It is important that they receive some form of training but it is difficult to see how this can be organized. One method that has proved successful in residential care settings and which can be adopted for use in the home is that of activity-centred programming. The

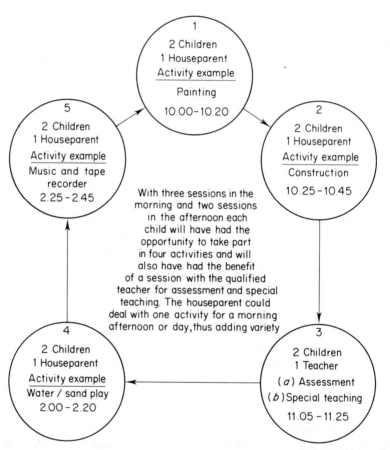

Fig. 40. An activity-centred programme. Each houseparent is responsible for a particular activity and takes each group of children for a session during the day. The advantage of this system is that the activities take less time to set and so block treatment is avoided. The houseparents deal with a variety of children although normal groups are maintained during other parts of the day. Activities may be varied; those shown are only examples. It is advisable to set up daily or weekly meetings to review progress.

example outlined in Fig. 40 shows how activities can be arranged for ten children, living in a hostel, between the hours of 10.00 a.m. and 3.00 p.m. The activities shown are painting, construction, sand and water play, music and tape recorder with a session included for assessment, special teaching, physiotherapy or speech therapy. These activities should be flexible so that if an outing is arranged or if it is a nice day, the programme can be shelved. Each member of the care staff is responsible for a particular activity for the morning, afternoon or day and by this means has the opportunity to work with all the children during the day. The advantage of someone being responsible for one activity is that it takes less time to set up for each individual child and goes some way to avoid block treatment. A base-line of developmental skills will have been completed for each child and suitable materials will have been organized before the sessions start each day. The activities can be varied for either child or adult. Suitable activities for an adult could include training sessions in self-help skills or social skills. In any event, the activities chosen should meet the learning needs of the individual. With three sessions in the morning and two sessions in the afternoon each child will have had the opportunity to take part in four activities and will also have had the benefit of a session with a teacher or other specialist.

Although it is much more difficult to arrange a programme like this in the home, it can be done with help and support. Home activities such as cooking and shopping could be incorporated into the programme. Other people such as peripatetic teachers, physiotherapists, speech therapists, psychologists and community nurses for the mentally handicapped could become involved in the programme on a daily, weekly, monthly or three-monthly basis. A recent study of how the families of the mentally handicapped managed the problems of caring showed that they often imposed a structure on their lives which enabled them to cope.[1] The activity-centred programme could help the mentally handicapped to gain skills and also give the parents or relatives the comforting knowledge that they are doing something positive for their child.

A variation of the activity-centred programme is that of zoning, suitable for residential care settings.[6] In this method each member of staff is responsible for a specific activity area but the children are free to move from one area to another as they finish a particular task. The member of the care staff assumes responsibility for the child who passes through his activity area or 'zone'.[6] As each child completes the activity he can be sent to another activity area and care staff. With children arriving singly in a zone the care staff can immediately provide materials to engage them in the new activity. A recent study undertaken in Kansas (USA) has shown that the 'zoning' method is not only efficient in use of time but also allows the teachers to evaluate the extent to which the children are involved in activities.[6]

For children or adults who are unable to attend activities in settings such as schools or training centres the techniques of activity-centred programming and zoning provide a structure within which programmes and activities can be organized to facilitate learning.

DEVELOPMENTAL APPROACH TO PLAY
AND LEARNING

'Play is not a purposeless activity only to pass the childhood hours; it is a vital factor in intellectual, social and emotional development'.[2] This opening statement of the Report of the Expert Group on Play for Children in Hospital serves to underline the importance of play.[2] No one would deny the importance of play for normal children but there is sometimes a reluctance to accept that the severely mentally handicapped child or adult needs to play.[12] It is the means by which the child learns the things he must know.[8] Through play the child develops an awareness of his body image, learns to use his senses and acquires skills such as hand-eye coordination; fine finger manipulation; gross motor movement; and visual and auditory discrimination. Through the development of language he learns both non-verbal and verbal communication which help in the acquisition of social skills. Play is an integral part of the continuing process of socialization which gradually changes the asocial child to an integrated adult with organized likes and dislikes, responsibilities, interests and an ability to survive successfully in a complex social structure.

When a normal child attends school for the first time he has already acquired a measure of independence.[11] He is able to dress himself and possibly tie his shoelaces. In some cases he may be able to read and write his own name; initiate and maintain a conversation; and play in a cooperative way.[13] The mentally handicapped child or adult may never achieve the skill level of the normal five-year-old but nevertheless they can and do learn,[11] particularly if the activities and toys are carefully selected to meet their level of development and staff are aware that the mentally handicapped child has to be taught to play.[9]

A useful formula for deciding on the most appropriate form of play is to consider the play materials and approach in relation to the developmental level of the child.[10] The first level is where unstructured materials such as sand, water, snow, mud or paper are combined with an unstructured approach.[10] An example of this combination can be seen in sand and water play. Sand and water are unstructured materials in that they have no form and cannot be destroyed. The unstructured approach is when the child is allowed freely to experience playing with and handling the sand and water. The child learns from this experience that he is able to manipulate his immediate environment.

The second level is a combination of unstructured materials and a structured approach.[10] The activity is more formal in that play is directed towards the child doing something with the unstructured materials. Examples might be making a sand castle or mud pie or attempting a picture using finger paints.

The third level is more sophisticated in that it aims to teach the child the appropriate use of the toy or play material.[10] At this level structured materials suh as toy cars, lorries, puppets, dolls, models or any manipulative toy are used. These materials are used with a structured approach, so that puppets, for example, could be used to simulate a social situation encouraging communication skills.

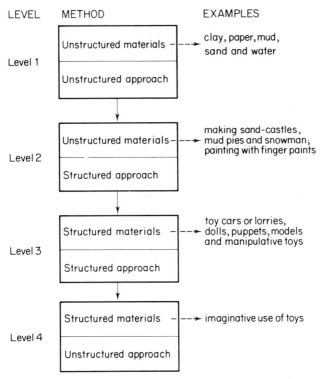

LEVEL   METHOD   EXAMPLES

Level 1
Unstructured materials ---→ clay, paper, mud, sand and water
Unstructured approach

Level 2
Unstructured materials ---→ making sand-castles, mud pies and snowman; painting with finger paints
Structured approach

Level 3
Structured materials ---→ toy cars or lorries, dolls, puppets, models and manipulative toys
Structured approach

Level 4
Structured materials ---→ imaginative use of toys
Unstructured approach

Fig. 41. Developmental levels of play with combinations of structured and unstructured material and approaches.[10]

Table 26. Colour code, play level and examples of graded toys used in Play Project[12]

Colour code	Play level	Examples of graded toys
Red	0–6 months	Rattles, bells, sticks, coloured balls, mobiles
Yellow	7–12 months	Small toys with wheels, squeakers, Mothercare Ball
Green	13–18 months	Simple inset boards, hammer-pegs, play dough, swing
Blue	19–24 months	Screw toys, play bath, big toys with wheels
Mauve	25 months and above	Fingerpaints, rocking horse, posting box, threading toys

Table 27.   Toys and activities suitable for developing the senses[5]

Sense	Suggestions for toys, games and activities
Sight	The problem with mentally handicapped children may not be a visual handicap but simply distractibility and inattention. They will need help in 'looking' and it may be necessary to start by developing the ability to maintain eye contact and attention. Physically handicapped children need to be placed in the correct position to see people, objects or toys. A mirror will be invaluable in broadening the range of visual stimuli and should be used extensively.
Activity	
Mobiles	These can be made from everyday articles found in any domestic setting and can be put across a cot or suspended near a mirror to produce a reflection
Shape Matching	Games such as 'the odd one out' and concepts such as large and small can be taught and encouraged
Colour recognition	Recognizing objects of the same colour on to naming colours
Painting	Requiring the child to paint within a circle. This is a very complicated skill that also involves fine finger manipulation and hand–eye coordination
Hearing	In just the same way as the child needs to be taught to look so he will need to be taught to listen. This is particularly true for the child with a visual handicap who will need to develop his other senses. Inability to communicate effectively is one of the major problems which mark out the mentally handicapped as different. An essential element of communication is the ability to hear and, as with normal deaf children, mentally handicapped deaf children often withdraw from normal contact, so making the problem more intractable
Activity	
Prepared tapes	There are a number of tapes of 'every-day' sounds such as farm-yard animals, trains or cars. These help identification of sounds
Percussion	Concepts such as loud and soft and listening to different sounds
Instruction following	Games like 'Simon says' where a child only carries out an action such as 'Simon says put your hands on your head' when the leader gives the instruction
Noisemakers	Almost anything will do providing it makes a noise. A good idea is to attach a number of articles such as bells or buzzers to a large piece of wood. The objective of these activities is to stimulate and hold the child's attention

Sense	Suggestions for toys, games and activities
Touch	Touch is probably the most neglected of the senses and probably one of the most important. This is particularly true for the mentally handicapped as they need to use every avenue of experience available to them. A young baby explores his environment largely by touch, holding things, twisting them round and putting them in his mouth. Mentally handicapped children and adults are often only at this stage of development despite their chronological age. Visually handicapped or blind children rely on touch to a much greater extent
Activity	
Texture boards and walls	A variety of different textures are provided from soft materials such as lambswool to hard ridged material like polythene lids. Sometimes a whole wall can be used in this way
Feely toys	Toys that are made in interesting materials, so providing a variety of textures
Hanging articles	Every-day objects that can be suspended across the cot or pram
Sorting and matching	Finding the same pattern, design or texture from a number of pieces of material. Matching a sample by feeling in a box with samples of different textures
Taste and smell	The senses of taste and smell are considered together as they are psychologically very closely linked. They are often neglected in terms of learning and teaching but can be very valuable particularly for the visually handicapped child. Again it should be remembered that the mentally handicapped child or adult may be at the development stage at which he puts everything into his mouth. The important task is to teach him to be selective. The sense of smell can provide important cues for the child and act as confirmation of the information gained from his other senses
Activity	
Parties	Parties for teddy bears and dolls can be a means of encouraging taste. A wide range of 'mini' foods are prepared and the children are given the chance to sample them
Tasting games	The child is blind-folded, given small samples of food and then asked to say what they are. These games are more suitable for more able children
Sprinkling perfume	For the physically handicapped child perfume could be sprinkled on his pillow encouraging him to turn his head
Matching smells smells	A number of smells are made up with two of the same smell. The child has to pair the similar smells together

The fourth level is a combination of using structured materials and an unstructured approach.[10] The aim of this level is to encourage the child to develop his own methods of play. He might fill a toy truck with sand, drive it across the floor and unload it. Play at this level requires a degree of knowledge and imagination that the mentally handicapped are often unable to achieve. This method of structuring the play environment can be represented diagrammatically as in Fig. 41.

A practical application of the developmental approach to play for the severely mentally handicapped child can be seen in a project described by Miss D. Roswell.[12] Approximately 60 children, all of whom were profoundly handicapped, were unable to attend the hospital school, as a result of shortage of accommodation, severity of handicap or behaviour problems. All the staff involved in the scheme received training in normal development and play and how this maybe altered in mental handicap, and in methods of assessment using progress assessment charts.[3] All the children were assessed to identify their developmental play level using PACs and the Griffiths developmental scale. A playroom was equipped which the children attended on a rota basis in addition to the play activities arranged on the ward. A colour-coded chart showed each child's play level. The toys were also colour-coded to correspond with six-month developmental stages, and kept in cupboards identified with the appropriate colour. With this information it was possible to match developmentally appropriate toys to each child. New staff could easily find suitable toys which the child had been playing with on previous occasions. Play levels were regularly assessed and adjustments made to the level of toy that the child could manage. Although the play setting and the toys were matched with the child's ability, opportunities were provided for exploration and use of toys that were just in advance of their present level to help them progress and widen their experience. Table 26 shows the play levels in months of age, the colour-coding used with examples of the toys and activities used in the project.[12] Although the grading of toys into developmental play levels appears crude, the scheme provides invaluable guidelines for those working with severely handicapped children and adults, and the same principle could be applied to the ward, hostel or home.

Another approach to play for the mentally handicapped is to use toys and activities that develop the sense.[5] The special senses have been described as the 'gateways of learning', as it is through the senses of sight, hearing, touch, taste and smell that the individual receives information about his environment. If the child can be helped to look, listen, feel and identify smells and taste, his opportunities to learn from his environment will be increased. This is particularly important when a child suffers the additional handicap of sensory disability such as visual or auditory impairment. Where one sense is impaired or lost, the other senses must be used in an effort to compensate for the stimuli that are lost. Examples of toys and activities suitable for developing the senses are given in Table 27.

The methods and activities described above are examples that could be used to improve the mentally handicapped in developing essential skills, through play. In any play activity there are a number of interrelated skills and the objective may be to teach a particular skill rather than to successfully complete the whole task. These skills may be listed:

1. Hand-eye coordination.
2. Fine finger manipulation.
3. Gross motor movement.
4. Visual discrimination.
5. Auditory discrimination.
6. Language development, both verbal and non-verbal.
7. Social interaction.

One activity that can include all these skills, at varying levels, is making pastry. Listening to instructions encourages auditory awareness. Measuring the correct amounts of fat, flour and water will develop visual discrimination and the formation of concepts such as large and small. Putting the ingredients into the containers involves varying degrees of hand-eye coordination. Mixing the ingredients calls for fine finger manipulation with the additional benefit of feeling the different textures. Moving about the kitchen, possibly carrying equipment, will assist in developing smooth coordinated gross motor movement. If the activity is planned for a group then social interaction skills such as cooperation and sharing can be encouraged. Language, including concepts such as colour and number, can be developed during the activity.

The technique of analysing the skills involved in carrying out a task can be applied to any play activity. The behavioural objective may be to teach or improve a specific skill such as hand-eye coordination or fine finger manipulation, with the total activity being used as a vehicle for achieving this objective.

SUMMARY

Learning opportunities in residential care are many and varied, but it is not enough to provide a stimulating environment alone; the mentally handicapped need a structured well-planned programme if they are to learn. This should be approached in a logical way with a period of observation and assessment so that their abilities and limitations may be compared with a developmental standard.[4] This in turn will indicate which skill or task should be selected for teaching. Having identified the child's learning needs, the next step will be to analyse the task. From this information it will be possible to formulate a graded teaching programme. The decision can then be made about how, when and where the teaching should take place. An important element in teaching should be the consistent use of rewards for the child so that he enjoys the learning experience.

The organization of the learning environment is important and one method that has proved successful is activity centred programming, where a number of activities are programmed for each individual throughout the day. Play is an important activity and the child learns vital skills through meaningful play. Play activities must be carefully selected so that they match the child's developmental level.[12] Play levels may be seen in terms of materials and approach and may be structured or non-structured.

The special senses have been called the 'gateways of learning' and every opportunity should be taken to develop the child's awareness through sight, hearing, touch, taste and smell.[5] A large range of toys and activities are available and should be carefully experimented with.

Finally, the environment should facilitate the acquisition of skills such as hand–eye coordination, fine finger manipulation, gross motor movement, visual and auditory discrimination and language and social skills. To achieve this the activities chosen will need to be intellectually stimulating, emotionally satisfying, socially valuable and related to the child's needs.

GLOSSARY

Activity-centred programming A method of organizing activities so that one member of staff is responsible for a specific activity catering for different children at pre-determined times.

Base-line A level of ability before training commences.

Fine finger manipulation The skill of using fingers and thumbs to carry out precise movements.

Griffiths developmental scale A detailed developmental scale measuring normal development from 0 to two years. The items cover the following major areas of development: locomotor, personal–social, hearing and speech, eye and hand, performance.

Gross motor skills Skills, such as walking, running and balancing, which involve large movements.

Hand–eye coordination The skill of relating visual stimuli to coordinated movement such as threading a needle.

Learning A change in behaviour, more or less persistent in nature, brought about by activity, observation or experience. It may be positive or negative.

Non-verbal communication Communication by sign, physical prompt or gesture.

Progress assessment chart (PAC) A developmental chart devised by Dr Gunzburg which itemizes skills under the headings of self-help, occupation, socialization and communication.

Peripatetic teacher	A teacher who travels from pupil to pupil, a home teacher.
Structured approach	One that teaches that a toy or piece of equipment has a specific function.
Structured materials	Items such as toys and games which have a particular function.
Task analysis	The breaking down of a task into elements.
Unstructured approach	Encouraging the child or adult to experience and experiment with particular toys or materials.
Unstructured materials	Materials such as sand and water which are not able to be destroyed.
Zoning	A method of managing an activity where children are directed from one area to another.

BIBLIOGRAPHY

1. Bayley, M. (1973) The community can care. *New Soc., 26*, 207.
2. DHSS (1976) *Play for Children in Hospital.* London: HMSO.
3. Gunzburg, H.C. (1977) *PAC Manual,* 5th ed. Birmingham: SEFA Publications.
4. Hester Adrian Research Centre (1971) *Working With Parents: Developing a Workshop Course for Parents of Young Mentally Handicapped Children.* Manchester: NSHMC.
5. Lear, R. (1977) *Play Helps.* London: Heineman Medical.
6. LeLaurin, K. & Risley, T.R. (1972) The organisation of day care environments: 'zone' versus 'man to man' staff assignments. *J. appl. Behav. Anal., 5*, 225–233.
7. Lovell, K. (1973) *Educational Psychology and Children.* London: University of London Press.
8. Matteson, E.M. (1965) *Play with a Purpose for Under Sevens.* Harmondsworth: Penguin.
9. National Development Group (1978) *Helping the Mentally Handicapped People in Hospital.* London: DHSS.
10. Panyan, M. & Boozer, H. (1972) *Levels of Play* (unpublished course material). Kansas: H. & H. Enterprises.
11. Perkins, E.A. & Taylor, P.D. (1976) *Learning through Play.* Birmingham: Institute of Mental Subnormality.
12. Roswell, D. (1974) Developmental play for severely subnormal children. In: *Experiments in the Rehabilitation of the Mentally Handicapped,* ed. H.C. Gunzburg. London: Butterworths.
13. Sheridan, M.D. (1975) *Children's Developmental Progress.* Windsor: NFER.

The principles of behavioural change 18

Human behaviour is complex, variable and often apparently unpredictable; it is maintained or modified by the effects of activity, observation or experience. In Chapter 4 the process of socialization is discussed and the point is made that the individual learns to behave in a particular way. This learning is largely determined by the behaviour of other people, such as parents, friends, peers, teachers and employers.[7] The quality, duration and intensity of these behaviours is determined by their consequences. The following example illustrates a typical situation in which behaviour can be seen to be both learned and determined by its consequences.

A mother takes her pre-school child with her when shopping in the supermarket. The child is tired and fractious and demands his mother's attention by whining and crying for sweets, to the extent that it interferes with her shopping. The mother has a number of choices available to her for dealing with her child's behaviour. She can give in to the child's demands and buy him the sweets he wants; she can ignore his demands completely; she can shout at him to be quiet or smack him for being naughty; or she can abandon her shopping trip and re-move the child from the shop.

If the mother 'gives in' to her child and buys him the sweets, two things may happen. The child may learn that if he wants something all he has to do is cry and whine. The mother will learn that by giving her child what he wants, her life is made easier and she is able to get on with her shopping.

If the mother ignores the child he may escalate his demands and behave in such a way that his mother will at the very least feel uncomfortable. The child will learn that even if his mother will not pay attention to him, other people will.

If she shouts at him or smacks him for being 'naughty' she will give him 'something to cry about', which may have the effect of stopping him asking for sweets but which will not stop him crying. The mother may learn from adverse disapproving reactions from other shoppers that she has behaved in an unreasonable way to her child. The child's behaviour will be maintained by the rewarding attention given by other people.

If the mother abandons her shopping as a result of her child's behaviour she will probably learn that it would be better to do her shopping without her son. The child will learn that his mother does not like him very much.

One element of the above example can be demonstrated by a simple diagram:

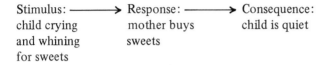

Stimulus: ⟶ Response: ⟶ Consequence:
child crying   mother buys   child is quiet
and whining   sweets
for sweets

There are, of course, countless examples of spontaneous unplanned modifications of behaviour occurring in every event or interaction involving people. They are subtle and very powerful in their effect.

The behavioural approach attempts to explain behaviour by applying scientific principles of learning to behaviour. Some of these principles are that behaviour is:[8]

1. Learned from other people.
2. Determined by its consequences.
3. More likely to occur if the individual finds it rewarding.

DEVELOPMENT OF THE
BEHAVIOURAL APPROACH

Many attempts have been made to explain human behaviour within the framework of a particular theory. The principles of the behavioural approach have gradually developed and have been drawn from extensive observations of human and animal behaviour in experimental and real-life settings. We shall consider the theories of classical, instrumental and operant conditioning by examining some well-known experiments. Conditioning has been defined as the process by which human beings and animals can be systematically taught to respond in a particular way to a specific stimulus or event.

Classical conditioning

In 1927 the Russian psychologist Ivan Pavlov was conducting experiments into gland secretion, using dogs. These experiments were lengthy and involved the dogs being restrained in harness. As a result of this they were usually fed during the experiment. Characteristically, the dogs salivated when they were given food. The event that led Pavlov to form his theory of classical conditioning was that whenever the man responsible for feeding the dogs came into the laboratory, the dogs started to salivate, whether he was bringing them food or not.[9]

Pavlov then set up a series of experiments to test his observations regarding the salivation response of the dogs. He presented a dog with a bowl of food which he called the unconditioned stimulus. In response the dog would salivate and Pavlov called this the unconditioned response. Then every time food was

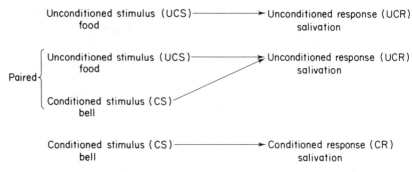

Fig. 42. The conditioned reflex as described by Pavlov.[10]

given to the dog a bell was rung which was called the conditioned stimulus. After a number of trials the food was omitted and only the bell was rung. The dog's response was to salivate just as they had done in response to the man who had fed them.[9]

The experiment was extended by substituting the bell with a buzzer which was termed stimulus generalization.This can be shown in diagrammatic form, as in Fig. 42.

Earlier, in 1920, an experiment had been carried out in America by two psychologists called J.B. Watson and R. Raynor. They were interested in the theory that phobias (irrational fears) were learned, and they set out to condition a phobia in an 11-month-old child called Albert.[9] The experiment centred around pairing a loud noise with the presentation of a white rat. The rat was presented to Albert who stretched out his hand to touch it; just as he was about to touch it a metal bar was struck with a hammer. After a number of trials involving pairing of the noise and the white rat Albert reacted by trying to avoid the white rat. Eventually the appearance of the rat on its own evoked fear in Albert to the extent that he cried and rapidly moved away. The experimenters then tried to generalize the stimulus to fear of all white furry objects. They presented a white rabbit, a dog, a sealskin coat and even cotton wool, all of which evoked fear in Albert, to a greater or lesser extent.[9] This can be seen in Fig. 43.

Classical conditioning involves physiological responses such as changes in smooth muscles and glands and is not under the voluntary control of the individual. The theory helps to explain some apparently irrational behaviour. An example of this might be seen in a child's fear of a doctor or dentist. Each time the child has been taken to see the doctor he has been feeling unwell and painful unpleasant procedures may have been carried out by the doctor. The paired stimuli of pain and the doctor may produce a conditioned response of fear. This may generalize to include fear of all men in white coats. One further point regarding conditioned stimuli is that if they are not repeated they gradually become extinguished and fade.[9]

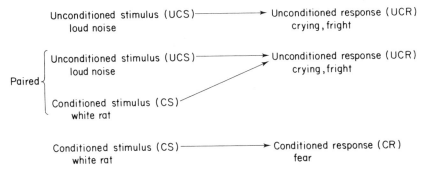

Fig. 43. The conditioned reflex as described by Watson and Raynor.[10]

Instrumental conditioning[10]

F. L. Thorndike, in 1911, was working on problems of animal learning. His research led to the theory of instrumental conditioning which is sometimes called 'trial-and-error' learning. He used a specially constructed box with a lever in the floor which, if pressed, would open the box. A hungry cat was put in the box, with food placed outside it. At first the cat rushed about the box in a random fashion until by accident it pressed the lever and escaped from the box. Over a large number of trials the cat took progressively less time to tread on the lever, until eventually it went straight to the lever and escaped at once.

From this research Thorndike formulated the 'law of effect' which stated that 'responses accompanied by satisfaction are more likely to recur'.[10] This 'law' has important implications for the teaching of children and adults and particularly the mentally handicapped who have difficulties with motivation and learning. In instrumental conditioning the reward follows the response and the association of the reward with a particular behaviour will increase the likelihood of the behaviour occurring again.

The main difference between classical and instrumental conditioning is that in classical conditioning the behaviour is not under the control of the individual, whereas in instrumental conditioning the response is voluntary.

Operant conditioning

The basis of the behavioural approach is rooted in the theory of operant conditioning first described by B. F. Skinner.[2] In the introduction to this chapter it was said that behaviour is learned as a result of activity, observation and experience. Operant conditioning theory seeks to explain in a scientific way how learning occurs and how it is maintained. As in any scientific theory, technical terms are used and it is helpful to define these before going on to discuss aspects of the theory.

An *operant* is defined as any observable action or behaviour that an individual does which is under voluntary control, such as walking, singing or eating.[10] The fact that the behaviour must be observable is critical in operant conditioning theory. Skinner was concerned with the cause-and-effect relationship between stimulus and responses, and not with the 'unseen' inner causes.[10]

A *stimulus* is anything that occurs in the environmental surroundings of an individual and may or may not affect the person's behaviour. Those stimuli that do affect individual behaviour are called reinforcers; a 'positive' reinforcer is anything that the individual finds pleasant and rewarding and which increases or strengthens a particular response; a 'negative' reinforcer is something that the individual regards as unpleasant or aversive and the removal of which increases or strengthens a particular response.[10]

By controlling and manipulating the causes of behaviour (stimuli) it is possible to control and determine the behaviour (response) of an individual. This can be demonstrated in diagram form:

Stimulus ⟶ Individual ⟶ Response ⟶ Consequence
or organism

Most of the theory of operant conditioning was derived from laboratory experiments in animal learning. Skinner carried out a famous experiment in which he taught a pigeon to walk in a figure-of-eight pattern using positive reinforcement.[10] The pigeon was placed in a special box, subsequently known as a Skinner box, into which food could be delivered. An analysis was completed of the elements involved in completing the sequence of movements, such as turning the head in either direction and the number of steps required. When the pigeon made one of the responses it was immediately given the food. The pigeon ate the grain and repeated the response which produced the food. Other responses required in the performance of the figure-of-eight occurred and were systematically reinforced with grain. Eventually the pigeon had to perform linked sequences before it was reinforced and finally it had to complete the figure-of-eight pattern before receiving reinforcement.

The description of teaching a pigeon to walk in a figure-of-eight pattern may seem mechanistic and inappropriate for teaching human beings. It is included to show a practical application of the principles of operant conditioning. The same principles have been used and are being used to teach children and adults. The following is a description of the application of these principles to a severely mentally handicapped boy, by P. Fuller in 1949.[9] It is included as it was the first recorded example of operant conditioning with the severely mentally handicapped.

The boy that Fuller worked with was described by the hospital staff as a 'vegetative idiot' and was thought to be incapable of learning anything. He was mute, severely physically handicapped and lay constantly in one position, on his back. He had very few behavioural skills, but was able to blink, open his mouth and move his arms, head and shoulders in a limited way. Fuller's purpose was to demonstrate that it was possible to teach a person as handicapped as this by using positive reinforcement. He noticed that the boy raised his right arm approximately once per minute and decided to increase this behaviour by using a solution of sweetened milk which he had seemed to enjoy.[9] Every time the boy raised his right arm sweetened milk was squirted into his mouth using a syringe. After 45 presentations the rate of arm raising had increased from 1 per minute to 1.12 per minute. At a subsequent session carried out the next day the frequency of arm raising had increased to three times per minute.[9] Fuller had demonstrated that it was possible to condition behaviour in a severely mentally and physically handicapped boy.

In summary, operant conditioning has been defined as strengthening an association between a stimulus and a response by systematically following the response with a reinforcing stimulus. It is based on principles derived both from laboratory-based experiments with animals and, more recently, from extensive experience in human learning.

Many people feel that experimental evidence derived from research with animals is neither appropriate nor applicable to human beings. There are, of course, limitations and even dangers in applying evidence directly from one to the other. However, animal research can have positive advantages. It is possible to exert a greater degree of control in a laboratory, so that a wider range of variables can be tested than would be possible in a hospital for the mentally handicapped. Findings in animal research may stimulate work with problems of human learning. A striking example of this is seen in the research of Premack and Premack who are teaching chimpanzees to communicate using behavioural methods.[9] Their research methods and findings may well be used in the teaching of autistic children. Pure experimental operant conditioning theory has been extended to include a wide range of applications. These may be seen in industry, where the principle of analysis of the behaviour required to carry out a task is extensively used, coupled with reward systems such as incentive bonus schemes designed to increase work output and efficiency and to teach new work skills; in education, in the development and application of programmed learning and teaching machines and particularly in remedial education with slow learners; in personal relationships, where psychologists and marriage guidance counsellors have used the principle to help individuals with relationship problems; in mental illness, where a considerable measure of success has been achieved in treating phobias, anxiety states and anorexia nervosa and in helping to rehabilitate long-term patients who have become institutionalized.

The area where operant conditioning has had the most impact is that of mental handicap, where it is used in a variety of ways. One major area is in teaching children and adults new behavioural skills.[6] These skills include the basic skills of feeding and toiletting; the self-help skills like washing and dressing; and the social skills of interaction and communication. A further important area is decreasing in frequency or eliminating behaviours that are disruptive or dangerous, such as excessive purposeless activity or self-mutilation. When operant conditioning principles are used to 'treat' a child or adult (that is, to teach new behaviours) the term behaviour modification is used to describe the approach, methods and techniques available to the teacher.

RATIONALE FOR USING BEHAVIOUR MODIFICATION

In Chapter 17 reference was made to the measure of independence achieved by the normal five-year-old and the skills we would expect him to have acquired. These included the ability to feed himself, use the toilet, wash and dress himself and to use language to express himself. In contrast the mentally handicapped child or adult will demonstrate varying degrees of 'backwardness' in acquiring these skills. This is sharply shown by the results of a survey of those people living in mental handicap hospitals, conducted by the Department of Health and Social Security in 1972. The survey revealed that of the 2000 children aged between five and nine years, 85% were not toilet trained, 95% were unable to wash and dress themselves and 91% were not able to use language in a meaningful way.

This failure or slowness to learn skills is often attributed to a physiological cause such as the degree of mental handicap, blindness, deafness or paralysis. Whilst it is true that physiological factors will alter the approach to learning, the central fact remains that mentally handicapped people can and do learn. They may be slow to learn and have difficulty in relating learning to practical everyday situations. They may not learn spontaneously and will require more experiences than usual. The learning itself will need to be broken down into easily assimilated increments. They will need to start learning as soon as possible and continue for as long as possible. They will need pressure to learn and repeated opportunities to practice skills.

It is lack of opportunity to learn that is the significant factor in the failure of the mentally handicapped to acquire independence.[11] By ensuring that the mentally handicapped have the opportunities to learn new skills as a result of planned systematic teaching using behavioural principles, they can move towards independence.

The above discussion raises the question of why, if behavioural principles and techniques are so effective, the mentally handicapped demonstrate so many behavioural deficits? One answer may be that it is due to traditional care practices which is sometimes described as the medical model.

Medical model

The medical model is exemplified by the way in which a general practitioner helps a person who goes to the surgery. The person describes his symptoms to the doctor who, on the basis of his observations and the person's history, makes a diagnosis and then selects a treatment, which is often in the form of drugs

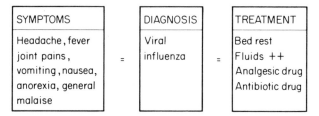

Fig. 44. The medical model (simplified).

(Fig. 44). If the patient fails to get better or shows signs of becoming worse he may be admitted to hospital. Admission to hospital is usually accompanied by an air of 'medical optimism': the patient will be cured. The patient admitted to hospital will be cared for by doctors and nurses who will aim to treat the disease the patient is suffering from by medical or surgical means.

Unfortunately, medical optimism and the medical model are largely inappropriate in the care of the mentally handicapped, either at home or in hospital. In an effort to arrive at a diagnosis so that the condition may be treated, labels such as 'low IQ', 'severely subnormal', 'autistic', 'Down's syndrome', 'intermittent neurological impairment', 'hyperactive' or 'brain damaged' are applied. However, the fact that a label has been applied to someone does not mean that there is any indication of how to treat the person; more importantly all the individual's behaviour may be seen as a direct result of the diagnosis. Often the psychiatrist or doctor is left treating behavioural symptoms with tranquillizing drugs, which have the effect of limiting the mentally handicapped individual's ability to learn new skills. Drugs affect all behaviour and are not limited in their effect to modifying specific disruptive or inappropriate behaviour. The treatment ethic of the medical model also influences nursing and care staff practices. Saying that a person is suffering from a condition for which there is no treatment encourages a move towards custodial physical care with an emphasis on maintaining an environment that may not be the most appropriate.

Fig. 45. Medical and behavioural models compared.

The behavioural model differs considerably from the medical model. The philosophy of the behavioural model is that 'inner causes' or underlying conditions are not important determinants of behaviour; it emphasizes the role of learning.[4] This difference can be seen in diagrammatic form in Fig. 45. The diagram shows how a simple adjustment in attitude and thinking can result in a change from the medical model to the behavioural model. Symptoms are no longer thought of as caused by a medical condition but simply as the behaviour that the individual does not does not do. The diagnosis, which is largely irrelevant, becomes the base-line, an objective record of existing specific behaviour. Treatment becomes a programme based on information gained from the base-line and may be aimed at teaching new skills or decreasing inappropriate behaviour.

Having discussed the need to teach the mentally handicapped skills that increase their independence, and examined some of the differences between the medical model and the behavioural model, the behavioural model will be examined in more detail in the following sections.

DEFINING BEHAVIOUR

In the section describing operant conditioning, an 'operant' was defined as an observable action or behaviour which is under voluntary control.[10] The quality of objectivity is crucial in the definition of behaviour. Often the problem in mental handicap is that the observed behaviour has been redefined in terms of the medical model and the assumption made that everyone concerned understands the same things about the term used. An example of this labelling is seen when an individual is simply described as 'aggressive'. Aggression can be shown in a number of ways: physical aggression in the form of hitting, biting, kicking, hair pulling, scratching or pushing; verbal aggression in the form of abuse such as nagging, screaming or swearing. It may be directed against the person himself (self-mutilation) or at specific people and may occur randomly or in response to particular stimuli. Other people will describe someone with an 'aggressive personality' or as having 'aggressive attitude', but this is merely a subjective description of how one individual sees the behaviour of another. It does not help in the teaching or management of the mentally handicapped. Indeed, the attitudes and expectations of those caring for the mentally handicapped may be determined by labels such as 'aggressive'. Fear of the consequences of aggression may make them avoid contact with the individual. Avoidance of contact lessens the chance of being involved in an 'aggressive outburst' and this avoidance behaviour negatively reinforces unhelpful attitudes.

Occasionally, major policy statements regarding standards of care in a hospital or department have overall treatment aims that are incapable of definition and application. A typical statement that may be used to describe the policy of the training departments in a hospital is: 'the stated aim of education and training of these units is to develop the individual to his/her maximum potential in order that he/she may lead as full, independent and unrestricted a life as possible consistent with what is best for him/her or the society in which he/she may reside'. A number of the terms used in the above statement are ambiguous and may mean one thing to the senior person who wrote the policy and quite another to the untrained assistant responsible for carrying out the programme and in continuous contact with the mentally handicapped child or adult. Expressions such as 'developing a person to his maximum potential' do not give guidance on the skills the person needs to develop and vague phrases like 'a full life' and 'what is best' are meaningless. Inaccurate subjective descriptions of behaviour, about which those involved cannot agree, lead to confusion and misunderstanding, even to the extent that different people will be teaching different skills within the framework of the same programme.

A useful model for describing behaviour in objective terms has been devised by R. Mager; he calls it the 'Hey Dad' test.[3] Behaviour is divided into two classes' fuzzies and performances. Fuzzies are vague statements about behaviour that 'Dad' cannot evaluate or see. A performance is a statement about behaviour that 'Dad' can see and evaluate in objective terms. Examples of fuzzies identified by the 'Hey Dad' test are:

1. Develop this child to his maximum potential.
2. Gives this child lots of individual attention.
3. Support the family during this crisis.
4. Develop the care staffs' understanding.
5. Help this child to enjoy painting.
6. Provide a supporting environment.

They are fuzzies because 'Dad' cannot see whether we have or have not done what we said we would do. Examples of performances identified by the 'Hey Dad' test are:

1. Set a specific goal that this person will achieve within one week.
2. Record the number of times he pulls the hair of other children in the ward in one day.
3. Guide his hands to the waistband of his trousers and pull his trousers to correct position.
4. Give the command 'pull up your trousers'.
5. Keep a record of individual progress by recording data daily in graph form.
6. Determine which of a range of commodities act as positive reinforcement for an individual child by conducting an experimental trial.

These are performances because 'Dad' can see whether we have or have not done what we said we would do.

It can be seen that the behavioural approach demands a move from broad general descriptions of behaviour to precise detailed descriptions of behaviour in performance terms. It is helpful to group these behaviours into categories:[5]

1. Those behaviours that need to be *strengthened*.[5] These are behaviours which the individual can already perform, but he may not perform them consistently, at the appropriate time or in the appropriate place. An example would be the child who can eat with a knife and fork but eats with his fingers if not supervised.

2. Those behaviours which need to be *developed*.[5] These are behaviours which the individual does not or cannot perform. Developing new behaviours involves teaching those skills that will enable the individual to be more independent. Examples of these skills may be washing, dressing, feeding or developing hand-eye coordination. Once these new behaviours have been developed they can be strengthened.

3. Those behaviours which need to be *reduced*.[5] These are behaviours that the individual does perform but which are either dangerous or inappropriate. The aim might be to reduce the frequency of the behaviour or eliminate it completely; reducing the frequency of disruptive manneristic behaviour which interferes with learning and eliminating self-destructive behaviour such as head-banging. Alternatively the aim may be to teach the individual to perform the behaviour at the appropriate time and place. An example would be the child who has learnt to undress himself but does this in public. The incidence of undressing in public would be reduced and undressing at bed-time or bath time would be strengthened.

The information that leads to the classification of an individual's repertoire of behaviour is based on observation carried out over a variable period of time, by the people associated with him in every-day settings. This last point is important, as, if the observation were to be carried out in a situation and by people with whom the individual was not familiar, a false picture of the person's behaviour may result. Daily contact and accurate observation enable parents or care staff to build a behavioural profile of the child or adult, so that behaviours which need to be strengthened, developed or reduced can be identified. This will form the basis for making the decision about which behaviour should be modified or changed, which new skills taught and in what order. Again, it is important that those most concerned with the child or adult should be involved in the decision about which behaviour should be changed. A parent, for example, may perceive a particular behaviour as more of a problem than others, whilst the psychologist advising the parent may see another behaviour as more important.

The aspect of the individual's behaviour which it is planned to modify is called the target behaviour.[4] Target behaviour has two dimensions: it is a statement of the behaviour that we aim to change and also a statement of the performance that we are aiming for, following successful completion of a training programme. As an example, we might aim to change a child's behaviour of stealing food at meal-times, to never stealing food at meal-times. It is a way of describing both existing behaviour and terminal behaviour. It is important to describe target behaviour in objective terms so that there can be agreement about the behaviour that is being changed and what it is being changed to. Once the target behaviour has been identified and defined it is necessary to establish how often and in what circumstances it occurs.

MEASUREMENT OF BEHAVIOUR

Information about the behaviour of a person is obtained through systematic observation and facilitates an accurate comparison of performance before, during and after training. A base-line is a record of existing behaviour before training takes place and usually refers to a specific behaviour. It is important that this is estimated accurately, as it will not only provide the data for evaluating the success of the programme of training but also indicate the stage at which the programme should be commenced. Two methods of observation commonly used are time sampling and continuous observation. In time sampling the usual technique is to divide the day into periods and to carry out observations for parts of this time.[4] These periods may be variable and designed to suit the particular circumstances. For example, it may be decided to observe a specific behaviour for five minutes on the hour every hour, which will provide a picture of specific behaviour during a day. Continuous observation is usually used to observe behaviour during a particular activity. An example of continuous observation would be observation of specific aspects of a child's mealtime behaviour. If you were interested only in mealtime behaviour, it would not be necessary to observe the child at any other time. Time sampling and continuous observation provide a framework for measuring different aspects of behaviour such as its frequency, rate or duration.

1. Frequency recording[1] involves counting the number of times a specific behaviour occurs during a given period of time. It may be used to establish a base-line measurement or the number of correct responses occurring during a teaching session.

2. Rate or percentage recording[1] is used when the behaviour recorded occurs over a variable period of time. It is calculated by dividing the total number of times the behaviour occurred by the time over which the behaviour was recorded. It can also be used to calculate the percentage of correct responses during a training programme.

3. Duration recording[1] is used to measure the amount of time an individual is engaged in a particular activity and the unit of measurement is time (seconds, minutes or hours). It is essential information in a programme to decrease the amount of time spent, for example, in dressing. Alternatively, the information may be needed in a programme designed to increase attention span or eye contact.

Accurate observation is vital to the success of behaviour modification programmes and several items of equipment will help to ensure accuracy. Specially prepared charts will help organize the recording of events. In frequency recording a counter should be used in conjunction with a stop watch.[6]

Once the information has been collected it is essential to record it in a way that can easily be understood by other people involved in the programme. Many different ways of recording have been developed as a result of the different experiences of different people. For example, a frequency count may be

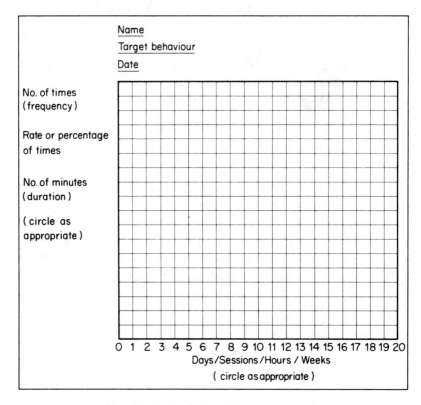

Fig. 46. A standard multi-purpose graph.

recorded as a number of marks on a chart or as a written figure. Experience has shown that recording the information in the form of a graph has the advantage of providing a record of behaviour over a period of time that is easily understood.[4] A standard form of multi-purpose graph is shown in Fig. 46.

REINFORCEMENT

At the beginning of this chapter the point was made that behaviour was determined by its consequences. This was borne out in the discussion of instrumental conditioning and Thorndike's 'law of effect', which stated that 'responses accompanied by satisfaction were more likely to recur'. Thorndike's 'law of effect' was defined operationally by Skinner in the theory of operant conditioning. Skinner described two classes of reinforcing stimuli: positive reinforcers are stimuli that the individual finds pleasant and rewarding, and which increase or strengthen a response; negative reinforcers are stimuli that the individual finds unpleasant or aversive and the removal of which increases or strengthens a response.[10]

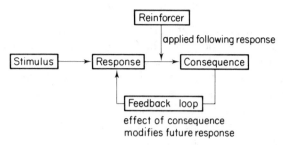

Fig. 47. Possible effects of a reinforcing stimulus on behaviour.

In behaviour modification programmes the aim is to identify an appropriate reinforcer for the individual and apply it in such a way that it is possible to change the individual's behaviour. This can be represented diagrammatically as in Fig. 47. A reinforcer is any event that strengthens or increases the behaviour that it follows.[8] However, although a reinforcer will act to strengthen the behaviour that it follows, it should be remembered that behaviour is not controlled by one reinforcing stimulus in isolation but by the interaction of multiple stimuli.[2]

Types of reinforcer

There are countless examples of reinforcers either occurring naturally or deliberately applied which may be used in the modification of behaviour. It is helpful to divide them into the broad categories of primary and conditioned reinforcers.

Primary reinforcers are those that relate to the biological functioning of the individual and may be described as consumable.[1] They include food (items of normal diet, sweets, chocolate, crisps, biscuits, ice cream) and drink (items of normal diet, tea, coffee, squash). Primary reinforcers are powerful in their effect largely because they do not require any special learning by the individual and are frequently used with the mentally handicapped.

Conditioned reinforcers, on the other hand, depend on learning in order to have the reinforcing effect. This effect occurs as a result of a repeated paired association between the reinforcer and a particular event. They include:

1. Social events: praise, attention, physical contact.
2. Activities: preferred activities such as playing with a particular toy, sitting in a favourite chair, going to a dance or cinema, watching television.
3. Tokens, perhaps in the form of plastic counters, a mark on a chart which can be exchanged for primary reinforcement in the form of sweets or a conditioned reinforcer such as a trip to a special event.

Conditioned reinforcers have the advantage that they can be given during a teaching session without interrupting the programme.

Selection of reinforcers

The previous section showed that a large number of reinforcers can be used in teaching the mentally handicapped. The selection of the appropriate reinforcer is critical, as behaviour modification is based on the principle that behaviour is changed or maintained as of the consequence of positive and negative reinforcement. One of the difficulties in selecting reinforcers for the mentally handicapped is that reinforcing stimuli are not always immediately obvious and cannot usually be ascertained simply by asking the person, although where this is possible it should be done.[2] The two approaches most commonly used in identifying reinforcers for the severely mentally handicapped are observing the individual in a situation of free choice or offering specific items or events and evaluating the response.[2]

The Premack principle is concerned with the first of these approaches. The individual is observed to see which activity he would spend the most time engaged in if given the choice. The preferred activity can be used to reinforce a less preferred or probable behaviour,[1] so that in order to do the preferred activity he would first have to do the less preferred activity. This is a particularly useful approach with the mentally handicapped as it is highly individual and can easily be adapted to particular preferences.

No one reinforcer is necessarily 'better' than another, as individuals vary so much in their response. A particular item like ice cream may work extremely well with one child but not at all with another.[6] Each child or adult should sample and experience a range of potential reinforcers before a teaching programme commences, to identify specific reinforcers for that person.

Generally speaking, the severely mentally handicapped respond to consumable reinforcers and the less handicapped to conditioned reinforcers of activities and tokens.

Tokens were mentioned briefly in the preceding section as 'counters' or 'marks' which have a value and can be given during an activity and exchanged for actual rewards following the activity. This system of reinforcement is modelled on normal economic practice, in which we receive money for work done and subsequently change it for goods. In behaviour modification this system is called a 'token economy'. Its application is particularly suitable for the less handicapped and when working with groups of people.

Schedules of reinforcement

In the previous discussion we have assumed that each correct or appropriate response will be reinforced. This is termed a *continuous rate* of reinforcement and is particularly useful in teaching and developing new behaviour.[9] Research has shown, however, that if continuous reinforcement is stopped the new behaviour will rapidly decrease in frequency. In order to maintain a behaviour that has been learned it is necessary to use other ratios of reinforcement. A *fixed ratio* of reinforcement is often used and means that the individual will be reinforced only after a fixed number of correct responses.[9] A further ratio used in the maintenance of behaviour is the *variable* or *intermittent ratio* of reinforcement which means that the individual will be rewarded on an average number of correct responses; that is, he does not always receive reinforcement after a fixed number of responses.[9]

Teaching should always begin with continuous reinforcement, progressing to a fixed ratio and finally a variable ratio to maintain the learned behaviour. Many of the reinforcers in the natural environment occur on a variable ratio in the form of success, profit or achievement.

Application of reinforcement

There are a number of 'reinforcement rules' which may help in the application of reinforcers. The first and most obvious is to identify appropriate reinforcers and then apply them selectively. Determine the target response and reinforce only that response. Random reinforcement will have the effect of establishing competing or inappropriate responses.[6] A correct response should be reinforced immediately it occurs otherwise there is a risk that the reinforcement becomes less effective and, more important, an inappropriate response may be reinforced if there is too long a delay.[6] Verbal praise can be used as a 'bridge' between response and reinforcement with a consumable reinforcer. The linking of verbal praise and primary reinforcement constitutes a further rule, in that as progress is made the consumable reinforcement can be withdrawn, maintaining the behaviour with verbal reinforcement.

We have already discussed the importance of the schedule of reinforcement with the general rule that teaching should start with a continuous ratio leading on to a fixed ratio and finally a variable ratio.

The effectiveness of the reinforcer should be constantly reviewed.[8] People change in their tastes and preferences and what started as a reinforcer may not continue as one, and so the reinforcer should be varied as and when necessary.

A problem that is often encountered is the quantity of a consumable reinforcer that should be given.[2] A general rule is that small quantities are best and not directly following a meal. If too much of a consumable reinforcer is given then satiation will occur.[4] Finally, the effectiveness of a reinforcer will be enhanced if it is given by someone that the child or adult likes and has established a good relationship with.

SUMMARY

This chapter has considered the principles of behavioural change as they have developed from learning theory. It has also discussed the application of these principles of teaching and helping the mentally handicapped and has included a discussion of the concept of reinforcement. Chapter 19 goes on to discuss the practical application of these principles by discussing techniques used to strengthen, develop or reduce behaviour.

GLOSSARY

Aversive   Regarded as unpleasant.

Base-line   A measure of what a person can do before any intervention to change that behaviour.

Behaviour   All the activity of an individual that can be observed by someone else.

Behaviour modification   The systematic use of principles and procedures derived from learning theory, particularly reinforcement theory, in a teaching situation.

Conditioning   The process by which individuals can be taught to respond in a particular way to a specific stimulus or event.

Classical conditioning   The conditioning of reflex responses by presentation of paired stimuli. Theory devised by I.R. Pavlov (1927). (See text for full explanation of unconditioned stimulus and response and conditioned stimulus and response.)

Duration recording   A method of measuring the amount of time an individual is engaged in an activity.

Fuller, P.   Dr Fuller first demonstrated the application of operant conditioning with a severely mentally handicapped boy in 1949.

Frequency recording   A method used to count the number of times a specific behaviour occurs in a given period of time.

'Hey Dad' test   A technique devised by R. Mager to define behaviour in objective terms.

Instrumental conditioning A process of learning described by F. L. Thorndike (1911), where behaviour is instrumental in gaining reward or avoiding punishment. Sometimes called 'trial-and-error learning'.

Law of effect   Formulated by F. L. Thorndike, it states that responses accompanied by satisfaction are more likely to recur.

Medical model   The model of care which assumes that behaviour has a physiological cause and is therefore treatable by medical means.

Operant   A class of behaviour that can operate on the environment to some effect. It can generally be considered to be all that behaviour not included under the heading of reflex behaviour, though there are exceptions.

Operant conditioning	The process of training operant behaviour using reinforcement principles. Behaviour modification consists mainly of techniques derived from operant conditioning.
Pavlov, I.	Dr Ivan Pavlov, Russian physiologist, who described the theory of classical conditioning in 1927.
Phobia	An irrational fear.
Premack principle	A technical term referring to the fact that a behaviour that occurs with a high frequency can be used as a reinforcer for a behaviour that occurs with a low frequency.
Primary reinforcer	Generally considered to be a reinforcer that is in itself rewarding without us having to teach that it is: the best example is food and drink.
Rate recording	A method of calculating the percentage of times a behaviour has occurred.
Positive reinforcement	The process by which a behaviour is strengthened when it is followed by a positive reinforcer or reward. The process of giving the reward to make the chosen behaviour more likely to occur again is called positive reinforcement; for instance we may pay attention to a child when he is behaving well in order to increase the number of times that occurs.
Positive reinforcer	Anything we provide that a person likes and that will make him more likely to repeat whatever he was doing at the time we gave it to him.
Negative reinforcement	The process by which a behaviour is strengthened when a negative reinforcer, or punishment, is removed. For instance, you might turn down the sound of a loud radio: the loud sound would be the negative reinforcer, turning down the sound would be reinforced by its removal.
Negative reinforcer	Anything that happens to a person that he does not like so that he learns how to remove it.
Fixed ratio	A schedule of reinforcement under which a reinforcer is presented following a specific number of responses. A special case is continuous reinforcement when every desired response is followed up by a reinforcer. On a fixed ratio we might reinforce only after, say, every four responses.
Variable or intermittent reinforcement	A schedule of reinforcement where the reinforcer is presented only intermittently; it can be on a number of different schedules such as fixed ratio or fixed interval. This

programme of reinforcement produces behaviour that is more resistant to extinction than behaviour reinforced on a continuous schedule.

Response   A specific unit of behaviour; for instance, in feeding, the filling of the spoon is a specific response in a whole chain of feeing behaviours.

Reward   Another name for positive reinforcer, serves to strengthen the behaviour that precedes it when it is presented.

Satiation   The state reached when a reward has been available for such an extended period that it is no longer effective as a reinforcer.

Skinner, B.F.   Professor B.F. Skinner who described the theory of operant conditioning.

Stimulus   Any event in the environment of the individual to which he might or might not respond.

Stimulus control When a given stimulus can be shown to control the occurrence of a specific response. Much of the training procedure involves building up new stimuli to control behaviour.

Target behaviour That aspect of an individual's behaviour which it is planned to change.

Thorndike, F.L. Thorndike formulated the theory of instrumental conditioning and the 'law of effect'.

Time sampling   A technique of measuring behaviour by carrying out observations at regular intervals in order to obtain a behaviour profile.

Token   A reinforcer, like money, that can be used to reinforce a wide range of activities and yet allow for individual differences in personal preferences for other reinforcers. The token allows the person the freedom to select his own reinforcers. By pairing a primary reinforcer, say a drink, with the token it soon becomes a conditioned reinforcer and can be used to reward the behaviour of someone we are teaching.

Token economy   Or token system. A therapeutic environment in which the reinforcers are available in exchange for tokens which are themselves contingent upon specific behaviours considered appropriate. The value of the tokens for any particular response can be changed to manipulate the economy in such a way that complex behaviour can be readily built up in small steps. Using a token system allows greater scope in 'paying' individuals for the work they do and in helping them develop new skills.

BIBLIOGRAPHY

1. Horner, R.D. & Whatmore, R. (1975) *Basic Procedures of Behaviour Modification* (Unpublished paper). Winchester: Health Care Evaluation Team.
2. Kierman, C.C. (1974) Behaviour modification. In: *Mental Deficiency: The Changing Outlook*, ed. A. Clarke & A.D.B. Clarke, 3rd ed. London: Methuen.
3. Kushlick, A., Felce, D., Palmer, J. & Smith, J. (1976) *Evidence to the Committee of Enquiry into Mental Handicap Nursing and Care.* Winchester: Health Care Evaluation Team.
4. Mackrell, K. & Remington, R. (1976) *Behaviour Modification in the Care of the Mentally Handicapped* (Unpublished paper). Southampton: Southampton University.
5. Morris, R.J. (1976) *Behaviour Modification with Children.* Massachusetts: Winthrop.
6. Panyan, M.C. (1972) *New Ways to Teach New Skills.* Kansas: H. & H. Enterprises.
7. Patterson, G.R. & Gullion, M.E. (1971) *Living with Children.* Illinois: Research Press.
8. Perkins, E.A., Taylor, P.D. & Capie, A.C.M. (1976) *Helping the Retarded.* Kidderminster: Institute of Mental Subnormality.
9. Whaley, D.L. & Malott, R.W. (1971) *Elementary Principles of Behaviour.* New York: Appleton-Century-Crofts.
10. Whitehead, J.M. (1976) *Motivation and Learning.* Milton Keynes: Open University Press.
11. Williams, C. (1978) An introduction to behavioural principles. In *Teaching The Profoundly Handicapped in Child: Care, Health and Development*, Vol. 4, pp. 21–27. Oxford: Blackwell Scientific.

The practice of behavioural change   19

In the previous chapter it was seen that behaviour is controlled by its consequences and that the essence of the behavioural approach is the control of behaviour by systematically following a correct response with an appropriate reinforcer. However, many naturally occurring environmental stimuli influence a person or cause him to behave in a particular way. This would seem to imply that human behaviour is subject solely to the vagaries of environmental stimuli and is determined in a completely random way. This does not happen because we learn to discriminate between courses of action available to us, in the light of our previous activity, observation or experience. The individual learns that by responding in a particular way he will either be reinforced or avoid unpleasant consequences. This is called 'discrimination learning' and involves learning to identify those stimuli that precede positive reinforcement, called discriminative stimuli, and those stimuli which indicate that reinforcement will not be forthcoming.[9] An example of discriminative learning may be seen when a child learns that if he cries his mother will always pick him up, but that his father will ignore him. Consequently, he will cry more often in the presence of his mother as her attention is reinforcing to him.

By arranging for particular stimuli to occur at a specific time or in a specific setting it is possible to determine an individual's response which can then be reinforced. These 'setting conditions', as they are called, help to determine behaviour.[4] This can be seen in the example of the child who is brought to the dining room and asked to sit at the table which is laid for dinner at the child's normal dinner-time. The environmental stimuli or 'cues' of the laid table in the dining room at dinner time will cause the child to respond in an appropriate way as a result of past reinforcement received at meal-times. Arranging for particular stimuli to occur which will determine a person's behaviour is termed stimulus control in that the stimulus controls the response.[5] Stimulus control is particularly important in behaviour modification and the following sections discuss how this may be achieved to strengthen or reduce existing behaviours or develop new behaviours.

TECHNIQUES TO DEVELOP AND STRENGTHEN BEHAVIOUR

A number of techniques may be used to strengthen existing behaviour or develop new behaviours. The more commonly used techniques include shaping, progressive and backward chaining, prompt and fade and modelling. The choice of technique will be influenced by the nature of the skill that is being taught, the degree of mental and physical handicap of the person being taught and the skill of the teacher.

Shaping

Shaping is a term borrowed from sculpture; just as the sculptor gradually shapes the material he is working with to the desired form, the teacher gradually shapes the behaviour of the mentally handicapped child or adult to the target behaviour. It is a technique that may be used when the target behaviour does not occur and new behaviour has to be developed.[6] Shaping is also called the successive approximation method becuase it involves using a behaviour that the individual can do and gradually reinforcing successive approximations to the target behaviour until finally the target behaviour itself is being reinforced.[3] Shaping requires a clear definition of the target behaviour; careful observation of the individual's existing behaviour to identify a behaviour that resembles the target behaviour; establishing this behaviour by systematic reinforcement; breaking the target behaviour into small steps and reinforcing successive approximations of the target behaviour until the target behaviour is achieved.[5]

An example of the shaping technique can be seen in a programme to develop speech. The child may not be able to say 'cup' but may be able to make a coughing sound. The coughing sound would be the initial behaviour that would be reinforced and gradually successive approximations to the sound of 'cup' would be reinforced until the child was able to say 'cup'.

'Pure' shaping is rarely used as it is dependent on the child making the initial and intermediate responses and consequently learning is very slow. Other techniques such as chaining and prompting are used to accelerate learning and these are discussed below.

Chaining

Chaining is a technique used to teach a number of behaviours which when linked together form a complete skill such as dressing or feeding. Each step in performing the task is a link in the chain of behaviour. The task must be analysed and broken down into small steps which can be taught to the individual. Gradually, as the child learns each new step, more and more behaviour is required in order to gain reinforcement until finally the target behaviour is reached, the last link in the chain. The procedure of teaching a skill from the beginning to the end is termed forward or progressive chaining and is not often used with the mentally handicapped as it can make learning difficult.[4] A far more effective method is that of backward or reverse chaining which involves teaching the last step in a chain first and working backwards. Backward chaining has the advantage that the child always receives reinforcement since each new behavioural skill he learns is followed by one he has already learnt and so provides opportunities to practice those skills he has acquired.[4]

An example of backward chaining can be demonstrated in teaching a child to complete a simple puzzle. Just giving a child a puzzle to do may be too difficult for him as he has no experience on which to base his actions. However, almost completing the puzzle, but leaving one piece for him to fit into place, makes the whole task easier. Gradually as this step is mastered another puzzle piece is omitted.

Prompting and fading

A prompt is any stimulus which influences an individual to behave in a particular way. Used systematically, prompting is a useful teaching technique that can help to bring about a desired response. Prompts can usefully be divided into three classes: verbal prompts in the form of simple instructions in a teaching programme; visual prompts in the form of gestures such as pointing to an object or beckoning to someone; and physical prompts in the form of physical guidance.[8]

Often, the three classes of prompt are used together in the same teaching programme. An example of this can be seen in teaching a child to put on a shirt. The visual prompt would be to hold the shirt up so that the armhole could be seen; this is accompanied by the gestural prompt of demonstrating the action of putting an arm into the shirt sleeve. The physical prompt would be taking the child's arm and physically guiding it into the shirt sleeve. This would be accompanied by the verbal prompt of telling the child to put his arm in the shirt sleeve. Prompting does more than just assist the individual to perform a skill or acquire new behaviour. The prompt leads to the child performing a behaviour which is reinforced and this sequence of prompt → behaviour → reinforcement is learned. In this way the prompt becomes a discriminative stimulus.[5] However, if this sequence was always presented, the child would not learn to perform a skill unless a prompt was available, and so, once competence is gained the prompts are gradually removed until the behaviours occurs without the need for prompting.[10] This technique is called fading and generally the prompts are faded in order of physical, visual/gestural and finally verbal.

Modelling

Modelling is a technique which may be successfully used with the more able mentally handicapped person.[3] It involves the individual observing someone else carrying out a task and then trying to imitate it himself.[4]

Several points should be borne in mind if a modelling procedure is used. The child must be able to interpret the actions he sees in order to reproduce them. It is helpful if the child is able to see another child or children modelling behaviour and being reinforced for it. The child may not be capable of reproducing a perfect imitation and it may be necessary to break the behaviour down into small steps and model one step at a time, gradually building up to the final performance.[3] This approach uses a combination of modelling and shaping successive approximations to the target behaviour.

An example of modelling is seen when a word is broken down into its phonetic elements, each element being modelled until all the sounds are learned and put in the right sequence to reproduce the word.

The above sections outline a number of techniques that may be used to strengthen and develop behaviour. The choice of which technique or combination of techniques to use is determined by the nature of the problem, the degree of handicap present and the skill of the teacher. The problem is often which behaviour to modify rather than which technique to use and the next section discusses a hierarchy of skills which the individual may need to acquire.

HIERARCHY OF SKILLS

The rationale for classifying skills into a hierarchy is that it helps to decide which skills to teach; groups skills with common components together; gives guidance on the sequential order of teaching; and grades the skills in order of complexity.

The skills listed in Fig. 48 are intended to be examples of the skills which

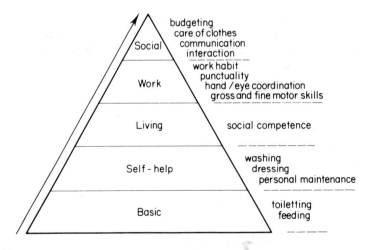

Fig. 48. A model of a hierarchy of skill, with some examples.

could be taught. The same model could be used to itemize the skills an individual already possesses or needs to develop in the light of his particular circumstances. The pyramid represents the order in which skills are normally taught, with the arrow indicating the progression from the basic skills of toiletting and feeding, to self-help skills and on to living and work skills and finally to the complex social skills of communication and interaction. It is the author's opinion that the progressive nature of the model is realistic, as it seems illogical to attempt to teach a complex social skill such as peer interaction when the individual is unable to feed himself or make any attempt to dress himself. Having said this, it is also true that in developing a person's social skills the interpersonal relationship between the teacher and the child may be strengthened and learning facilitated as a result. The question of which skill to teach is taken up in the next section which deals with the selection and writing of programmes with illustrative examples.

ASPECTS OF PROGRAMMING

A number of factors should be considered when planning programmes of training, including the selection of the target behaviour, the sequence of steps used to teach the skills and physical factors such as the time, duration and location of the training sessions. The selection of the skill should result from an analysis of the skills the child already performs. This can be determined by systematic observation of the child's behaviour using the results of continuous observation or time sampling or by using a developmental checklist such as the progress assessment charts.[2] The skill selected should allow for a smooth progression of developmental ability in all areas. Two further criteria are important: the selected target behaviour should be both realistic and relevant. Sometimes children are taught skills that are not realistic, as for example a child who is taught to button his shirt when he is unable to put his shirt on. An example of an irrelevant skill is seen when a child is taught to tie shoelaces and then given slip-on shoes to wear.[7] If there are no opportunities to practice what has been taught the ability to perform the skill will be quickly lost. Once a target behaviour has been identified for an individual a base-line recording should be taken to determine the frequency or level at which the behaviour occurs. This information is essential as it provides a record of behaviour before any teaching begins so that the success of the programme can be evaluated, and also indicates the stage at which teaching could commence.

However, before teaching can begin on any programme the individual will need to have developed some basic skills. It is impossible to teach anyone anything if they cannot or will not pay attention and it is made more difficult if they are unable to follow basic instructions. Paying attention and following simple instructions may be the first skills that the individual will need to learn so that he may acquire more complex skills.

Once the target behaviour has been identified, the next step is to break the behaviour down into the elements or steps which will form the teaching programme; this process is called task analysis. A large number of published programmes, particularly self-help programmes, can be used as a guide, although it should be emphasized that each individual requires an individual programme. The following programmes are taken from Panyan[7] and illustrate the principles of task analysis and programme writing.

Feeding[7]

Self-feeding sessions last for 15–20 minutes rather than the customary 10 minutes. If 20-minute sessions are held, require 20 successful trials for two straight sessions as the criterion.

1. Assist the child in raising spoonful of food to within 8 cm (3 in) of the mouth. After he takes the bite, assist him in returning spoon to the plate.

2. Assist child in raising food and assist to half-way between plate and mouth. Once he has taken food assist him back to the plate.

3. Assist child to scoop food with the spoon and let him take it to his mouth. After he takes the food assist him back to the plate.

4. Assist child in dipping, gradually fading your support. After he takes the food assist him in returning to the plate but release your support 8 cm (3 in) from the plate.

5. After he takes the food assist him in returning the spoon half-way down to the plate. Do not assist him in dipping or raising.

6. After he takes the food, touch his wrist briefly as soon as he removes spoon from mouth for the return movement down to the plate. Do not assist him in dipping or raising. Fade out touching the wrist.

Bathing[7]

1. Pick up the soap.
2. Pick up the wash flannel.
3. Rub some soap on flannel.
4. Wash face and neck.

Each rubbing motion which leaves soap on the area is counted as a success.

5. Wash stomach and chest.
6. Wash both arms.
7. Wash thighs and genitalia.
8. Wash legs and feet.

Each rubbing motion which leaves soap on the area is counted as a success.

9. Rinse: each motion which removes soap from the body is a success.
10. Dry: each motion which removes water from the body is a success.

Putting on socks[7]

1. Put the socks all the way over the foot and 2.5 cm (1 in) from top. (Command: Pull up your sock.)

2. Put the socks on the feet, stopping at the ankles.
3. Put the socks on stopping at the heels.
4. Put the socks on stopping at the middle of the foot.
5. Put the sock just over the toes.
6. Place the sock beside the foot. (Command: Put on your sock.)

Handwashing[7]

1. Put hands in the water.
2. Pick up the soap.
3. Rub hands together with soap (ten strokes equal ten successes).
4. Rinse hands, rubbing hands in water.
5. Dry hands (ten patting motions equal ten successful trials).

Buttoning[7]

For steps 1–4 use large coat buttons.

1. Hold button between thumb and forefinger.
2. Hold the edge of the other side of the shirt (or blouse) between the thumb and forefinger of the opposite hand.
3. Push one side of the button through the buttonhole and pull the button through.
4. Complete steps 1–3 for all five buttons.
5. Complete steps 1–4 using medium-sized buttons.
6. Complete steps 1–4 using standard-size buttons.

One of the most common difficulties experienced in teaching programmes is that the steps in the programme are too far apart in terms of skills. In this case intermediate steps will need to be written to allow for the smooth acquisition of the skill. Indeed it may be necessary to write the complete programme rather than relying on prepared programmes. When writing new programmes attention should be paid to the following points. The target behaviour should be defined in objective behavioural terms so that there is no ambiguity and everyone involved will understand the aims of the programme. An example might be: 'on completion of the programme John will be able to put his coat on by himself when asked'. This statement of behaviour should then be analysed into task elements and generally should contain not more than ten steps. These steps are arranged in sequence and form the programme as seen in the self-help skills programmes outlined above. Finally it is necessary to decide what constitutes the successful learning of a particular step; for example ten successes at ten opportunities, and when the individual can progress to the next step in the programme.[7]

Before teaching begins consideration should also be given to the time, duration and location of the teaching sessions in order that they may be as realistic as possible. Generally speaking the skill should be taught at the normal time, so that dressing skills are taught on getting up in the morning and undressing taught when getting ready for a bath or going to bed. Similarly, the location should be the one in which the behaviour would normally occur; feeding skills would be taught in the dining room at a normal mealtime. Finally, the duration of the teaching session should be limited to the time that the individual is able to attend, usually no more than 10 or 15 minutes.

The above methods may be varied to take account of individual circumstances. The following examples show these variations: a child may be taught dressing skills in the morning or afternoon to give more opportunity to learn and when there may be more staff time available; a child may be disruptive and distractable in the presence of other children and so he is taught on his own and gradually integrated with others; a child may be able to concentrate only for a brief time and so sessions are kept to a minimum and lengthened as the attention span increases. Occasionally quite dramatic measures may be taken in order to provide increased learning opportunities. This may be seen in the 'mini-meal' procedure, where the total daily diet is divided into ten equal portions and the child is then fed at ten sessions throughout the day.

In this section various aspects of programmes and programming have been discussed. The choice of teaching method, whether to forward or reverse chain, which prompts to use and the range of reinforcers will be determined by the individual circumstances. The techniques and programmes have all been directed towards strengthening behaviour or developing new behaviours. It is often necessary to reduce or weaken behaviours so that the mentally handicapped child or adult may benefit from other more positive ways of behaving. These techniques are discussed in the next section.

TECHNIQUES TO REDUCE
OR WEAKEN BEHAVIOUR

The previous chapter discussed the process of describing behaviour in objective terms and then measuring its frequency, rate and duration. This process is applied in exactly the same way to inappropriate behaviour. After a base-line recording the target behaviour is identified and an appropriate technique for managing the behaviour is decided on. The techniques which may be used to reduce or weaken behaviour include extinction, time out, response cost, shaping incompatible behaviours, differential reinforcement of other behaviours and punishment.

Extinction

In the introduction to this chapter the concept of discrimination learning was briefly discussed with the example of the child who learned that his mother would always pay attention to his crying but that his father would ignore him. The child's crying behaviour was reinforced by his mother's attention but was extinguished by his father ignoring him when he cried. Extinction is the withholding of reinforcement following a behaviour so that the behaviour decreases in frequency.[9] It involves identifying the reinforcing consequences that maintain the behaviour and systematically removing them.[6] It is important to remember that human behaviour is complex and not a single stimulus–response chain and therefore extinction is often inappropriate as it is not possible to eliminate all the reinforcing consequences maintaining the behaviour. Extinction can be used only when the consequences of ignoring the behaviour are not dangerous to the child or others.[5] An example of this can be seen in the case of a child who bangs his head. The 'normal' response would be to pick the child up to stop him from banging his head, and this social attention serves to reinforce the child for head-banging. However, it would be almost impossible entirely to ignore head-banging in a child because of the physical damage that would occur.[5] Similarly, it would be irresponsible to ignore physical attacks such as kicking, biting or hair-pulling.[5]

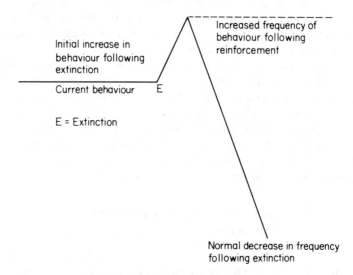

Initial increase in behaviour following extinction

Increased frequency of behaviour following reinforcement

Current behaviour   E

E = Extinction

Normal decrease in frequency following extinction

Fig. 49. The principle of extinction.

A further drawback in using extinction is that it is often a very slow process, requiring a highly consistent approach by all those who are concerned with the child. The reason for this is that behaviour is normally maintained by intermittent reinforcement and it requires only one incident to be reinforced rather than ignored for extinction to be ineffective.[5] This is particularly significant when it is realized that initially behaviour that is being extinguished increases in frequency before it decreases.[6]

However, extinction may be used very effectively for some forms of inappropriate behaviour, particularly when the behaviour is maintained by social reinforcement such as attention. The child who constantly demands attention by screaming, crying and pestering parents, teachers or care staff by pulling their clothing and interfering with their work with other children poses a problem which may well respond to the systematic application of extinction.[5]

Time out from positive reinforcement

'Time out' is essentially an extension of the extinction procedure and involves the planned temporary removal of the opportunity to gain reinforcement. There are a number of ways in which 'time out' can be implemented. The method usually associated with 'time out' is the physical removal of a child who is behaving inappropriately from an area where he can gain positive reinforcement to a special room or 'time out' area. The 'time out' area or room should be unstimulating so that the child is unable to gain reinforcement from his environment.[8] The child is placed in the room immediately after the inappropriate behaviour and left there either until he comes out by himself or until three to five minutes have elapsed.[6] The time spent in the room is important because if the child is left in the room for too long appropriate behaviour may be punished. On return from the room the child should receive social reinforcement for appropriate behaviour.[6] In some hospitals patients are 'secluded', which means that they may spend varying amounts of time in a side room. Seclusion should never be confused with time out. Seclusion is prescribed and authorized by a doctor, whereas time out is a short term (three to five minutes) procedure which can be used by care staff to help reduce inappropriate behaviour. Other 'time out' procedures do not involve physical removal of the child but removal of an activity which is reinforcing to him.[4] Examples of this can be seen where a child plays with his food using his fingers. The plate may be moved for a period of 30 seconds so that he cannot do this and then returned, or his arms may be physically held to prevent him putting his hands in his food. A further use of 'time out' is seen where the person working with the child deliberately turns his back on the child for a short period of time following inappropriate behaviour, ensuring that reinforcement is unavailable to the child for this brief period.

The effectiveness of 'time out' depends on a number of factors. The environment from which the child is removed must be reinforcing to the child and the 'time out' environment must be unstimulating.[4] If 'time out' is being used it must be used consistently otherwise inappropriate behaviour may be reinforced and subsequently occur at a higher frequency than before, as seen in the discussion of extinction.[6] 'Time out' should be used only in connection with a defined target behaviour as part of a programme to reduce an inappropriate behaviour and not indiscriminately for all inappropriate behaviour.

Response cost

Response cost is similar to time out, in that it involves the withdrawal of positive reinforcement but in addition requires the child to lose reinforcement. The payment of fines for inappropriate behaviour is an example of response cost in every-day life.[5] If a library book is overdue you are required not only to return the book but also to pay a fine.

Response cost procedures are obviously more effective when used with people who can understand and appreciate a loss; because of this they are often used in conjunction with a token economy system.[6]

Variations of the simple response cost procedures are restitution and over-correction. Restitution involves the child 'making good' any damage that he may cause by his behaviour. If the child throws something on the floor he would be required to pick it up. This helps to ensure that he is never reinforced for throwing things. Overcorrection is an extension of restitution: the child is required not only to replace the article that has been thrown but also to practice the appropriate behaviour involving the thrown object. In this way both restitution and overcorrection not only ensure that inappropriate behaviour is never reinforced but also provide opportunities to practice appropriate behaviour and gain positive reinforcement.[1] This last point is important and is discussed in the next sections.

Shaping incompatible behaviour

Occasionally it is possible to reduce or weaken inappropriate behaviour by shaping other behaviours which are incompatible with the behaviour it is desired to reduce. This has the dual effect of reducing inappropriate behaviour and building up and strengthening appropriate behaviour.[3] An example of this technique can be seen in a child who is distractable to the extent that it is impossible to teach him anything. Gradually eye contact would be established, the child being taught to follow instructions with the consequence that his attention span is increased. Paying attention is incompatible with being distractable.

The aim should always be to substitute an appropriate behaviour for a behaviour that is reduced, weakened or eliminated.[6] If a child spends three hours a day behaving in a specifically inappropriate way and this is eliminated, the child will usually find other inappropriate behaviour to engage in, unless new appropriate behaviours are taught.

Differential reinforcement of other behaviours (DRO)

This technique is similar to shaping incompatible behaviour in that it is designed to increase one class of behaviour and decrease another.[3] The difference lies in the fact that positive reinforcement is given whenever the inappropriate behaviour does not occur, coupled with extinction of the inappropriate behaviour when it does occur. An example of this can be seen when a child is reinforced for interacting with other children but is ignored when not interacting with others.[3] Initially the reinforcement schedule is almost continuous but the aim should be to fade the reinforcement to a fixed ratio as soon as possible. In this way inappropriate behaviour may be reduced and appropriate behaviour strengthened. This technique requires that the environment should afford the child the opportunity to gain positive reinforcement.

Punishment

Behaviour modification techniques, at their simplest level, are based on the principle of reward or punishment. Time out or extinction can be said to be punishing in that either an aversive stimulus is presented or a positive reinforcer is removed.[5] Punishment is more usually thought of as being either verbal, in the form of a reprimand, or corporal, in the form of a smack. In just the same way as the effect of a potential reinforcer has to be observed to see if the behaviour it follows increases in frequency, so the effect of punishment has to be observed. If a behaviour does not decrease following punishment then the event is not punishing to the individual.

Generally speaking punishment should be used only as a last resort and only after extensive consultation with all those caring for the individual. Quite apart from the ethical problems of using punishment, it is not a very effective way of managing behaviour. Punishment at best only teaches a person what not to do and may have the effect of suppressing inappropriate behaviour rather than changing it; when punishment is withdrawn the behaviour recurs.[5] The person administering the punishment may become so aversive to the child that it would adversely affect the programme of training.[4] An apparently contradictory effect can be seen when the child regards the punishment as reinforcing. This occurs because the act of reprimanding or smacking involves giving the child personal attention and as a result the child learns to behave 'badly' in order to continue receiving attention.[8] Finally, punishment may have the same effect as a major tranquillizer in that it will damp down all behaviour so that the child withdraws from all activities.

The choice of which technique to use in modifying inappropriate behaviour should always be influenced by the knowledge that teaching using positive reinforcement is always more effective.[6] In view of this the techniques of shaping incompatible behaviour and differential reinforcement of other behaviours should be tried first. However, for some behaviours, particularly those that involve injury to other children, a more suitable technique might be time out. The important considerations are that once a technique has been selected its effectiveness should be regularly reviewed and it should be applied consistently by all those concerned with the child's programme.

SUMMARY

This chapter has discussed practical applications of the principles of behavioural change by describing the various behaviour modification techniques that may be used to strengthen, develop or weaken behaviour.

The concept of discriminative learning was shown to be critical in the acquisition of skills by the mentally handicapped.[9] Achieving stimulus control accelerates learning and helps to maintain consistently appropriate responses.

The techniques that may be used to develop and strengthen behaviour include shaping, chaining, prompting and fading and modelling. Each technique has its particular application and the selection will be determined by the nature of the problem, the degree of handicap and the skill of the teacher. Reinforcement, discussed in the previous chapter, should always be systematically applied. The selection of which skill to teach was discussed, using the model of a hierarchy of skills which has the advantage of grouping skill with common components, determining the sequential order of teaching and grading skills in order of complexity. This discussion led to the consideration of the various factors involved in programming, including illustrative examples of self-help skills. A number of behavioural techniques that may be used to reduce or weaken behaviour were described, including extinction, time out, response cost, restitution, overcorrection, shaping incompatible behaviours, differential reinforcement of other behaviours and punishment.

Many people have difficulty both in accepting and in applying behaviour modification techniques, believing them to be 'mechanical' or 'inhuman' and in some way contrary to the concepts of caring for someone who is mentally handicapped. Other criticisms include the view that controlling and manipulating another person is unethical and morally wrong, and that behaviour modification is merely common sense confused by psychological jargon. The use of behavioural techniques does not preclude a warm and loving relationship with a child; in fact, the stronger the bond between the teacher and the child the more effective will be the teaching. Behaviour modification programmes have a defined goal that is designed to increase the mentally handicapped child or adult's degree of independence and clearly this is a very positive way of caring for someone. The particular strength of behaviour modification is that it can be used to teach the most severely handicapped child or adult of any age when other methods have been less than successful.

GLOSSARY

Aversive   Regarded as unpleasant.

Base-line   A measurement of what a person can do before any intervention to change that behaviour.

Chaining   A technique used to teach a number of behaviours which when linked together form a complex skill. Forward or progressive chaining involves teaching a skill from the beginning to the end in the normal sequence. Backward or reverse chaining involves teaching the last step in a chain first and working backwards.

Discriminative stimulus	The stimulus event which an individual learns to associate with the presence of absence of reinforcement.
Differential reinforcement of other behaviours	A technique designed to increase appropriate behaviours and decrease an inappropriate behaviour. It involves the combined use of positive reinforcement and extinction.
Extinction	The witholding of reinforcement following a behaviour so that the behaviour decreases in frequency.
Fading	The gradual removal of either prompts (cues) in the order of physical, visual/gestural, verbal or reinforcement during a programme.
Hierarchy of skills	A graded order of skill development from the basic skills of toiletting and feeding, self-help skills and through to social skills such as communication and interaction.
Incompatible behaviour	A behaviour that competes with another.
'Mini-meal'	A specific procedure for increasing the available opportunities to teach feeding skills, it involves the child's daily diet being divided into ten 'mini-meals'.
Modelling	Learning of a skill through imitation.
Over-correction	A technique for modifying inappropriate behaviour which involves the child repeatedly practicing the skills needed to carry out the appropriate behaviour.
Phonetic	Relating to the sounds of spoken language.
Prompt	Any stimulus which influences an individual to behave in a particular way. Prompts may be physical, visual/gestural or verbal.
Response cost	A technique which involves withdrawal of reinforcement in conjunction with the payment of a 'fine' from previously gained reinforcement.
Restitution	The 'making good' or repairing of any damage that may be caused by an individual.
Shaping	The technique of gradually increasing and strengthening successive approximations to the target behaviour.
Stimulus control	Use of a given stimulus to control the occurrence of a particular response.
Target behaviour	That aspect of the individual's behaviour that is planned to be changed.

Time out   A technique which involves the planned temporary removal
                    of the opportunity to gain reinforcement.

Token economy   A therapeutic environment in which the reinforcers are
                    available in exchange for tokens which are themselves
                    contingent upon specific behaviours considered appropriate.

BIBLIOGRAPHY

1. Fox, R.M. & Azrin, N.H. (1973) *Toilet Training the Retarded.* Illinois: Research Press.
2. Gunzburg, H.C. (1977) *Progress Assessment Chart Manual*, 5th ed. Stratford-upon-Avon: SEFA Publications.
3. Horner, R.D. & Whatmore, R. (1975) *Basic Procedures of Behaviour Modification* (Unpublished paper). Winchester: Health Care Evaluation Team.
4. Kiernan, C.C. (1974) Behaviour modification. In: *Mental Deficiency: The Changing Outlook*, ed. A. Clarke & A.D.B. Clarke, 3rd ed. London: Methuen.
5. Mackrell, K. & Remington (1976) *Behaviour Modification in the Care of the Mentally Handicapped* (Unpublished paper). Southampton: Southampton University.
6. Morris, R.J. (1976) *Behaviour Modification with Children.* Massachusetts: Winthrop.
7. Panyan, M.C. (1972) *New Ways to Teach New Skills.* Kansas: H. & H. Enterprises.
8. Perkins, E.A., Taylor, P.D. & Capie, A.C.D. (1976) *Helping the Retarded.* Kidderminster: Institute of Mental Subnormality.
9. Whaley, D.L. & Malott, R.W. (1971) *Elementary Principles of Behaviour.* New York: Appleton-Century-Crofts.
10. Williams, C. (1978) An introduction to behavioural principles. In: *Teaching the Profoundly Handicapped Child: Care, Health and Development*, Vol. 4, pp. 21–27. Oxford: Blackwell Scientific.

PART VI
Conclusions

Conclusions 20

The care of the mentally handicapped is at a crossroads. This is reflected in government policy,[3,4,6] the recent literature,[8,9,13] and the views and attitudes of representative organizations[12] and direct care staff.[2,10,12] The current debate is concerned with four central and inter-related issues: the rights of the mentally handicapped; patterns of care; the degree of integration and the forms it should take; and the training required by the care staff.

The uncertainty about these issues is due to a number of factors. One crucial factor is the historical development of services and care, which has resulted in patterns of care all too often based on the outdated concept of institutional and custodial care. An acceptance of the continuing role of the hospital for the mentally handicapped will influence consideration of the rights of the mentally handicapped, the degree of integration that is possible or desirable and the training requirements of the care staff.

The situation is further confused by the dichotomy of care provided under the present system of National Health Service and local authority care related to different dependency levels. This, in turn, is linked to the professional status and training of those involved in caring for the mentally handicapped in both health and social services, resulting in a seemingly intransigent desire to maintain the status quo.

The ways forward to resolve these issues have been discussed in recent government reports and legislation and by contemporary writers and these are reviewed in the following sections.

HUMAN RIGHTS AND THE MENTALLY HANDICAPPED

Significant progress has been made in the last ten years in the adoption of the principle of basic human rights for the mentally handicapped. Particularly in view of the fact that as recently as 1952 a leading writer on mental handicap advocated euthanasia for 'the 80 000 or more idiots and imbeciles in the country'; largely on the grounds that the money spent on them could be more beneficially used for the normal population.[8] This view is in direct contrast to the United Nations 'Declaration of the Rights of Disabled People' adopted in 1975. This stated that the mentally handicapped '... whatever the origin, nature and seriousness of their handicaps and disabilities ... have the same fundamental rights of their fellow citizens of the same age, which implies first and foremost the right to enjoy a decent life as normal and full as possible'.[9]

This principle was reiterated in the Jay Committee's philosophy of care:[2]

1. Mentally handicapped people have a right to enjoy normal patterns of life within the community.
2. Mentally handicapped people have a right to be treated as individuals.
3. Mentally handicapped people will require additional help from the communities in which they life and from professional services if they are to develop to their maximum potential as individuals.

A further example of this recongition is that mentally handicapped children have the same rights to education as other children. A right that is unequivocally stated in the 1970 Education Act as 'no child is ineducable'. This theme of educational rights is developed by the Warnock Committee's recommendations of a comprehensive range of educational facilities, within the mainstream of education, for 'children with learning difficulties'.[1]

However, recognition and acceptance of the rights of the mentally handicapped are not sufficient in themselves, but must be seen to be translated into positive action at all levels of society. It must also be remembered that the issue of rights for the mentally handicapped should include their right to reject community care in favour of living in a hospital,[13] which may be the rational choice in view of the disabling effects of long-term institutionalization. The rights of the mentally handicapped to lead a normal life should be accepted, protected and planned for in the form of an individual 'life plan'.[2]

PATTERNS OF CARE

This concept of an individual life plan must be reflected in the range of residential care options available. Chapter 13 discusses a number of imaginative developments scattered over the country, but these are dependent on local initiative and do not form part of an overall rational plan.[8] This means that optimum facilities are, more often than not, a matter of random chance determined by available funding and priorities rather than the result of systematic planning based on identified needs.

The Jay Committee proposed a range of residential care settings, based on 'life stages'.[2] They rejected the hospital as 'quite unacceptable' for children, a view that is endorsed by the government,[4] and proposed a number of alternative care options. These alternatives include substitute family homes, 'normal' children's homes and small special homes that are locally based. The guiding principle of small group living is applied to the residential care needs of adults using ordinary housing, shared accommodation and staffed homes, across the range of dependency levels. They suggest that elderly mentally handicapped people would be able to use the normal residential services for the elderly.[2]

The government's response to the Jay Committee's recommendations has been disappointing; whilst accepting the philosophy and model of care it feels unable to move forward 'in view of the current necessary restraints on public expenditure'.[3] And yet the necessary money could be available if a plan put to the government were implemented. The plan involves the legal transfer of mental handicap hospitals to the local authorities, so that the land may be sold and the money used to buy, build or rent more appropriate residential care facilities.[6]

Whichever pattern of care is provided there should be a measure of accountability. Mittler makes the point that there is an increasing demand for accountability, not only from the consumers but also from the professional staff.[9] He describes the accreditation procedure in the USA, which takes the form of a programme or professional audit which includes an evaluation of the aims, objectives and success of the organization.[9] He goes on to suggest that each 'facility' should state its aims and goals and how these should be evaluated, possibly by publishing an annual report detailing the progress made.[9]

The National Development Group have published a 'Checklist of Standards' with the aims of 'translating theory into practice'.[11] The *overriding principle* is that mentally handicapped people are entitled to the same range and quality of service as are available to other citizens, and to services designed to meet their special needs. Services for children should recognize their distinctive needs.

Principle 1 is that the services provided to a mentally handicapped person, whatever his ability, should be based on interdisciplinary assessment of his individual needs and a training plan designed to meet them. Such plans should be regularly reviewed and revised.

Principle 2 is that services should be available to help families to look after a mentally handicapped person at home and to enable adults to live in homes of their own if they wish.

Principle 3 is that mentally handicapped people require day and residential services that promote their development and independence.

Principle 4 is that services should be jointly planned and delivered by health and local authorities in partnership with voluntary organizations and those directly providing the services. The needs of clients and their families are the prime consideration.[11]

INTEGRATION

The above principles put forward by the National Development Group are 'relevant to a comprehensive community based service',[11] which is central to the debate concerning integration. Integration is the degree to which community facilities are used by the mentally handicapped and reflects a normal range of life experiences in the areas of accommodation, employment, education and leisure. Successful integration is dependent on comprehensive support not only for the mentally handicapped but also for their families. This support may take the form of training workshops for parents to help them in managing their child at home; integrated classes for mentally handicapped children in normal schools; help from disablement resettlement officers in finding employment; and help from the social services in finding accommodation.

A concept that has recently evolved is that of the 'named person', proposed by the Warnock Committee 'to provide a point of contact for the parents of every child who has been discovered to have a disability or who is showing signs of special needs or problems'.[1] The 'named person' can assist the transition from segregation to integration through an expert knowledge of the resources and facilities of other agencies.

Experience has shown that integration is a very slow process and although this is usually thought to be due to public antipathy, there are a number of other factors. One is the lack of knowledge about mental handicap amongst planners, managers and professional care staff which often leads to the formation of low expectations and a denial that, with support, the mentally handicapped can learn to live in the community.

CARE STAFF TRAINING

At the present time nurse training leading to the certificate of Registered Nurse for the Mentally Subnormal (RNMS) and enrolment as a State Enrolled Nurse (SEN(MS)) constitutes the only specialist training in caring for the mentally handicapped. The 1970 syllabus for the RNMS is currently under review by the General Nursing Council and the following represents a personal view of the emphasis that the revised syllabus should have.

Any review of the syllabus of training should start from the premise that the training should enable the nurse to meet the physical, psychological and social needs of the mentally handicapped child or adult, in a wide variety of settings: at home, in the community or in hospital.

As a first step, concepts such as 'caring' and the 'quality of care' should be defined. Caring should be seen as an enabling process and the mentally handicapped should make progress towards independence as a consequence of receiving care. The quality of care can be measured in two inter-related ways. High-quality care allows the mentally handicapped person to acquire appropriate behaviours and lose inappropriate behaviours. This, in turn, is achieved by a high level of engagement by the care staff, who consistently utilize environmental opportunities for learning. The converse demonstrates a low quality of care: the mentally handicapped people make little or no progress and the staff spend large parts of their day not interacting with them. In view of this, the major emphasis in the syllabus of training should be placed on those skills which will solve the problems of learning and adjustment experienced by the mentally handicapped.

These 'core' skills include those of behavioural assessment; the identification and selection of target behaviours; writing individual teaching programmes using the principles of task analysis; implementing the programmes and recording progress; the appropriate application of reinforcement and techniques such as shaping, chaining, prompting, fading, modelling, extinction, time-out, response cost and shaping incompatible behaviours.

Interdependent skills involve those procedures which will initiate and maintain environments that will support the development and application of these 'core' behavioural skills. These include procedures for delivering on-going treatment; personal safety; personal care on a daily basis; physical nursing care in illness; maintaining the mentally handicapped individual's rights in relation to care and treatment; and providing conditions of choice.[7]

These skills cannot exist in a technological vacuum and it is essential that the nurse acquires skills in communication and inter-personal relationships so that the core skills may be more effectively applied.

A profession may be judged by the degree of autonomy of its practitioners and the body of knowledge associated with its training requirements. Autonomy of practice may be gained as a result of nurses making informed decisions about the individual needs of the mentally handicapped and having a range of behavioural skills that will enable them to meet these needs. These behavioural skills should be taught within the wider framework of knowledge gained from other disciplines.

It is essential that the nurse should understand society's norms, values, customs and institutions and how these affect the mentally handicapped. Equally, it is essential that the nurse should have a background knowledge of psychology, particularly normal development, learning theory, attitude formation and change, and group structure and function.

The setting in which the practical training takes place is important. The arbitrary assumption that training for the RNMS should take place in a hospital is no longer valid in view of the numbers of people cared for at home and in the community. Wider practical experience is essential and should include experience of helping mentally handicapped people and their families in the home and in community residential care as well as in hospital.

The 'philosophy' as outlined requires a fundamental re-appraisal of the existing syllabus of training for the nurse for the mentally handicapped. It involves the adoption of a new role, the learning of new skills and a new approach to the problems experienced by the mentally handicapped in living and learning.

The RNMS and SEN(MS) qualifications provide a basic training only and Mittler makes the point that there is a need for a 'national plan for staff development for all staff working in services for the mentally handicapped'.[9] He proposes a national college which would develop post-experience training, eventually leading to a special qualification in mental handicap following 'successful completion of a specific number of study units'.[9]

There is clearly an urgent need to share knowledge and expertise between the various professions concerned with the care, education and treatment of the mentally handicapped.

NURSING PROCESS

One example of an approach to care that may usefully be shared with other professions is the nursing process.[5] This approach is a four-stage model in the delivery of care. It is essentially a problem-solving technique, involving assessment of the individual's care needs, the planning of the care necessary to meet these needs, the implementation of the care and finally an evaluation of the effectiveness of the care.[5]

At first sight it may seem so obvious that it does not need saying, as this is what nurses have always done. However, the nursing process is more than just four tasks to be carried out in a total care package. Implicit in the philosophy is the recognition that each individual in need of care *is* an individual requiring care to meet his special needs with a built-in accountability.

The first stage of *assessment* identifies problems that may be helped by intervention and consists of collecting information about the person. This may be achieved in part by assessment techniques such as the progress assessment charts or the Vineland social maturity scale or by using development charts. This will give base-line information about the skills that the individual needs to acquire in terms of appropriate behaviours that need to be strengthened or developed and inappropriate behaviours that need to be weakened or eliminated.

The second stage of *planning* involves the setting of goals that will meet the assessed need and communicating this to others involved in the individual's care in the form of a plan.[5] In mental handicap this would take the form of a behaviourally based programme with specific learning objectives relating to a particular skill or behaviour.

The third stage of *implementing* the care plan includes all those interactions between the nurse and the individual receiving the care. Specifically it concerns the implementation of a carefully designed programme using those behavioural techniques that will assist the achievement of the learning objectives.

The final stage of *evaluation* concerns the effectiveness of the programme which may be measured by the extent to which the individual is enabled to function in particular circumstances or settings.

The four stages of the nursing process are carried out simultaneously. There is a continuous assessment which may necessitate further planning, in turn altering the programme which will affect the evaluation critera. Although the nursing process was originally developed in the USA for use in general hospitals it can readily be adapted and provides a systematic approach to the many problems experienced by the mentally handicapped and those caring for them.

SUMMING UP

Peggy Jay in her preface to the Report of the Committee of Enquiry into Mental Handicap Nursing and Care said that 'we are convinced that change is not only necessary but inevitable'.[2] The questions that need to be answered concern the changes that should be made.

The rights of the mentally handicapped should be accepted, protected and vigorously promoted using the very powerful media resources available. The gradual shift in the balance of hospital care to a range of options, linked to life stages allowing small group living in the community, should be accelerated. This acceleration in residential provision should be complemented by greater numbers of staff who would be equipped through basic and post-experience training in those behavioural skills which help the mentally handicapped child or adult towards independence, in a variety of settings: at home, in community residential care and in hospital.

Any changes that are made should be based on the principle that the mentally handicapped deserve understanding, guidance, teaching and support from a more fortunate society.

BIBLIOGRAPHY

1. DES (1978) *Special Educational Needs—Report of the Committee of Enquiry into the Education of Handicapped Children and Young People*, Cmmd 7212. London: HMSO.
2. DHSS (1979) *Report of the Committee of Enquiry into Mental Handicap Nursing and Care*, Cmmd 7468-1. London: HMSO.
3. DHSS (1980) *Press Release—Government's Response to Jay Report*. London: DHSS.
4. DHSS (1980) *Mental Handicap: Progress, Problems and Priorities*. London: DHSS.
5. Hargreaves, I. (1980) Theoretical considerations. In: *The Nursing Process*, ed. C.R. Kratz. London: Baillière Tindall.
6. Herbert, H. (1980) No cost plan to aid mentally handicapped. *Guardian*, 10 Nov. 1980.
7. Kushlick, A., Felce, D., Palmer, J. & Smith, J. (1976) *Evidence to the Committee of Enquiry into Mental Handicap Nursing and Care*. Winchester: Health Care Evaluation Research Team.
8. Malin, N., Race, D. & Jones, G. (1980) *Services for the Mentally Handicapped in Britain*. London: Croom Helm.
9. Mittler, P. (1979) *People not Patients—Problems and Policies in Mental Handicap*. London: Methuen.
10. National Development Group (1978) *Helping Mentally Handicapped People in Hospital*. London: DHSS.
11. National Development Group (1980) *Improving the Quality of Services for Mentally Handicapped People—A Checklist of Standards*. London: DHSS.
12. Olson, R.M. (1980) Take the Jay train. *New Society*, 11 Sept. 1980.
13. Ryan, J. & Thomas, F. (1980) *The Politics of Mental Handicap*. Harmondsworth: Penguin.

Index